Glimpses
of India

About the author

Ian Douglas Macdonald was born in India in the Himalayan town of Mussoorie in the 1960s. He has also lived in Belfast, Inverness, Hampshire, Sheffield, Verona, Colonsay, Cantabria, London and Devon.

Since qualifying as a teacher, in 1999, he has worked in nine schools in Devon and London. *Glimpses of India* is his first novel.

He is also the author of two non-fiction books:

*The First Half-Empty Book of English Villages** (2007) – hardback;

The Word Cup: A Tournament of Old Words Seeking New Favour (2014) – paperback & eBook.

* This book is ring-bound, with a silver-embossed front cover. Each alternate page lists English villages which are linked by their name. It was printed on high quality art paper, so that the opposite blank page could be painted or sketched on.

For reasons obscured by the mists of time, it has only ever been available in one retail outlet in the world.

First, the shop opposite the Duke of York in Iddesleigh (until the shop closed). Then, on Sarah Henshaw's extraordinary Book Barge (until it sailed across the English Channel en route to Burgundy). Rumours that it will find a 'blooming' new home, in 2023, are yet to be verified...

Glimpses of India

A Novel
(not a Travel Guide)

Ian Douglas Macdonald

figfarm Books

First published by Figfarm Books in 2020
eBook edition first published in 2022

5 7 9 10 8 6 4

This novel is a work of fiction.
Names and events are either the product of the author's imagination or used in a fictitious manner. Any resemblance to actual persons, living or dead, is entirely coincidental. Medical research, including research into transplantation, is a fast-moving science. Descriptions of procedures, timescales and medical interviews should never be used as a substitute for up-to-date advice from medical professionals.

Paperback ISBN: 978-1-8381394-0-7
eBook ISBN: 978-1-8381394-1-4

Cover Design by Paul Tippett @ VitaminP

Set in Garamond and Corbel

figfarmbooks@gmail.com

For Sue

December 24th, 2018

'India's in the Pacific.'

No one in M3 responded to George P Salt's statement.

'India,' George repeated, 'is on an island in the Pacific Ocean.'

'And you're supposed to be a Geographer,' Marina said. She nodded towards the world map on the ceiling, while topping up a pint of Oakham's Citra IPA.

George smiled and adjusted his leather baseball cap. 'You're right Marina. I'm talking about India Farr, Zoe's mother. I met her last week. She is, or at least recently was, on Easter Island. In the Pacific.'

'*Asombrosa*,' Marina said. 'That's amazing. Colin drove Zoe to the hospital early this morning. There's a chance the transplant team might have found a suitable kidney for her. Though she's only the reserve.'

'What do you mean?'

'Zoe's the backup. She's there in case the donated kidney isn't a good match for the primary recipient. Can we speak about this later?'

'Of course, Marina. Oh, and Merry Christmas for tomorrow.'

'And *Felices Pascuas* to you as well, George.'

Marina watched as George walked across the yard to his shop, and smiled as he paused to check out the Citroën H Van's latest menu. She put her elbows on the bar and rested her chin on her knuckles. Then noticed that she had put on odd socks underneath her transparent wellies. Marina felt sick and excited. She looked up at the map again and placed India. In the Pacific, yes, but surely needed back in Europe?

December 24th, 1999

Colin and India ignored the small crowd at Speakers' Corner and headed towards the Serpentine. A few riders were still about. But last-minute Christmas shopping, and the fading light, made for an almost deserted Hyde Park.

'I've always liked your full set of whiskers, Colin. If you put on thirty kilos, you'd make a cracking Father Christmas. Perhaps I could make you a suitable suit.'

'P'raps you could. Now, India, I don't blame you for avoiding the issue. But in the New Year, you'll need to sort things out with your mother. It's been over a year since you and Abigail spoke. It's a bit odd too.'

'What is, Colin?'

'Your mother living in the main house and you camping out round the back at Number 17. In the chilly mews cottage.'

'It's not ideal, but it sort of works.'

'Not for too much longer, I'm afraid. I know Manchester's your preferred option for next year, but there are also three universities in London that have made you offers. Wherever you end up, you'll be leaving the Hop Yard and Suffolk for three years. And if you do study in London, then you'll need to live with your mother.'

'Couldn't I just live in Number 17? It wouldn't take too much more money, time and effort to make it a liveable space.'

'That's part of the plan, India. But I need to sell the main house, partly because of your mother's increasing care costs. So the two of you, for the first time in your lives, would need to live together. I've already started moving some of her stuff into the second bedroom. As you know, Abigail's coming back with me to spend Christmas in Peasenham. I'm still not sure it's a good idea for you to stay here, in London, by yourself. Are you really sure, India?'

'I'll get the train up to Suffolk on the 29th. You, of all people, know how tricky my relationship with Abigail has been. And my social calendar is full, including supper with Natalie at Number 11 this evening. Then Christmas lunch at Number 26 tomorrow. Freda and Bouke will be hosting that, of course, and the Duffy clan is always on good form.'

'Marina and I will look forward to seeing you for the New Year. We've almost finished restoring another of the outbuildings at the Hop Yard. Skye suggested we use the space for a bookshop. Maybe you could help get it up and running. Talking of running, let's speed up and get a winter warmer over the road at the Paxton Head.'

'That would be great. And I'll make time to sit down with Abigail in the New Year. Maybe the two of us *can* start to find a different way forward. It would be a good way to start the new millennium.'

'I'll raise a glass to that, India, when we get to the pub. Mine's a Midori and soda, if you're buying . . . '

After she had helped Nat clear the supper dishes, India popped back to Number 17 to put on a pair of jeans and her chunkiest jumper. She had the key to Abigail's locked bedroom, and decided to have a peek inside. *It's not just a door that I need to unlock—*

'Hey, Indy. Are you there? The others have gone on to the William Wallace.'

India hesitated, but was suddenly grateful for the interruption. 'Is that you, Richard? Just give me a minute.'

'Where is everyone?'

'Oh, they'll probably be here soon, Indy. And call me Duffy.'

'Alright, Duffy. But I prefer to be called India. What are you having?'

'I'll have a Bacardi Breezer. Oh, that couple are just leaving. I'll grab their seats.' Richard went and sat on one of the low wooden stools next to the leaded window. A stained-glass red lion added to the Scottish feel of the pub.

India nudged her way through the busy bar and quickly caught the eye of the tallest barman. 'Hi there, can I get a Bacardi Breezer — yes, watermelon's fine — and a pint of Deuchars IPA?'

'Would your fella like it in a handled glass?'

'No thanks. He's not my boyfriend and he's happy to drink his from the bottle. The pint's for me. In a straight glass, please.'

'Aye, and why not, lass?'

'Get some crisps as well, Indy.'

'He's a charmer, for sure. I think you might enjoy these haggis-flavoured ones. Just don't choke on the black pepper.'

'Thanks. And sorry about all the shouting from my companion. Can I get you a drink?'

'Nae bother, and thanks. But I need a clear head for the family gathering tomorrow.'

'What was that you said? Something about another William Wallace?'

India had been about to head back to Pershore Place Mews. However, a soft Highland whisper, perhaps not even meant to be heard, stopped her in her floral Doc Marten-booted tracks. India tugged back Duffy, so they could both hear what the kilted young man had to say.

'I overheard your conversation. This *is* the WW, but I think The Gunmakers round the corner *also* used to be called the William Wallace. Which is a wee bit surprising, as yer man didn't really feel the love when he was in London. He never swore allegiance, so how was he convicted of treason? It was brutal wha' they did to him, quartering his body and burning his internal organs. Bastards! I get the shivers whenever I'm walking through Smithfield Market towards St Bart's. Which I try to do in his memory, every 23rd of August. Ach, I'm sorry. What I was trying to say, is that your pals might be in the other pub. It's worth a try. Eh, hen?'

India ran her fingers through her hair, grabbed a quick breakfast of blueberries and cold turkey, and switched off the festive lights. *Not that she'd ever really switched them on in the first place.* It had been good of Freda to bring round a warmed and foil-wrapped plate yesterday. She would drop in a thank you note before she went back to Peasenham. India headed outside into Pershore Place Mews. A few olive leaves, blown from the terracotta planter over at Number 22, swirled around her feet. Normally she'd have turned right, and headed north towards Baker Street tube station. However, she wanted to avoid Richard. So, she—

'It's my Indy girl. Are you heading to Hyde Park for a Boxing Day leg stretcher? Or do you fancy another form of exercise?'

'Hello, Duffy. What are you doing up so early? I'm getting a train to Manchester to—'

'Manchester?'

'Yes. I'm in a bit of a hurry, so maybe we could meet up later.'

'I suppose so. Hang on though. You're going in the wrong direction.'

You could be right about that. 'I want to get a new Muji pen, with a 0.1mm nib, and then catch the Northern Line from Tottenham

Court Road.'

'You and your pens. I thought I'd get a new desktop computer in the sales. We could walk down together and maybe grab a coffee.'

'Not a good idea, Duffy. You should wait until the New Year. If the Y2K bug really does exist, then your computer would be useless. And whilst your riding cap, striped shirt and tweed jacket are lovely, your lower half is a tad worrying. Shiny shorts, knee socks and slippers do not make for a good look. I'll walk alone.'

'Why did you sleep with me, Indy?'

'We had sex. Once. Messily. We didn't sleep. And I only let you stay over, on the sofa, because your parents were still at Midnight Mass. You'd locked yourself out of Number 22. Or so you said. And I prefer India, not Indy. You know that.'

'Okay, Ind . . . ia. I enjoyed last night and it sounded like you did too. Enjoy your daytrip to Manchester. I reckon you'll have time for a quick look round and a panini before you have to head back. You're a strange one, that's for sure.'

'Thanks for the advice, Duffy. Let's meet at the Dover Castle, at 10pm.'

'I'm guessing that you're talking about the pub in Marylebone, not Kent. You wouldn't want to make a mistake like that twice.'

India decided to walk from Piccadilly Station, rather than risk getting a bus that went past Manchester University. If she was pregnant, then her academic plans would probably be on hold. For another year. And with Colin's finances getting tighter, it would make more sense to study in London. So she walked down Whitworth Street, with the wind in her face. India then took a right up Deansgate, stopping briefly to admire the awesome John Rylands Library once again. She thought the exterior was wonderful. However, it was the contents that had filled her with awe during the Uni Open Day.

India checked the directions she had been given late on Christmas Day, then headed west past the Granada TV studios. Then she crossed over the River Irwell to Salford. There were definitely more red shirts in this area, but she was feeling blue. And a little green. And, phew, pink too. India hesitated when she got to the pharmacy. Then took a deep breath, and walked in.

'Hi, my name's China Marr and I'm here to get a prescription to buy a morning-after pill.'

'Hello, China. We were expecting you. Our pharmacists are fully trained, but we supply rather than prescribe. And the supply is free, subject to the results of the short interview. Uzma, the duty pharmacist, will take you through all the details. She'll see you over in that side room, in about half an hour.'

'Can you tell me when your last period started, China?'

'That would be twelve days ago, on December 14th.'

'And how many hours is it since you had sex?'

'Hours?'

'Yes. The pills prevent three-quarters of pregnancies if taken within 72 hours of unprotected sex.'

'Actually, it was a couple of hours after midnight on Christmas Eve. So let's say 2am. I'd had a few drinks at the William Wallace pub. But I knew what I was doing, even though I didn't really know how to do it. It was my first time. And it's now just after 4pm on Boxing Day, so that would be about, doo-duh-doo, 38 hours.' *Was it really only yesterday?*

'I don't know that pub, China. Is it in Manchester or Salford?'

'Actually, it's in Marylebone, between Hyde Park and Regent's Park in London. Although I live in Suffolk, where my GP is.'

'Oh, I thought you were a student here. You've come a long way. And this pilot scheme only started on Christmas Eve.'

'Yes, I got lucky. One of my neighbours, Bouke, is a nurse. He gave me the info and the NHS Direct number. I caught a train from Euston to Manchester Piccadilly this morning, though I had to change at Crewe.'

'You mentioned your GP in Suffolk. Although you'll need to sign the notes I make, she or he will not be informed. And the supply of the pills will not appear on your medical record. Linked to that, are you on any prescribed medications?'

'No, but I do sometimes take anti-histamines when there's a high pollen count.'

'That's fine. Finally, and this isn't part of the formal interview, did you use any form of contraception? We ask this to help the NHS build up a picture of some of the reasons leading to unwanted pregnancies.'

'A condom was unwrapped, and, er, placed. But I think it was the first time for both of us. And it didn't seem to do its job.'

'China, I am satisfied that you have a genuine need for this service—'

'Doesn't everyone who comes to see you?'

'No. Some women want to have the morning-after pill at home in case of emergencies. But it shouldn't be viewed as an after-the-horse-has-bolted form of contraception. You should be aware that some women *still* become pregnant despite taking the medication. And other women decline to answer some or all of the questions. In such cases, we would suggest they contact their GP. Can I ask you to sign and date these notes, to show your consent?'

'Thanks for being so supportive, Uzma. Should I take the pill when I get home?'

'It's more complex than that. The morning-after pill is actually a combined treatment of four pills. You'll take two before you leave and then another two in twelve hours. So don't forget to set your alarm clock for 4.30am tomorrow morning.'

'Can I get you a drink, India? I don't recognise any of the brands, so I went for a vodka and tonic rather than my usual Hofmeister lager. You might want to stick to spirits, too. Why did you choose this pub? We're the only one's here.'

'It's a Sam Smith's pub, so they brew all the beers, including the lagers. And there are no electronic distractions, so it's a good place to talk. I'll just have a grapefruit juice, with two lumps of ice, please.'

'No problem, India. Weymouth Mews is a lot wigglier than our one. How did you know about this place?'

'Colin likes to search out interesting places. Did you see the signs etched on the door panes? One says *Bottle Room* and the other says *Retail Entrance*. I know it's more open-plan now, but this part of the pub used to be divided. Coachmen used the ceiling mirror to spot when their employers were ready to leave. However, what Colin really loves is that World War Two photo on the wall. Last time we were here, he spent over ten minutes looking at it. It was as if he had recognised someone.'

'It's an atmospheric photo. With all those civilians and service personnel, both army and navy, standing outside this very pub. Just before D-Day. Dangerous, but exciting times.'

'Indeed, and they probably had better reasons for reckless sex.'

'That's not fair. Well, it's a little unfair.'

'Duffy, I went to Manchester because of our reckless sex. The NHS is running a trial morning-after scheme up there.'

'You don't even know you're pregnant. And even if you were, don't you want a baby?'

'Are you serious? People patting me on the tummy, offering me random words of advice and criticising my lifestyle? Having something inside me for nine months, growing from the size of a bean to a basketball. My hormones going crazy with all those endorphins. And that's before the baby is born.'

'Yeah, but Indy. Sorry, India. That's what most mothers go through.'

'Despite my rant, it's not the pregnancy that bothers me. In fact, I think I might enjoy, as they say, being in an interesting condition, full in the belly, carrying a packet from Paris . . . It's motherhood that scares me, and even if it didn't, how's it going to work out for me at university? Or later on, when I start my career? Anyway, it's too late as I've taken the first two pills.'

'First two?'

'Yes, I was a bit surprised as well. I have to take the other two in the early hours of tomorrow morning. There's a three in four chance that, if I'm pregnant, conception will be prevented.'

'And if it isn't, let's have the bambino.'

'You're joking. And after all I've said about—'

'No, India. You have the baby and then I'll look after it for us. Hey, I could even take another gap year before Durham. It would also be a good distraction for the aged parents. It might even slow down their divorce proceedings. And Trundle, my old nanny, still lives nearby in Paddington. So she could help out with the practicalities. Daddy Duffy, it's perfect.'

'A *small* part of me is persuaded by your weird logic. So let me get this right. You're saying, that if I *am* pregnant, you'll take full responsibility for the baby?'

'Yes, I will. You haven't taken the other pills yet, have you? Is that them in your bag? Shall I throw them away?'

'Not yet, Duffy. It *might* come to that. Even though part of my brain is screaming, "No, no, no!" at me. But let's walk back to Pershore Place Mews and have a chat with your parents first.'

The Main Cast,
as of May 1st, 2018

Colin Pargeter, 84

Skye Hunter, 77

Angelique Vonk, 58

Marina Rueda, 51

Richard Duffy, 39

India Farr, 38

Hatsu Akahoshi, 34

George P Salt, 34

Gita Chaudhury, 29

Kenesha Baxter, 25

Pippa Luscombe, 24

Warren Wagstaffe, 20

Zoe Pargeter (aka Farr-Duffy), 17

Chapter 01

'Hooray, hooray, the first of May, the *Chatter Broth* podcast starts again today. Hi, I'm Skye Hunter. Regular listeners might know that this fortnightly podcast is recorded on whatever day May 1st happens to fall on. In 2017, it was on Mondays. So this year, it's on Tuesdays. There have been a few changes, most importantly, the addition of my new researcher, Warren Wagstaffe. You'll be hearing from him soon. But first up, let me introduce you to today's guest, Marina Rueda. She runs M3, Marina's Moreish Micropub, which is diagonally across the Hop Yard from our *Chatter Broth* studio.'

'Hola, Skye. And thanks for inviting me onto the first show of the new season.'

'You're welcome, Marina. Before we hear more about M3, what has caught your eye from our In This Fortnight selection?'

'I could hardly ignore Joseph Bramah's patenting of the beer-pump handle in 1785. I know there's a trend towards the sale of canned beers and nitrokegs in micropubs. But I always try to have at least three beer barrels *de grifo* — on tap — over at M3. And then my eye was drawn to Wisbech. On the River Nene, it's home to Elgood's Brewery, which in itself is a good enough reason to visit. The National Trust's Peckover House is also interesting, but what I really love is its garden. I took Zoe there for her first ever game of croquet, almost ten years ago, when she was nine. The volunteers were so friendly. I loved the sign on the edge of the lawn, which read something like, "*If your ball ends up in the bushes, please do not fret. However, would you be so kind as to inform a member of staff of the general direction the ball was last seen travelling?*" But the actual event which happened, in Wisbech, in this fortnight of history is, how can I say it, frozen in time. What I mean to say, Skye, is that, in 1937, Smedley's of Wisbech became the first company in England to retail frozen vegetables. Not peas or carrots, as you might expect, but asparagus. This is the perfect time for fresh asparagus, but seeing frozen asparagus in the inter-war period must have been some sight. One of my favourite pubs, the Fleece Inn in Bretforton, has an asparagus festival. The locals there gather in the back room to discuss all matters '*gras*, as they call it. But I think you'd need to travel, to South Yorkshire or Portland in Oregon, to find asparagus as an ingredient in an experimental brew.'

'Talking of experimental brews, what's your current favourite brew over at M3, Marina?'

'Skye, it's a Belgian-style wheat beer by Elgood's called Cherry Wheat. Though it also has lush raspberries in it. Very refreshing *en el sol* — in the sun.'

'Are there any other events which happened in this fortnight in history that jumped out at you?'

'I think that two events on May 13th are well linked. In 1607, Captain John Smith made landfall on the coast of Virginia. He established the first permanent English settlement in the New World, calling it Jamestown. There's a great road there called the Colonial Parkway. There was also another kind of road, a watery one, which took Pocahontas from Jamestown to her death in Gravesend. But Great Britain lost control stateside, and a new colonial outlet was needed. So 180 years after 1607, the First Fleet sailed from England, transporting the first convicts to the new penal colony of Australia. And I think I'll finish this part with two protests. On May 2nd, 1980, Pink Floyd's "Another

Brick in the Wall" was banned by the South African government. It had been adopted as a song of defiance by schoolchildren in the townships. Almost ten years earlier, on May 4th, 1970, US National Guardsmen shot thirteen students at Kent State University, Ohio. Four of them died. I was only a toddler at the time, but I remember my parents speaking about it after Watergate. Richard Nixon seemed to justify the shootings at the time with his comment that, "when dissent turns to violence it invites tragedy". And let's not forget the two students who were shot dead at a college in Jackson, Mississippi, later in the month. Maybe Neil Young could have written a song about them too. What do you think, Skye?'

'I think this would be a good time to play that Pink Floyd song. Ah, I think that has triggered something in Warren's memory. He moved to Peasenham last year and has quickly become part of our family of misfits.'

'Thanks, Skye, and hello listeners. I was thinking back to my first Field Party. I'd just arrived in the village and I was blown away by the mix of people, stalls and entertainment. I didn't know you could feed over seventy people from one giant frying pan. There was a teacher from the local secondary school performing at the Open Mic session. I think her name was Kenesha. Anyway, she sang "Another Brick in the Wall" brilliantly. But someone, who wasn't even at the party, complained to the school. It was along the lines of, "How *dare* a teacher sing about children not needing education". The school failed to spot the deliberate irony and she was given a formal warning. It was still a great party though. As I don't really drink, I had a clear head and helped make breakfast the next morning. Which was the first time I spoke to you, Skye.'

'That's right, Warren. And the Field Party is coming up again in August. Kenesha, or Miss Baxter as Zoe knew her, has now left the teaching profession. A pity, because she changed the lives of many students during her short career. I know Zoe misses her, and not just because the first two lessons on a Monday morning were Photography. Oh, I do hope that Zoe's first meeting at the hospital is going well.'

'She's lucky to be living in a country with such an amazing healthcare system. Many of my American friends don't really believe that the NHS exists. You know, free access to healthcare for *everyone*.'

'I agree, Marina. I was only six when the National Health Service began. However, we must never take it for granted. What a great song it was that Miss Baxter sang. I remember seeing *The Wall* performed in 1990. It was a scorching day on the dusty expanse of Potsdamerplatz. I admit to crying; indeed I was sobbing with big gulps, during "Comfortably Numb". Then later there were the sirens and searchlights, which might have been upsetting for some of the older residents of Berlin. It must have been traumatic for the bomber crews too, watching cities fall. I'll play that Pink Floyd song which made me cry, followed by The Scissor Sisters' version.'

~

'Hello, Zoe. My name's Laura Tisdale and I'll be your designated transplant coordinator. To start, can you tell me a little bit about yourself?'

'Hi, Laura. Are you related to that civil servant who was jailed for leaking information about American cruise missiles being sent to the UK?'

'I remember that case. No, she was Sarah Tisdall. I'm a Tisdale. Like Paul Tisdale, the nattily-dressed football manager. Anyway, what about you?'

'My mother is called India Farr. She didn't want to have children, and I still don't know why. But she became pregnant during the Christmas holidays, just before the millennium. My father, Richard Duffy, said that he'd take responsibility for me. India agreed, and didn't end her pregnancy. But then Richard had an accident in Australia, just before I was born.'

'Are you in touch with your parents, Zoe?'

'I've met my father a few times, but he hasn't fully recovered from what happened Physically, he's fine. It's the mental health side of things that Richard still struggles with. I don't remember ever meeting my mother. Luckily, I think, Abigail was being cared for by Colin Pargeter.'

'Who are Abigail and Colin?'

'Abigail was India's mother and my grandmother. She died when I was fifteen. I didn't like visiting her in London. It was really tricky getting into her bedroom. She had surrounded herself with stuff that she didn't need. At least, stuff that I didn't think she needed. Sometimes she'd be super-friendly, but then sometimes she would push me away. I think she sometimes confused me, in her time-jumping mind, with my mother. Also, I didn't like the unpredictability of our meetings. Though things got better, when she started to forget people's names. Including mine.'

'Your mother didn't get on with *her* mother?'

'That's right. India was brought up in Suffolk, with Colin. Though she and Abigail lived together in London, for a couple of years, before my mother dropped out of university. I was just a baby then.'

'I thought you said that you'd never met your mother?'

'I did say that, Laura. She left when I was two, so I've no memories of her.'

'How do you feel about that?'

'Can we talk about Colin?'

'Ok, Zoe. Where does Colin fit into all this?'

'Colin is my legal guardian. Abigail and Colin first met in

Bologna, but neither of them likes to talk about how or when. Colin had inherited the two London properties from a childless couple after the Second World War. And some land in Suffolk. He sold the main London house, just after I was born, but kept the mews property to the rear. Colin based himself in Suffolk, at Peasenham, where he built up the Hop Yard.'

'I've been there. There's an interesting bookshop. With a small pub and a gallery on the other side of the courtyard. And a map shop that also sold donated vegetables. Can that be right?'

'Indeed it can. That shop is called Globe+Artichoke, and it's run by George. Hey, I'm glad you've visited. The micropub is run by Marina Rueda. I'm not exactly sure of the relationship, but she and Colin are very close. When my mother left, Colin successfully applied to become my guardian. In fact, I recently changed my surname by deed poll from Farr-Duffy to Pargeter. It's all quite complicated, but I'm lucky in many ways.'

'Let me get this right. Colin provided care for your grandmother. And then took on the responsibility for bringing your mother up, and then you.'

'He did, and it's not just us. Colin has supported many people, mainly at the Hop Yard. Particularly if they were trying to sort themselves out. Some people stayed for just a few days. Others have been with us for years. For example, I've known Marina since I was three. They've all kind of adopted me, maybe because I'm the only child there. In fact, I used to think that Marina actually *was* my mother. I hope that helps.'

'That's great. Thanks for coming in today to start the process. And it's quite a process. It will hopefully end with you, the recipient, being successfully matched with a kidney from a living or a deceased donor. The transplant team, guided by the lead surgeon, has to ensure you're suitable to receive a kidney transplant. Not all patients are. Also, sadly, kidney transplants don't last as long as healthy kidneys. As you are only eighteen, you will probably need more than one transplant during your lifetime. And it's best to have a transplant *before* you go on dialysis. Your kidney function is reducing, but you're still about a year away from needing dialysis.'

'Why is it best to have a transplant before dialysis starts?'

'Dialysis flushes toxic food waste and excess water from your body, but will also take away a lot of your independence. I know you're young, but almost all women on dialysis are unable to have children. And you would probably feel less energetic and have more difficulty coping with everyday life, including studying. Speaking of which, what are your academic plans?'

'I'm taking my A-levels later this term. Chemistry, History and Photography. But I'm going to postpone any plans for university. I might not even go. So how long is the waiting list?'

'There's a national pool of people waiting for a kidney from a deceased donor, typically for three years. But it's not a waiting list.'

'What do you mean it's not a waiting list? And if I had to wait three years, I'd need to go on dialysis. Probably for the rest of my life.'

'As I said, it's a process. A complicated, demanding and emotional process.'

'But, three years?'

'Zoe, there's a huge shortage of suitable kidneys in the UK. The gap between kidneys donated and the number of people waiting for one is increasing. Currently, over 5,000 people in the UK need a kidney transplant. And sadly, hundreds of people die every year while waiting for one. Shall we go and get a drink from the canteen? It's a lot to take in.'

~

'Hello again, listeners. What a great song "Comfortably Numb" is. I love both versions. Listeners, whether you're out there or *in there*, I wonder if *your* hands ever felt like balloons. Southwold overlooks Sole Bay. And at the Battle of Sole Bay there was smoke on the horizon, from ships coming through in waves. That was the sea battle that inspired one of my favourite beers, Adnams Broadside. To get back on track, as I see Warren smiling out of the corner of my eye, let me tell you about In This Fortnight. Listeners might know that I used to run an On This Day section. Warren suggested extending the timeframe to a fortnight. Why was that, Warren? And what events have you picked out?'

'Thank you, Skye. I can definitely hear what you're saying. You've certainly made waves ripple, from Berlin to the Suffolk coast. I thought a new format might throw up more interesting links and coincidences. Although, as it happens, I think that today, May 1st, was a fascinating day in this fortnight of history. The breathtaking Great Exhibition had its opening day in Hyde Park in 1851. That's where my time travelling machine would make its first landing. I'd send a letter home using Rowland Hill's Penny Black, which had gone on sale exactly eleven years previously. Though why it took another thirty years, from 1840, to introduce the Halfpenny Lilac, I've no idea. And, in 1928, the voting age for women in Britain was reduced from thirty to twenty-one. I'm amazed it took over forty years to bring that down to eighteen. Skye, do you think that's the right age, or should it be lowered to sixteen, as it is for some elections in Scotland?'

'That's a tricky question, Warren. But if you can vote, then surely you should be able to stand as an MP. It's now almost three years since, aged twenty, the Scottish National Party's Mhairi Black became Westminster's youngest MP since the reign of Charles II. Could you imagine an MP who was aged sixteen in the modern era? Anyway, Warren, do you have any Lost Four Words?'

'Yes, Skye. Listeners may or may not know that we are trying to 'release' obscure words back into common use. You did it over a decade ago, with discombobulated. Now it's time for a new word to soar. Or at least emerge into the light. Right, Skye?'

'Certainly, Warren. Each fortnight we pin a shortlist of words, with a space for further suggestions, onto our *Chatter Broth* noticeboard in M3. Thanks for letting us use that, Marina. People can then add any words they think should be on the list. One of our regular listeners chooses their four favourite words. And then turns them into a poem. On our last Monday podcast, before we switched to Tuesdays, we were looking for words beginning with the letter A. And the final four are?'

'Thanks, Skye. They are abeigh, adventitious, antelucan and apricate. And they were turned into the following lines:

She was more abeigh than aloof,
And liked to apricate alone.
Though fond of antelucan experiences,
Her adventitious nature
Often made her a disruptive houseguest.'

'And just in case any listeners need some help, Warren?
'Well, Skye, does this interpretation make any sense to you?

She was distant more through shyness than aloofness,
And liked to sunbathe alone.
Though fond of events in the hour before dawn,
Her habit of accidentally appearing from an unexpected place
Often caused havoc when she was staying with friends.

My suggestion was absquatulate, to depart in a hurry. Have you ever absquatulated, Skye?'

'I have been known to, Warren. Although, do you remember those two bank robbers in Tibor Fischer's *The Thought Gang*?'

'Oh yes, Edouard and Hubert. And thanks for lending me the book. They didn't absquatulate after their heist. They dined in a restaurant overlooking the bank and watched the police arriving. The getaway *lunch*.'

'And I had to get away, swiftly, after an adventitious experience in Austria some years ago. Although it was while travelling, rather than staying with friends. Having visited my favourite lingerie shop in Melk—'

'Was it called *The Name of the Rose*? Ah, Adso of Melk, and Sean Connery playing William of Bas*h*kerville, in the film of Umberto Eco's book.'

'Thanks, Warren. As I was saying, following my brassiere purchases, I had a rather delightful lunch in a brasserie, washed down with a half-bottle of chilled Gruner Veltliner. Later, I was exploring the precinct of the hilltop monastery and came across an interesting wooden door. It was slightly open, so I ducked through and found myself, in a display behind a glass screen, being stared at by tittering tourists on the other side. I smiled, didn't make my excuses, but returned swiftly to the town square. I think some Four Play is required. Over to you, Warren.'

'Yes, Skye. Another of our new ideas is to link up to four songs to the word or event being discussed. I've promised Skye that I'll not use this as an excuse to play songs from some of my favourite bands such as Cruising Julie or Stark Reality. And she has agreed to leave Goldfrapp, Prefab Sprout and Dionne Warwick at home. So this is a tune, linked to abeigh, that became a song. Duncan Gray was a Glaswegian who whistled while he worked. A local musician overheard him and wrote down the tune. In the 1790s, Rabbie Burns added the words. The Scots language has some unfamiliar words, so look out for: blythe — carefree; fu' — tipsy; asklant — sideways with a squint; unco skeigh — very proud or very saucy, and gart — made. Oh, and the second fu' is full, not tipsy:

"*Duncan Gray cam' here to woo,*
Ha, ha, the wooing o't,
On blythe Yule-night when we were fu',
Ha, ha, the wooing o't,
Maggie coost her head fu' heigh,
Look'd asklent and unco skeigh,
Gart poor Duncan stand abeigh,
Ha, ha, the wooing o't.'"

'Thanks for that, Warren. Though, maybe, something a bit easier to understand next time? I think I might need to buy a Scots dictionary to keep next to my *Hobson-Jobson* Anglo-Indian one. Would you like to borrow it as well, Marina?'

'Definitely. I would use *tímido* for abeigh. However, I need to absquatulate. Colin said he'd let me know how Zoe's first transplant meeting went. But before I go, she asked if you could play a song for her. She's looking forward to hearing how the show has developed and she's quite happy for us to discuss her need for a new kidney. The song she chose was "Just Like Me" by The Ancestors. They became The Grand Slambovians, who played at the Field Party a few years ago. There was a deluge that day, but they helped make it a memorable Saturday in the rain. So thanks again for the invite, and *hasta luego* — see you later.'

'I like that song, Skye. The Hop Yard feels like my magical community, where I feel protected. And, although I think we all need some fantasy in our lives, I need to be connected, with different threads, to the real world. Does that make sense?'

'Yes, it does, Warren. And if you're in a life-threatening situation, like Zoe, then you can't live in dreams. You also have to get organised, do your research and make decisions.'

~

'Thanks for the coffee, Laura. It was great to see it was made with Fairtrade beans. Anyway, could you tell me more about the waiting list?'

'Yes, Zoe, but remember that the national pool is *not* a waiting list. Each kidney from a deceased donor is assessed and then questions are asked. Which patient has the greatest need? Which patient will the kidney have the best chance of succeeding in? The success probability is based on blood group and tissue type compatibility between the donor and you, the recipient.'

'I've done some background reading. And as well as studying Chemistry, one of my History modules, ironically, is the History of Medicine. Am I correct in thinking that the body tissue proteins are called HLAs?'

'That's right. HLA-type proteins, known as Human Lymphocyte Antigens, are responsible for the unique tissue type of every person. Unique, unless you have an identical twin, that is. Some people have likened it to a bar code imprinted on the surface of cells. And the more similarity to your bar code that the donor has, the better. So linked to blood group compatibility, having more HLA similarities makes for a better matched donor kidney.'

'So which part of the body is the tissue sample taken from?'

'Oh, I see what you're thinking. No, there's no need to take a tissue sample. It's all done with a blood test.'

'That's a small relief. Am I right in thinking that tissue type is

24

linked to the body's ability to get rid of viruses?'

'You're right and, once again, well done for doing prior research. I'm really proud of you. . . Hey, have I upset you?'

'The *situation* has upset me, not you. It's all become a bit overwhelming. You, however, have been really thorough, helpful and supportive. Please carry on, Laura.'

'If you're sure. There are six key proteins in your body cells involved in getting rid of viruses. They're called HLA antigens and each has been allocated a different number. You inherited three from India, your mother, and three from Richard, your father. Let's say that India's HLA numbers were from one to six and Richard's were from seven to twelve. Yours might then be 3, 4 and 6, from India, with 8, 9 and 11, from Richard. Or 1, 5 and 6, with 7, 8 and 9. And so on. Good matches are much more likely to come from your biological parents, rather than people you are not related to. For example, your guardian Colin. Or his friend, Marina. Although sometimes, these tests do reveal unexpected results. Hopefully, we won't need to worry about that in your case.'

'So have I got this right, Laura? The HLA proteins will detect that the new kidney is a virus, that it's foreign. And naturally work to cause my body to reject the kidney. But with close blood group and tissue type matches, especially from a close relative, the chance of rejection is reduced.'

'That's a good summary, Zoe. Did you ever consider pursuing a scientific career?'

'I wanted to be an astronomer when I was younger. But I really enjoy the different elements and skills involved in the three courses I'm taking at A-level. Maybe they could all have their uses, especially now that I'm thinking about becoming an archaeologist. I don't know. But I'm feeling more positive about the future, now that I know more about the science behind the transplant process. Overall, it means that I might have to wait a long time until a good match becomes available.'

'Yes, Zoe. However, there's also a points system based mainly on three factors. These are age, the younger the better. Then age difference, the smaller the better. And thirdly, time spent waiting.'

'So it's good that I'm young, and bad that I haven't already been in the national pool for some time. And my chances of success would only be improved if the donor kidney came following the death of someone who was close to my age. That's a horrible thought. Would I be able to find out the name of the person?'

'If a suitable kidney becomes available you can be told the approximate age, gender and cause of death, as long as there are no confidentiality issues. We'll also talk to you again about the individual risks and benefits. If you then decide to go ahead, and it is your decision, you will be asked to sign a consent form. But waiting for a suitable kidney from a deceased donor increases the chance of delays and rejection. The transplant is more likely to be successful if the time between donation and transplantation is minimised. This is most likely to happen if there's a planned operation, with the new kidney coming from a living donor. As we've discussed, the best scenario is that the donor should be compatible with you in terms of blood group and tissue type. If they're not, this is known as a mismatched transplant. However, medical advances have made it possible for a mismatched transplant to take place between a donor and recipient with a different blood group or tissue type. Also, a kidney from a live donor is 20 percent more likely to be functioning well after ten years. Can you think of any family member, or close friend, who might be prepared to donate one of their kidneys?'

'Phew, that could be tricky, Laura. I'm not sure who I'd want to ask.'

Chapter 02

Yellowstone National Park, 2003

Marina had other favourite places in the park, but she never tired of Old Faithful. Though it made her slightly guilty, she enjoyed the bison chili. Which she ate on the open-fronted porch overlooking the geyser basin. She loved being close to such dynamic, explosive force. Natural power, rather than human destructiveness. It was only two years since the New York skyline had been blown apart. Marina still couldn't get some of those images out of her mind. Yellowstone was where she headed whenever she needed some space. And with both of her brothers away on military duty, it was up to her to sort out her father's estate.

She'd left Boise a couple of days earlier. The sight of early morning hot air balloons, as they slowly gained altitude, had given her a lift. So rather than speeding down I-84, she'd pointed her Subaru northeast and headed up towards the Sawtooth Wilderness. Like the writer William Least Heat Moon, as described in his epic *Blue Highways*, Marina preferred life *off* the Interstate.

Marina had stopped off at the Baking Company in Stanley for provisions — "Yes, Madam, *Pale Rider* was filmed here by Clint Eastwood" — which she ate in the parking lot of the Craters of the Moon National Monument.

After her early lunch, she had kept to the marked trails as she walked among the moon-like mini volcanoes known as spatter cones. President Calvin Coolidge had described the area as "a weird and scenic landscape, peculiar to itself". And NASA had sent Apollo astronauts to the area, so they could learn about volcanic geology, as they prepared for their lunar missions.

As with so many places, Marina thought there was a delicate balance between tourist access and habitat destruction. A sign, reading '*Are we loving them to death?*', made her nod in agreement.

After a night just outside Rexburg, Marina had followed the Teton Scenic Highway into Wyoming. Escaping the honeypot that was Jackson Hole, she had been struck by the raw, imposing beauty of the Grand Tetons. And although she had understood Bill Bryson's point about homesick men having vivid imaginations, she had not been reminded of female breasts. Grand, or otherwise.

Even though it was almost the end of season, there were no lodgings to be had at Grant Village. So Marina headed north, knowing she could find a bed just outside the park in Cooke City or Red Lodge. She crossed over the Continental Divide again. This time the sign showed an altitude of over 8000 feet. People sometimes forgot, or didn't realise, how much of the West was a high plateau.

Marina thought about how much time she had before nightfall, and pulled over at the Midway Geyser Basin. It was a short stroll to the Grand Prismatic Spring. Sulphur-scented steam covered the shallow lake. But then the light breeze gathered strength and the fall sun broke through. Much of the waterscape around the boardwalk was a rich brown, cut through with vivid orange stripes. And beyond was a turquoise pool with steam puffs drifting over it—

'It's almost too beautiful.'

Marina had to agree. She walked over to the woman who had

whispered the remark. She seemed ten, maybe even fifteen, years younger than Marina. It was difficult to tell, as most of her face was covered by wavy brown hair.

'Hola, my name's Marina. Do I detect a British accent? I've never been, but I'd love to one day.'

'Oh, hello. Yes, I live in England, though my father was from the States. I'm India. This is the third day in a row I've been here. This place moves me. So are you Spanish?'

'I have Spanish heritage. My grandparents moved to Idaho from Northern Spain, hence my surname Rueda. They were shepherds. But their son, my father, got into construction and married a Boise local. It's an interesting place. Have you been?'

'No, but I've seen it on a map of American state capitals. Do you live there?'

'I was brought up there. But I manage a brewpub in Bend, Oregon. Well, I did until a few weeks ago. My father died recently and I'm trying to sort out the estate. And get the house sold. It's a daunting task, so I've sidestepped it by coming here.'

'Oh, I'm quite good at sidestepping as well. Not off the boardwalk, though. Why are there no fences?'

'This is a wild place, and probably the most geologically active place on earth. More people die from falling into hot springs than from encounters with wild animals. I think the National Park Service believes that people shouldn't get too complacent. So signs, but no fences. Are you here by yourself?'

'I was with three friends, but they needed to get back to Flagstaff. I decided to stay on, in one of the cabins up at Roosevelt Lodge. It's their last night of opening tonight. Where are you staying?'

'I was going to head out and look for a motel room just outside the park.'

'Stay with me, there's a spare bed. It's a basic Rough Riders cabin, with no facilities, but there's a cute little potbelly wood-burning stove. And I think there might be a place left on the chuck wagon cook-out this evening.'

India had got some coffee, while Marina had bought stamps at the tiny Mammoth Hot Springs Post Office. She sipped it while admiring the landscape.

Suddenly, Marina put her foot on the brake. 'It's a bison and elk jam.'

India just managed to avoid spilling her hot drink. Seven cars had pulled over to watch, and there was no safe route past.

'The minimum recommended distance is 25 yards for bison, and 100 yards for bears and wolves. And you should only park in designated pull-outs. Oh no, that guy is getting out of the lead car. Has he seen the elk?' Marina and India watched as the elk lowered its head and rammed the car door. Three times. The driver managed to get back in through the passenger door.

'That's going to take some explaining to the insurance company,' India said.

Marina nodded. 'It happens too often. Last time I was here, I was stuck in a bison jam for almost an hour. I couldn't go forwards or backwards. I felt very vulnerable. Now, are you sure about tonight?'

'Absolutely. Hey, I think things are starting to move.'

'Howdy y'all and welcome to Roosevelt Lodge. It was just horses and wagons here, until automobiles were allowed into the park in the early 1900s. By 1915, the horses were getting spooked real bad by the general racket. So get this, the authorities banned the horses. For fifty years. I'd prefer it if they'd banned all vehicles here, but that's another story. Anyways, my name's Jed and my pardners over there are Justine — she's from Europe — and Timmy. He'll be driving the wagon. Cook's been out there for six hours, preparing for our arrival. So let's get moving, and I hope you're all hungry. Cook usually cooks up a storm. We've only had to abandon her three times. Once for snow, once for an earthquake, and once because of a Grizzly Bear.'

'Stop teasing them, Jed. It's a 45-minute trip, and the cook-out is held on the site of an old staging post.'

'Aw, I was just fooling around, Justine. I'll see y'all later. Safe travelling, folks. And don't forget to fill in your feedback forms when you get back from your feed.'

Timmy gave a flick on the reins and the wagon started to move. Justine sat up front, her blue jeans almost covered by her green leather chaps. A few minutes later, she asked Timmy to stop. A hundred yards away, there was a movement in the grass. Then a pale, almost ghostlike, mammal appeared.

'Is that a wolf?' India asked.

'No, it's a solitary coyote. Wolves are more likely to be up in the Lamar Valley. What do you think, Timmy?'

'I agree, Justine. And a pack of wolves is a powerful sight.'

The wagon continued along the old trail, until it came to the cook-out area. Cook was smiling as she walked up to the front of the wagon.

'Hey, Justine. Howdy, Timmy. It's the last cook-out of the year, so I hope all you people are hungry.'

Marina and India both watched as the first guests filled their plates: ribeye steak, mash, grilled corn, slaw, Roosevelt beans and apple cobbler.

'When in Rome,' India said, with a chuckle.

After everyone had eaten, and most had gone for seconds, Justine brought round the blue enamel jug of coffee. 'It's warm and it's sticky, and it stops Timmy yodelling. But when he's cleared his throat, he'll play you a few cowboy songs on his guitar around the campfire. His fingers pick well and his voice sort of grows on you.'

Night had fallen, but there were still a few guests sitting on rocking chairs outside the main lodge. Marina had opened a bottle of Kung Fu Girl Riesling and there was also a steaming jug of hot chocolate.

'India,' Marina said. 'I remember seeing two hikers in Utah a few years ago. It was near a place called Escalante, just off Highway 12. I offered them the foil-wrapped remains of my previous night's pizza. They treated the gift as if it was a gourmet breakfast. Later that day, I was resting on the rim of Bryce Canyon. A National Park Ranger must have realised I was tired, and gave me a crunchy granola bar. I thanked him, but he said it was just another bit of "trail magic". Something along the lines of, "Sometimes you give it, sometimes you receive it". You sharing your cabin with me, a stranger, also seems like trail magic. Thank you.'

'You're welcome, Marina. In fact, I've had an idea. You said you'd never been to Britain. Well, you could stay at a place called the Hop Yard. It's in a small village in Suffolk, near the East coast. And there are loads of interesting pubs and breweries in the area.'

'I like your enthusiasm, India. And it's a neat idea. But I need to sort out things in Boise first.'

'I'll do it for you. Sort your father's stuff out.'

The quiet confidence of India's response caused Marina to pause. 'It's a bit wild, but there's something in your idea. Let's speak about it in the morning.'

~

Marina's entry in The Ancient House Logbook, 2003

The Ancient House in Clare (a town, not a person) is a wonderful survivor. Some of it dates from the 14th century. And though very old, I feel snug and protected in this timbered house. Snug from the heat of the open fire. And protected by the 'woodwoses' (wild men of the woods), carved in oak. In the 1720s, Daniel Defoe wrote that Clare was '*a poor town and dirty, the streets being unpaved*'. Things have taken an upswing since then.

So much so, that an American offered to buy The Ancient House in the 1920s. So that he could dismantle it and ship it back to the States. I'm glad the offer was rejected. Though I once had a great weekend in Lake Havasu City. It took Robert McCullough three years to reassemble London Bridge in the parched landscape of Arizona. But he made millions from the purchase, even if some people thought he'd been conned.

The Swan's locals have been very friendly to me. But they were a bit dubious about Robert making a fortune from a bridge in a desert. And I've surprised them by ordering beer. Sometimes, even in a straight pint glass. Although I prefer halves or thirds. I decided *not* to tell them that I have a degree in brewing.

This has been a year of firsts. My first visit to Britain. My first time in Suffolk. My first stay in a Landmark Trust property. My first jigsaw, and with 'whimsy' pieces at that. And all because of a chance meeting, in Wyoming, with a young woman in September. I chose to rent this property because of the name of its external plasterwork. It's in a style called pargeting, and my host in Suffolk is a man called Colin Pargeter. Which is kind of neat.

The plaster used in pargeting often included lime, sand, oil and horsehair. Even cow dung was sometimes added. They seem keen on unusual building materials round here. Maybe it's because there's no local stone to quarry. And the pargeting tools used on the walls are *raro* — strange — as well. Trowels, I understand. Teaspoons, not so much. The raised designs are unusual themselves, and they change over time. I would love to have seen past examples, such as a dragon, a griffin or a hippopotamus*.

But pargeting does not last for long. The plaster gets heavier with each new layer of limewash, and eventually has to be removed. The '1473' date outside is definitely not original, and probably isn't even accurate. If an interesting text, that I found in the library, is anything to go by. It recorded that the Ancient House, '*attracts attention from its ornaments. . . but, being much defaced with whitewash, it is nearly impossible to ascertain exactly the figures.*' So renewal happens each time the pargeting is replaced.

Buildings change. For instance, there used to be a billiards room in the garden. And at a different time, a bakehouse. Those buildings are gone, but the knowledge, or thought of them, feels like *un puente* — a bridge — to the past. And the past can be difficult to translate. There's a sundial, outside the porch of the adjoining church. On it is written, '*Go about your business*'. What does that mean? Work? Don't linger here? Something else entirely?

I came across another interesting text from the bookcase (there is an excellent selection of books here, both reference and fiction, relating to the local area). In the text, two medieval characters are slightly confused by an inscription on a gravestone at Clare Priory. From what I can just about make out, a modern interpretation might be:

'*What man lies here?*'
'*No man.*'
'*What else (could it be)?*'
'*It is a woman.*'

Marina Rueda (Boise, Idaho)

PS I love the washroom, with its diamond-shaped glazing and wooden shutters (though the angles are crazy). Not the Angles who settled here in East Anglia, but the dramatic slope of the floors upstairs. You can roll a cork from the door to the lavatory, which is diagonally opposite. I was alone (but not lonely) in the bedroom of the Ancient House, but couples might have some unexpected *divertido* — fun — in there too.

* I've read some of the logbook entries. They inspired me to visit places like Castle Hedingham, Long Melford and a tiny, quirky pub in Bury St Edmunds. But I've not been tempted to travel more than fifteen miles from Clare, especially given the speed of the H Van that Colin lent me. Like this house, it has attracted some attention. An 'ancient' French van, with its quirky crinkly panelling, next to The Ancient House. A combination that's been irresistible to photographers and tourists.

The logbook, as I wrote, has been useful and enjoyable to read. But some of the entries strike me as unreliable, or even mischievous. Hence the '*' next to hippopotamus. The author of that entry (which mentioned the hippo) also admitted to some unlikely feats of athleticism in a local hostelry. So enjoy the logbook, but read it with *una pizca de sal* — a pinch of salt.

~

'Hi, I'm Skye Hunter and welcome to *Chatter Broth*. It's May 15th and today's guest is Colin Pargeter. He usually likes to keep a low profile, but he's agreed to join us on air for the first time.'

'Hello Skye and Warren. It's nice to see you both. I liked the word apricate, to sunbathe, from last time. Though, if you apricated too long you might begin to look like a prune. Is prunicate a word, p'raps?'

'I don't think so, Colin. On that thought, perhaps we should go straight into Lost Four Words. Over to you, Warren.'

'Thanks, Skye. In the last fortnight, we've been looking for words beginning with the letter B. The final four are bindlestiff, bowet, bruckle and buvette:

Though considered bruckle by some,
She would often head out
With just a bindlestiff.
Stopping only when she saw a welcoming bowet,
In the porch of a buvette.'

'And your thoughts on what meaning there may be, Warren?'
'Well, Skye, does this make any sense to you?

Though considered fragile by some,
She would often head out
With all her possessions carried in a bundle and tied to a stick.
Stopping only when she saw a welcoming candle-lit lantern,
In the porch of a small pub.

Marina's place is definitely a buvette, and there's a bowet in its porch. Battledore, a wooden laundry paddle, was my choice. It sounds more violent, than domestic, to me. The kind of item, as a last resort, you might actually use in a battle.'

'There are many kinds of battles, Warren. What sort were you thinking of?'

'Good question, Skye. But first, here's some Four Play linked to the word bruckle aka fragile. It's The Stranglers with "Strange Little Girl".'

'Does anyone out there know what her name was? Or why she ran away, and where she went? Perhaps she decided to warm up a bit on Mediterranean beaches. Enjoying ripe peaches and becoming a European female.'

'Warren, you didn't exactly *run* away. But you did move last year from a city to a hamlet, from Portsmouth to Peasenham, when you were just nineteen. Most people run away to somewhere larger, more anonymous, don't you think? Like the "Smalltown Boy" in that haunting song by Bronski Beat.'

'Probably, Skye. Although where would Londoners run away to, if that's the case? Lagos? Mexico City? Tokyo? I decided to move where I'd be noticed. Where I couldn't be easily ignored. And I realised just how unusual this place was, and still is, shortly after I arrived. When I walked into the pub, past the creaking door, the locals *didn't* stop talking. By the way, Colin. How did you get to Peasenham from London? Were you evacuated?'

'As it happens, I was. Three times. Actually, four, if you count the rehearsal. It was a strange and exciting time. A time of upheaval, physically and emotionally. Some evacuees didn't want to come home, because they'd come to love their new foster parents.'

'Like in *Goodnight Mr Tom*? Have you seen it?'

'A few times.'

'Time for a song, Colin?'

'I know what you're saying, but the young chap's interested. And my thoughts and feelings need an airing. Stuff gets stuffy. Memories get crusty, Skylark.'

'You haven't called me that since the Fifties . . . Over to you then, Colin.'

'The first time, *that* didn't go so well. However, the second time was much better. My school went to Waterloo Station by double-decker, a green one. I was on the top deck, or up in the attic as we used to call it. I remember looking down to wave to my mother and my sister Edith. I had my gas mask, a label and a small duffel bag. We didn't own a suitcase. Then we steamed down through Alton, all the way to New Alresford in Hampshire. Although the town looked quite *old* to me. That bit of line closed in the 1970s, but has re-opened as the Watercress Line. I was billeted along with a brother and sister the first night. Something must have happened, because they were re-billeted the next day. I was with the Blenkinsops, Anne and Geoffrey. He was a cobbler and had a workshop in the backyard. It seems strange, but I think he used hog bristles, rather than needles, for sewing. Geoff also had a wheelchair with two wheels at the back and a tiller at the front. He called it The Chariot. Geoff took the dog, I don't remember its name, for a long walk every day. Down Broad Street and along to the watercress beds. Sometimes we walked alongside the River Arle and back up The Dean past my school. The Chariot was pushed by a neighbour. They used to trick me. The dog would often catch a rabbit. Or rather, it was handed over, having been caught elsewhere. The dog was a lurcher, in more ways than one. Three-legged dogs don't often catch wild rabbits, do they? We sometimes went through the churchyard of St John's. There were graves with the names of French PoWs from the Napoleonic Wars. I liked that spot, but also found it a bit odd.'

'I think Hampshire was a bit of a hotspot for French PoWs, Colin. Thousands were imprisoned down at Porchester Castle. They dug out some of Portsmouth harbour by hand. An island, near to the Royal Dockyards, was formed by the spoil they created. Were you in Hampshire for the whole of the war?'

'No, Warren, I wasn't. Most of the action was going on in Europe, so my mother came down to collect me, just after my sixth birthday in early 1940. But then in 1941, there was a landmine in our street. The windows of our home were blasted in. We had a Morrison shelter, under the table, but I was the only one at home. Mother and little Edith were coming back from the park. They both got caught by the full blast.'

'You don't need to talk about that, Colin.'

'I know, Skylark. But talking about it has become unexpectedly important for me. A small group of us were evacuated from Liverpool Street Station. We were all orphans; I never knew who my father was. We were sent out of London because of the risk from bombing. So it was ironic that our train was attacked by a German plane, which strafed the Mid-Suffolk line near Stradbroke. Eventually, we were picked up by taxi at 3am and taken to Peasenhall. Just down the road from here. We bunked down in an old Women's Institute hut. I remember being woken up early the next day by the sound of the nearby blacksmith's bellows being pumped. We were taken across to what is now the New Inn. A lady doled us out some warm bread, with a proper dollop of butter. There was an evacuee called Sydney Madge staying there. He'd been there since 1939. So he was able to tell us a bit about the local people and places. Syd also advised us not to use the toilets in the yard. A few hours later, I found out why. They were very basic. Remember that scene in *Slumdog Millionaire* where the Indian kid gets covered in the bad stuff? The New Inn toilets were a bit like that. It'll be much more pleasant there, now it's a Landmark Trust property.'

'I've heard that name, but I don't know much about the Landmark Trust. Hang on, isn't the Martello Tower in Aldeburgh one of theirs?'

'That's right, Warren. The Landmark Trust is a charity that rescues buildings, sensitively restores them, and then turns them into holiday accommodation. Zoe's mother, India, introduced Marina and me to them. I know Skye has stayed in a few.'

'Indeed I have. My first was an old fishing lodge, up near the Scottish border, called Coop House. Like all the Landmarks, it had a good library and an absence of modern electronic distractions. It was an oasis of calm. Last April, I had a week on Lundy Island, staying in The *Radio* Room. Which, I think you'll agree, is appropriate. That Lundy Landmark is actually designed for just one visitor. And of course, Colin will remember his belated, but elated, 70th birthday, which we celebrated at the White House. The name *Chatter Broth* was inspired by something that Marina wrote in the logbook there over a dozen years ago.

~

Marina's entry in The White House Logbook, 2005 with additional comments by Zoe, Colin, Skye, Angelique, Mel & Richard

What a privilege to stay in Aston Munslow at Miss Purser's 'four-houses-in-one', which she donated to the Landmark Trust in 1990. The architectural mix (medieval, Tudor, Jacobean and Georgian) makes for an atmospheric stay. In 1966 she opened the Museum of Country Life in one of the outbuildings. Did she hire a consultant or use an agency?

No, she borrowed a schoolboy. I wonder what his name was. And whether it was the same boy who directed an earlier visitor to the White House, by pointing out the grounds next to a conker tree. What's a conker tree? I was also fascinated by the History Room, with all its research on the people, especially the Stedman family, who have lived here over the centuries.

A note of caution though. Do not linger in this room by yourself after midnight. Especially if you believe in ghosts, which I don't. Although the contents of the Galician wines I brought with me seemed to evaporate mysteriously fast. The White House seems to breathe, with the medieval oak trusses still supporting the roof. I can understand why an Oxford professor saw buildings like this as 'historic documents', which could be read.

I can imagine a horse in the cider house, slowly moving the millstone. The millstone is made of something called ocean conglomerate. The sea seems a strange place to source such a heavy piece of machinery. The cider was poured from a big barrel into a leather container called a costrel. Maybe that word come from costard, which is a type of apple. I only know this about this fruit variety because we had costard custard (ho, ho) in Ludlow on Wednesday. And on the subject of food, we tried to recreate one of Constance's traditions. Local farm workers were traditionally fed on broth twice a day, and Miss Purser used to raise funds by hosting Broth Mornings. Soup and a good natter? I think I'd call that *Natter Broth*. The soup, or broth, was made in large pots, mainly made with vegetables and herbs from the garden. Apparently, the prep was done with a century-old vegetable slicer. For our version, we used a peeler we'd bought en route in Bridgnorth. By the end of the meal, everyone declared themselves to be full of soup. I wonder if there's a word for that. We didn't pop any pigeons into our pot. The dovecote, which once housed over 500 pigeons, is now derelict. I think the 'cote' part means a cottage, but why a 'dove' cottage, rather than a pigeon one? You had to be, at the very least, a knight to eat pigeons legally. Although I imagine some were poached by the locals, before being roasted.

Marina Rueda, The Hop Yard (originally from Boise, Idaho)

Marina didn't know what playing conkers was, so I told her. She laughed. I don't know why. Is it such a funny game? I was a bit scared of the moles. I didn't see any, but I saw the mounds they made. My Daddy said it made the croquet interesting. I hope a mole didn't pop its head up when a ball was zooming across the lawn. We saw some jumping sheep on Wenlock Edge. They might be better at avoiding croquet balls than moles.

Zoe, aged 4 years and 10 months (written up by Angelique)

Thanks to the Housekeeper for presenting the property so beautifully and for the vase of flowers left on the kitchen table. The seven of us have had a wonderful week. We ventured to Clun, Stokesay Castle and Ludlow. And a few of us might have popped down the lane to the pub for last orders. More than once. But most of the time was spent in this house and its grounds. After all, the village is called Aston Mun-SLOW.

Colin Pargeter, The Hop Yard, Suffolk

We agree with all of the above, and both of us admit to aiding wine evaporation. I'd never even heard of Albarino. It's delicious, though maybe not after apple custard. Oh, and we have come to a different definition of what a costrel is. I agree with Angelique's idea, that it's actually a small bird of prey which is recovering from having fallen into a cider vat.

Two More Hop Yarders (Skye Hunter and Angelique Vonk)

Maybe you are thinking about which Landmark to stay in next. The Hop Yard is very close to three LT properties, two are which are on either side of a medieval hall. Unless you're reading this soon, I won't be there (Colin chooses people to run the bookshop as they wish for six months or a year, and my stint ends next month). But please bop in, hop in or pop in anyway. Maybe in years to come it will be *you* living above Bay Six Books. And deciding whether to arrange the books by author surname or by genre. Or by however the mood takes you.

Mel Cooper, Fife

My doctor gave me permission to reduce my medication for the week, as long as I didn't take any other drugs, including alcohol. Fortunately, there's lots of apple juice to be had in this part of the world. This old house has lots of exit points. I like that about a place. I saw my daughter, Zoe, for the first time in over four years. She seemed unfazed by me turning up. How is it that children are, so often, more resilient than adults? Or do they just appear to be? Those are two of the questions I'll be asking my new therapist next week.

Richard Duffy, Marylebone

~

'By the way, Skye, how old were you when the war ended?'

Skye glanced at Colin, and he gave her a small nod. 'I was three and three-quarters. But the war didn't really end for me until 1948, just after my seventh birthday. Gosh, I haven't talked about this for years, decades even. And I will, but not today. It's time for another song. Have you got one about a buvette, Warren?'

'I don't know if the pub in *this* song was small, but here goes.'

'That was "Baggy Trousers" by Madness. I can understand the teachers all being in a pub, with that pre-smoking ban fug. But would the naughty boys have damaged all those tools? The woodwork room would surely have been a place they *enjoyed* working in.'

'I agree, Warren. I loved working with my hands. But my absolute favourite things at school were the cross-country runs. More so in Alresford, with its softer chalk. Rather than here, where my plimsolls gave little protection from all the sharp flints. And my love of running is why I've chosen Jesse Owens. Not his record-breaking performances at the Berlin Olympics. It was another event within this fortnight of history, but a year earlier. On May 25th, 1935, his Ohio State team drove to Michigan for the university championships. Jesse was still recovering from falling into a stairwell the week before. He needed a long soak in the bath before competing. First up, just after 3.15pm, was the 100-yard dash. Whoosh, 9.4 seconds. That equalled the world record. The timing was very tight, so he only had time for *one* attempt in the long jump. He smashed the world record by 15cm. By 4pm, he held another *four* world records.'

'I feel exhausted, just thinking about it. How about you, Warren?'

'I'll certainly need a kip later. Did anything else catch your eye, Colin?'

'Jesse enjoyed his hot soak, just as people did a couple of centuries earlier in London. The first English indoor swimming pool, Bagnio, was opened on May 28th, 1742. Bagnio was in Lemon Street, which sounds rather refreshing too. For a guinea, Richard and Elizabeth Haddock offered their male customers "*Sweating, Bathing and Cupping*". Multi-tasking waiters were also on hand to offer swimming tuition. Such bathing houses were often suspected to be fronts for brothels. William Hogarth painted *Bagnio*, which suggested that other services *were* readily available.'

'I've often wondered why we still use the guinea, especially in the north of Suffolk at Newmarket. And very few people could have afforded to pay that much.'

'Perhaps that was the point, Skye.'

'Talking of cupping, I think it's time for a brew. Though I can see you're thinking of something else, Colin.'

'I am, Skye. 1980 was an unsettling year. Not just Bologna in August. The senseless deaths at the station. And the shock to Abigail Farr, which caused the premature birth of India. The hospital staff were amazing, showing great care as the injured were brought in by ambulances, and even by buses. Though they couldn't save everyone . . . Indeed, I don't think her mother ever really recovered from the trauma. However, I'm thinking about another explosion from 1980, back on May 18th. People knew there was going to be an eruption. One was an old-timer called Harry Truman. He refused to leave the danger area. But when

Mt St Helens erupted, I found it truly shocking. Physically sickening. I remember hearing Jimmy Carter on the radio, saying that the moon was more like a golf course, compared to the destruction he'd seen. Marina was on holiday with her family, in Portland, just over the border from Washington. When she saw the images on CNN, she thought the world had come to an end. A Forestry Service worker wrote a poem about it, "Pondering The Immensity Of Change". I'll see if I can dig it out for you.'

Chapter 03

'Hi, I'm Skye Hunter and welcome to *Chatter Broth*. It's May 29th and today's guest is Gita Chowdhury. Some of our listeners will have bought a book or attended a book club at Bay Six Books. Gita has now been with us for nine months. To get things started, what has sparked your interest in this fortnight of history?'

'Good morning, Skye. And thank you, Warren, for providing me with such a good selection of research notes.'

'I enjoyed it, Gita. I'm looking forward to hearing your choices.'

'One choice I've made, is to attend my first life modelling class later this week. As an artist, not a model. I could never do that. Well, not without my full war paint.'

'I think Warren meant your In This Fortnight choices. But I'll see you there on Thursday. I don't really know what to expect. But as Angelique has organised it, it should be interesting. Back to your choices?'

'Of course, Skye. Not surprisingly, I'll start with a book. My heritage is Indian, but I was born in the UK. The author of the book was born in India, but he was British. There's a strange synchronicity there. And when he changed his name, from Eric Blair, he chose a Suffolk river for his surname.'

'The Orwell. And I think his parents were then living further up the coast at Southwold.'

'Spot on, Skye. Almost seventy years ago, on June 8th 1949, George Orwell's *Nineteen Eighty-Four* was published. It was originally going to be called *The Last Man in Europe*. But Orwell simply reversed the last two digits of the year he had finished the novel. Who knows how a title impacts on sales and readership? Or even an author's name? Kenneth Miles and X were just two of the pseudonyms which the then Eric Blair rejected. I chose *Nineteen Eighty-Four* as my second book club selection, back in October. There were all the usual discussions and comments: Big Brother and Room 101. The Thought Police and telescreens. Ignorance is Strength, Freedom is Slavery and War is Peace. And a few that were new for me. Like "Oranges and Lemons" and Rewrite Squads. I had asked everyone to bring in a glass paperweight. Winston Smith buys one from Mr Charrington's so-called junk shop for four dollars. Upstairs was the bug-ridden room in which Winston and Julia's affair was finally discovered. Winston was fascinated by the paperweight. By the age of it. How delicate it was. Its uselessness. And by the fragment of coral inside it. Talking about the book, with everyone's paperweights on the coffee table, was a special experience.'

'I remember that evening well, Gita. I took along a small paperweight I'd inherited from my great-aunt Winifred. It stirred up memories for me, about a time that seems like another life. Another world almost.'

'I know what you mean, Skye. Ordinary or unlikely objects can take on meaning, often at an unexpected time.'

'Which book have you chosen for next month?'

'It's *How the States Got Their Shapes* by Mark Stein. Marina recommended it to me, and she comes from Idaho. Look at the strange shape of *that* state in the book or on one of George's maps. I can see you're both doubtful, but it's a fascinating read. I'm not sure if it's *as* fascinating, but on June 9th, 1790, *The Philadelphia Spelling Book* became the first book to be copyrighted.

Its aim was to "*expedite the instruction of youth*". India told me about it. She came across it when she was living, about a decade ago, in the Old City district of Philadelphia. And there's a Dickens connection there, Warren. You were born in Portsmouth too. It's something about a stuffed bird, I think.'

'I don't know about the bird, but I love the reclining statue of Dickens outside Portsmouth Guildhall.'

'I was once invited to play polo near there. It was at a place called Cowdray Park. The official matches had finished, but a group of us stayed on. It's tricky playing polo in the dark.'

~

Philadelphia, 2008

'I'm guessing you must be India.'

India looked up at the wild-haired and velvet-suited man. 'And that means you are Zebediah Raggio?'

'Yer got that right. Folks call me Zeb. I need some eats, and you look kinda hungrified. So stay there, while I forage.'

'I've not tried a Philly Cheesesteak yet.'

'They're real good, India, especially on a hearth-baked Amoroso roll with thinly shaved rib-eye, Cheez Whiz, sautéed onions and 'shrooms. Maybe a twist of black pepper. And a splash of ketchup. Takes me right back to my South Philly childhood haunts. But we've hooked up here at Reading Terminal Market for a different reason. A DiNic's roast pork sandwich, simply served with sharp provolone cheese, roasted peppers and grilled broccoli.'

'Sounds good to me, Zeb. This is quite a place.'

'It aches and creaks with history. The kind of place that sings, making sweet harmonies out of strange frequencies. It was purpose-built under the old railroad tracks. They squeezed eight hundred stalls in here. Now there are only about eighty.'

'It still seems pretty crowded.'

'It's on the way back up. When my family moved up to Old City in the 1970s, to avoid the Italian-Irish shenanigans, it was kinda spacious. Just a few dozen vendors. I'll join the queue.'

'I enjoyed that, Zeb.'

'An army marches on its stomach. But I split our sandwich, so we could get some apple dumplings from the Dutch Eating Place.'

'Dutch?'

'Comes from the word *Deutsch*, as they were originally German-speaking immigrants. It's hosted by Amish and Mennonite families from around rural Pennsylvania. Do you remember the movie *Witness?*'

'It came out when I was about five, but I saw it later on DVD. I remember Harrison Ford feeling quite awkward one morning — AM-ish, if you like — watching Kelly McGillis.'

'You *do* remember it. Detective John Book and Rachel. Most of the urban scenes were shot on location, here in Philly. Lots of the production roles, like carpenters and painters, were filled by Amish folk. Out of the picture. But most of the extras were Mennonites. The scene where young Samuel witnesses the murder was filmed nearby at Amtrak's 30th Street Station.'

'I didn't like it when the corrupt cops arrived at the farm. It felt like an invasion.'

'But they under-estimated the opposition. Do you remember that scene in the silo? The actor was totally covered in corn. He had to have diving gear and an oxygen tank, so he could breathe. Do you want cream or ice cream with your dumplings?'

'Ice cream sounds good. Though probably not avocado this time.'

'Avocado?'

'There's a great ice cream parlour called Capofitto near my hotel. The owner persuaded me to try it. I was dubious, but it was strangely delicious.'

'As it happens, there's a Bassetts here, over at the 12th Street exit. They also do interesting flavours. Though I think I'll stick to classic peach.'

'That was a good hike. Time to introduce you to more of my city, through the power of mini golf.'

'It looks like an interesting course, Zeb.'

'They've jazzed up this area around Franklin Square recently. Pay eight bucks and get yerself a mini eighteen-hole history lesson.'

'We haven't talked about the property yet. I don't even know where it is.'

'Plenty of time for that. I'm still trying to get my very peculiar head around the idea. I trust Ana Logan, and she spoke so highly of you. What you did, out there on the Outer Banks, and the care you did it with. Especially as her aged parent was still living in the converted garage.'

'I made good use of the time whenever Mrs Logan was collected for her weekly check-up in Ocracoke. I also shifted a lot of stuff at night, making sure I dodged the beam from the lighthouse.'

'India, no-one's living in the property here. But it isn't empty. Just the opposite, in fact. It's full of stuff. Shall we start our round of golf before the crowds arrive?'

Zeb still looked confident, despite having lost the first three holes. 'Early days, India. Though I wouldn't bet against yer!'

'I like the thought that has gone into this course. Like having Philly singers, back at Hole Two.'

'We like our music here in Philly. Even Benjamin Franklin could have played a part. I love the theremin, but he invented the glass armonica. He played it by moving his fingers around the rims of glass bowls. Kinda neat, but probably wouldn't survive in a tour bus. Now, this is the first Par 3. Elfreth's Alley. It's based on the oldest street in the city. Rudyard Kipling lived up in Vermont for a time. But he wrote about the alley in 1910: "*There's little left, indeed, of the city . . . the pigeons strut in the narrow way*". Even then, there wasn't much of Old Philly left. It was growing fast. In the 1770s, it had overtaken Dublin and Edinburgh to become the second largest city in the British Empire.'

'Elfreth sounds Anglo-Saxon.'

'It was the surname of two English chaps, Jeremiah and Josiah. We like a good biblical name in the City of Brotherly Love. Though the street started off as Gilbert's Alley, then Elfreth's, then Preston's. It somehow even became Cherry Street for a while.'

'I'm staying on Chestnut. I like that some of the main streets are named after trees. Oh, good shot.'

'A hole-in-one and I'm back in the game.'

'Hole Six had the Ben Franklin Bridge going over the Delaware. When that bridge was built in the Roaring Twenties, the Alley was in its *Cherry* phase. Just survived being torn down. A decade later it survived a plan to turn the area into warehouses. Later still, some of the houses were zoned off to make way for a new Interstate. Luckily, *that* plan was squashified. Ben Franklin is rumoured to have stayed at No. 108, when he first arrived in Philadelphia. Philip Syng, a friend of his, worked as a silversmith in the alley. If you look carefully at the $2 bill, you—'

'Two dollar note? Is there such a thing?'

'There surely is. Jefferson's on the front, but it's the back that's really interesting. It shows the signing of the Declaration of Independence in 1776. If you look closely at that image, you can make out a quill. Resting in an inkstand made by, you guessed it, Mr Syng. However, Ben Franklin was a complicated man. By way of example, he promoted freedom while being a slave owner. But make sure you visit the B. Free Franklin Post Office. Not only does Ben appear on the one-dollar bill, he was also on our first postage stamp. It's quirky, and unique among US post offices. It doesn't have a ZIP code, it doesn't fly the flag, and it's named after a signature. The clerks still use quills and wear Colonial-era uniforms. If you go, remember to get your mail hand-franked at Franklin's.'

'Five-all, so all to play for, Zeb.'

'Well done on the last hole, India. We walked through the *real* Chinese Friendship Gate on our way up here. That was a popular meeting place during the Beijing Games, earlier this year. And we'll go past the Love Park sculpture on our way to the Free Library and the Museum of Art. You managed to avoid your ball coming *down* its steps on the last hole.'

'The steps that Rocky ran up?'

'He did, though I like to walk. My favourite work in the museum has a different kind of steps in it. Charley Peale was quite a painter. He even named some of his kids after famous artists, such as Titian and Rembrandt. Two of his sons pop up in *The Staircase Group*. The bottom of that painting even has a step attached to it. Gives yer even more of a feeling that you could step right into it. When we visit my property later, you'll see why I love it.'

'Fourteen is my favourite hole, India. I love the atmosphere of Boathouse Row on the Schuylkill River. If you're feeling daring, you can aim your ball into the river. It might even emerge on the other bank and pop straight in the hole.'

'I'm glad there's a hole based on Philly teams. Eagles fans are an optimistic bunch. There's a slogan that reads, '*Every Fall We Will Rise*'. Will we ever win the Super Bowl? Not this year, but it's gonna happen.'

'What a great time to get your first hole-in-one, India. The match is tied and you rang the bell. And don't worry. There was a crack in that old bell *before* you played your shot.'

'Just coming through the doors, you knew this was going to be a great library.'

'The Free Library is more than great. It's also the hub for more than fifty branches around the city.'

'So why are we here, Zeb? Is there a mini golf course down in the stacks?'

'Not yet. Heh, heh. I'll just turn off my cellphone. I don't want it ringing wild where we're going.'

'Which is where?'

'It's just round this corner.' Zeb and India turned right, into a quiet corridor. 'Have a look in that glass case, India.'

'It's a stuffed bird.'

'Not just any bird. It was the pet raven of Charles Dickens.'

'Very impressive, but why's it here?'

'Dickens visited the city a couple of times. He quite liked it, but found the streets too straight for his—'

'He wrote, "*I felt that I would have given the world for a crooked street*". Sorry for interrupting. I work here at the Rare Books Department'

'The more the merrier, I say. My friend here is visiting from England.'

'Oh, that's wonderful. Do you know the story?'

'Didn't Dickens buy the raven as part of his novel research?'

'That's right, for Barnaby Rudge. Grip, the raven, was a

character in real life too. His main hobby seemed to have been trying to bite children. Dickens must have overlooked that kind of behaviour, as he called him the 'best of birds' on Grip's memorial. Though painted on wood, as you can see, it was more detailed than many a deceased person would have got. Dickens wrote that his raven, on the day that it died, made a bequest. Grip said he would like to dispose of "his little property, consisting chiefly of a halfpenny". Grip's last words were, "Halloa old girl!" And Grip came here as part of a bequest. We have been left some wonderful donations, such as a desk and chair which belonged to Dickens. Have you seen his statue yet, with Little Nell at his feet?'

'I haven't shown that to my British friend yet. I'm sure she'll have come across one.'

'Not unless she's visited Sydney.'

'I haven't. Why did you say it like that?'

'The only two statues are here and in Australia. It was quite a scandal. Charles Dickens, in his final will, left a detailed set of instructions. Including that his funeral be inexpensive, and that attendees avoid wearing, "*black bow, long hat band or other such revolting absurdity*". And he was very clear that he should not be the subject of *any* monument. He wished instead to be remembered for his published works.'

'So why did we Philly folk ignore his wishes?'

'Good question. The statue was commissioned in 1890, but struggled to find a buyer. At one point it was even sent over to England and offered to Sir Henry Dickens, a son of Charles. He was furious. Maybe he even said, "What the Dickens!", in response. But there still isn't a statue in England, though I've heard a whisper about plans for one in Portsmouth. Our statue was eventually bought in 1900, for $7,500, by a local charity based nearby in Fairmount Park. What's your interest in Dickens?'

'I inherited a property in Old City. It's mainly stuffed full of junk, but there are a few sparks of light. Like a five-shilling note from 1773, which has the warning, "*To counterfeit is Death*". Then there was a scrap of a letter, in which the writer mentioned hearing Charles Dickens in Chestnut Street. And holding the audience in the "*palm of his hands*". Who knows what else might be waiting to be discovered and released?'

'I'd love to see that letter. You found it in Old City?'

'Yes, in Elfreth's Alley. Though my place is a bit more rundown than the miniature version up at Hole Four in Franklin Park.'

'You've picked an interesting watering hole for us, India.'

'It's halfway between my hotel and Elfreth's Alley. I thought we could grab a drink, and a snack, before we head over.'

'It's called Skinner's Tavern now, but last time I was here it was called Anthony's. This table's a bit wonkified, so let's head over to a booth.'

'Evening folks and welcome to Skinner's. Yes, that booth is free. I'm Ophelia. See anything you fancy? On the menu, that is.'

'What do you suggest, Zeb?'

'A mid-winter's night dream? Actually, I think Ophelia was in *Hamlet*. I'll have a pint of Kenzinger, please. What kinda beers do yer like, India?'

'Nothing too hoppy, but preferably local. What do you think, Ophelia?'

'We know what we are, but know not what we may be. As for *drinks*, I'll get you some tasters. Let's see . . . I'm thinking Dock Street's Pilsner and Carol Stoudt's Scarlet Lady Ale. Carol was a real pioneer, and that particular brew is made in an English style. You should try the fries too. They come with a tasty South Asian-style sauce. Did I hear you guys mention Elfreth's?'

'You did. India here's gonna be living over there for a while. Sorting through, seeing what's good. That kinda stuff.'

'Hey, that's neat. But all by yourself? That's brave. If you need a break, come on over here. Unless there's a ballgame on the screen. It gets a little rowdy on *those* nights.'

'This street is so atmospheric, Zeb.'

'It's certainly is. It's almost as if it's got a will to survive. But don't let appearances fool you. These cobblestones were only laid in the run-up to the Bicentennial in 1976. I remember when it was just Belgian Blocks. My grandma had this place and we lived three blocks north. She could tell you some stories about the area. Have you heard of Jemina Wilkinson?'

'No, who was she?'

'This was before Grandma Raggio's time. Jemina liked to wear pants — that's trousers in your tongue — and tell folk that she'd been resurrected, like Jesus. And that *her* gospel was feminism. She got stoned for that. Another thing I remember, scared the living daylights out of me. I was sitting down in the family room, drinking black tea. A face appeared at the window. Its owner had leapt up to peek inside. Grandma called people who did that jumpers. Sometimes, curious folk would even try the door. Now, here we are.'

Zeb stopped outside a boarded-up property. 'It might look under-loved, but it was in an even worse state back in the 1970s. It had been near-derelict since before Pearl Harbor. That's why it was on the market for $47,000. My father fixed it up, for his parents, but he didn't mess around with it too much. Most of the properties here have a modern interior. I'm thinking of turning it back into more of a trinity house.'

'What's that, when it's at home?'

'Pretty simple. With just one large room for each of the three storeys, with the kitchen tucked away down in the basement.

Though I'll probably create a 21st-century sanctuary up in the attic. How long do you think you'll need?'

'The way I work, it can take up to a year. But it's more typically six months.'

'I've also got a short-term lease on a store nearby. You could use that for sorting. And then maybe selling stuff my family don't want. I've found some good stuff already. But some of the rooms are tricky to get into. I don't know what happened after Grandpa died. Grandma kept a tidy house downstairs. None of the family knew what was being stored and stacked on the *upper* floors. It's very—'

'Don't worry, Zeb. I've seen it before. And older people have more experience in being secretive. This is what I do.'

'And you're positive that you want to do this alone?'

'I want to and I need to. When I started out, in Boise, there were people around. At least, they tried to be. My second project, in Rehoboth Beach, was almost my last one. I loved that part of Delaware, and I certainly had a few Dogfish Head brews. But the family couldn't sit back and wait. They would phone up and ask me if I'd found this trinket, or seen that beloved heirloom. I had to threaten to leave them to it. That would have been tricky. As they were based down by the Gulf of Mexico, near Pensacola. So I work solo. India Farr, by myself. IF, only.'

'I like your firm attitude. My family are scattered now, so it's a relief. And I'll enjoy spending some of the next year in England. Which heritage property are we going to stay in before I head on to Suffolk?'

'I've chosen a place called Obriss Farm. It's not so far from places that Charles Dickens used to haunt.'

'Hurrah, hurrah, hurrah!'

'You *are* excited, Zeb.'

'That's a fact. But I was just quoting that curmudgeonly raven, Grip. Shall we go in?'

'This is a wonderful property. I love the wooden flooring and all the exposed brickwork.'

'It holds many happy memories for me, India. Though the outside privy took a bit of getting used to.'

'I see you've got a print of *The Staircase Group*. With a mini step attached at the base.'

'Just like the real one we saw earlier at the museum. Charley Peale originally had it attached to a door in his studio. Then he added a *real* step. Now, check out those two doors next to the fireplace.'

India walked across the room and opened both of the doors. The first doorway led down to a cellar. The second one, accessed by a raised step, led upstairs.

'Just like Charley's painting, though ours spirals the other way. I almost had to tunnel my way through, to access the rooms up there. I'll show you tomorrow. For now, please tell me more about how you work. You take the seat, I'll perch on this tea chest'

'Thanks, Zeb. Sometimes I'll spend two or three months living in a property before I start clearing. Reading documents and looking at photographs. Talking to the neighbours and exploring the local area. Getting a feel for the person whose home it was. It's an emotional process, even though I'm normally dealing with the possessions of a stranger. For many reasons, as you might imagine, my service is niche. And it needs to be personal.'

'That's not how estate sales or house clearances usually work.'

'I don't see my work in that way. I try and tune into the history of the home, then sort and sift.'

'Like a curator of memories and meaningful memorabilia?'

'Just like that. It's quite an emotionally draining process. Which is why I need to get the right sort of clients. More for their sake, I suppose. They have to place a lot of trust in me.'

'So you get all your new clients via recommendations?'

'Yes, so far. But it's not an instant process. Partly because I organise holidays as well, like I did for Ana. Each year, I invite potential clients to meet up with me in Britain. I create a five to ten-day trip for them based on their family history, tailored to their professional and leisure interests. Then we meet up, usually at a mews house in Marylebone.'

'What's a mews when it's at home, India?'

'Colin, a very good friend, used to own two houses in London. A grand one on Pershore Place. And a smaller one, attached to the rear, with access to a service road. It had previously been used as stables, with staff quarters above. The smaller property, which Colin still owns, is just one of a row of such properties. And such rows are known as mews. Like Elfreth's Alley, they're often more appreciated now than they were in the past.'

'Yer got that right. Though we shouldn't become too complacent. Who knows what improvement scheme City Hall might dream up? For our edification and delight.'

'My mother used to live at Number 17, the mews house. Now, Colin and the other Hop Yarders use it as their London base. But I'm allowed to have lunch with my clients there. It's strange, though. My mother used to live in the main house. But it took over a year to sort and move her possessions to the smaller property. Most of the rooms were full of all kinds of stuff. Which Colin and I had to sneak out. Abigail was very curious about what we were doing in her old home. Maybe it was a bit like the rooms upstairs here.'

'So you know the kind of things that might be squirrelled away upstairs. But why don't you live with your mother?'

'Good question, Zeb. My twin brother died on our birth day, and my mother never forgave me. That's how it feels anyway. She has a live-in carer now, so there'd be no room for me.

Luckily, for her and for me, Colin has supported both of us. As well as my daughter, Zoe.'

'Ana told me you had a daughter. Who does Zoe live with when you're working?'

'She lives with Colin and Marina, at the Hop Yard. I haven't seen her since she was a baby, over six years ago.'

'Sounds like there's some strong emotions being submerged. Some hard rocks, and hard knocks, between you and a clear channel. Between you and your mother. Between you and your daughter . . . It must be very tough for you all. Living near and yet so far away from each other. How does Zoe feel about things?'

'I've heard that she seems quite happy. And she's surrounded by a group of people who have time for her. I think she's better off without me, but I know that's a controversial viewpoint.'

'There'll always be someone who wants to slam your name. Even if *you* think you're doing the right thing. You know, we're *all* strange in our own special ways.'

'That's so true, Zeb. For me, this work seems to be the right thing. Right for me, if not for my relationships. I'm IF, only . . . In more ways than one.'

'I'm glad you're here. And that we first met on my home turf. Though I'm looking forward to seeing London and staying with you at Obriss Farm.'

'I think you'll love the Hop Yard too. You'll quickly become part of the family.'

~

'That was fascinating, Gita. I'll never look at jodhpurs in the same way again. I think we'll give you a break and allow you to fully unsaddle, so to speak. So what are the Lost Four Words this time, Warren?'

'Thanks, Skye. And what a great story, Gita. You maintained your dignity, and came out smiling. In very challenging circumstances, despite only wearing—'

'Last time, we were looking for words beginning with the letter C.'

'Thanks, Skye. Of course. I'm back in the present. Our final four are chark, chummage, cloop and contranatant:

The cloop in the corridor,
Hinted at how the chummage
Had been spent.
She could chark all day,
But being contranatant often came at a price.'

'And your thoughts on what meaning there may be, Warren?'
'Well, Skye, how about this?

Outside the cell, the noise made by a cork leaving a bottle,
Showed how the new prisoner fee, paid to the other inmates,
Had been spent.
She could grind her teeth all day,
But going against the flow could be expensive.

What do you think, Gita?'

'I suggested chirospasm, Warren, a writer's cramp. Though I like the selection, especially cloop. That's a sound I like, although most of my wine purchases now come with screwtops. But contranatant is a powerful word. And the price sometimes paid, when going against the flow, isn't always economic. There's often a human cost as well. For example, protestors come up against many obstacles, and not always the ones you might expect. A letter written on May 29th, in this fortnight of history, is a good example. It includes, "*Feminists ought to get a good whipping . . . By claiming equality with men, they — that is women — would become the most hateful, heathen and disgusting of beings and would surely perish without male protection*". And that was written by a woman in 1870. Queen Victoria, in fact. Luckily, not everyone listened to her. One who didn't was a Suffragette called Emily Davison. We'll probably never know if she intended to kill herself at the 1913 Derby. She had a return train ticket, but then everyone was issued with one of those on big race days. I'm undecided. But I think getting struck by *Anmer*, the king's horse, was a coincidence. I've been on the rails at Goodwood. The horses pass in a blur . . . I love what happened two years *before* her death, during the 1911 census. Suffragettes typically tried to avoid being recorded. They were known, by some, as census-slinkers. A satirical magazine of the time threw a weak punch when it wrote, "*The suffragettes have definitely taken leave of their census*". But Emily was recorded twice. Inaccurately, at her lodgings. And then, in the Palace of Westminster, when she was discovered hiding there. Her diet, while she hid in a parliamentary broom cupboard, was unusual. It consisted of meat lozenges — a bizarre mix of dried meat and jelly — and lime juice.'

'Definitely not something we'll be serving up at the Field Party. I think it's time for some Four Play. What have you got for us, Warren?'

'I'm going with the theme of contranatant, going against the flow. If people just accept unfairness and prejudice against others, then they shouldn't be too surprised when it's *their* turn to be targeted. So here's The Manic Street Preachers, with "If You Tolerate This, Then Your Children Will Be Next".'

'I remember seeing the Manics at the Eden Project a few years ago. I was staying at Frenchman's Creek, a remote Landmark

Trust cottage between Falmouth and Helston. The Manics produce good albums, but they're even better live. Just like Snow Patrol are, and The Scissor Sisters. The Proclaimers too. And Toyah Wilcox, of course. She can definitely still rock it out. Though sometimes it's better if you don't focus on the lyrics too much. Like that bit about rabbits and fascists, from the song you just played, Warren.'

'I'm with you there, Skye. It's like that song by Adele. I always thought, bizarrely, she was chasing *penguins*, not pavements. And sometimes people think they remember things that didn't even happen. A kind of false news, rather than deliberately faking news.'

'Can you give me some examples?'

'I can, Skye. When I was researching the In This Fortnight notes, I came across some 'facts' that surprised me. On May 31st, eighty years ago, the last of over fifteen million Model Ts rolled off the Ford production line—'

'Any colour, so long as it's black.'

'That's right, Gita. Or rather, it's not. For the first five or six years after its introduction in 1908, black was not even an option. The four paint choices were blue, green, grey and red. For instance, if you bought the touring version it could be either green or red. The non-option of black only came in during 1914. My other 'fact' bookmarks the era of the Second World War. Television transmissions ceased at the outbreak, and didn't resume again until June 7th, 1946—'

'Ah, Leslie Mitchell. With his "As I was saying before I was so rudely interrupted".'

'I wish it had been, Skye. You were only a kid at the time, so you can be forgiven for the error. And you probably didn't have a TV.'

'Actually, I did. Sort of. I've had time to think about it more since we were speaking about evacuation with Colin, a fortnight ago. I was evacuated to Peasenham in 1944 with my mother, a few weeks before my third birthday. Earlier that month, the government had said that the battle for London was all over. Later that day, the first V2 rocket landed, just three streets away from our home in Chiswick. My mother was terrified. We left in a rush and I left my birthday present by the front door. I wonder what it was. Probably not a paperweight. Anyway, in January my mother went to London one day and never came back. I don't think she abandoned me. It was just one of those things. My father had died in 1942. He'd been removing incendiary bombs from a burning cinema, The Regal, when the roof collapsed. They never found him either.'

'Oh, Skye. I can't imagine how you felt. Was it terrible? And how is it that you're still in Peasenham?'

'I suppose it should have been terrible, Gita. But I was lucky in other ways. I was passed around various foster parents, but then in 1947—'

'You couldn't have been an evacuee in 1947. Could you?'

'I was, Warren. There were tens of thousands of displaced people, mainly adults, in the years after the war. I was one of them. There were still even around 1500 unclaimed evacuees in July 1948. Yes, 1500. Three years after the war ended. But Colin had stepped in on my behalf a year earlier. He'd been formally adopted by the Pargeters. They had no children of their own, and of course he was an orphan too by then. He was only twelve, but he somehow managed to persuade the Pargeters to 'adopt' me as well. I suppose I was the first of what you might call his waifs and strays. When the Pargeters died, back in the late Fifties, he was the sole beneficiary of their will. He sold Peasenham Hall, and most of its land, to pay off death duties. Though he kept this yard — which became the Hop Yard, where we are today — and one of the fields. The main London house at Pershore Place was later sold to give Colin some funds, but he kept the mews property behind it. Many people say the Sixties were good, but the early Seventies were delightful. And having a London bolthole, even though it was in an almost derelict state then, was terrific. Let's just say that my 29-year-old former self found it liberating. You've been there Gita, haven't you?'

'Yes. And I'm twenty-nine now. For a few more months, at least. I kept Zoe company when she was looking at various University options in London. We shared a room because Abigail's possessions were still waiting to be sorted in the other bedroom. Why—'

'Oh, I know where we were. Televisions. The Pargeters had a TV, Warren.'

'So back to Leslie Mitchell. It wasn't him who restarted the BBC broadcast after the Second World War. Although that would have been brilliant. It was actually a BBC announcer. She said, "Good afternoon, everybody. How are you? Do you remember me, Jasmine Bligh? Well here we are, after a lapse of nearly seven years ready to start again, and of course we are all terribly excited and thrilled". I love that. Even if it *is* true. Linking to the TV theme, is my final thought on 'false' information. Some people think that the first video recorder came out in 1965. A Sony, costing a whopping $995. But Ampex brought one out in 1956. That was a staggering $50,000. But it wasn't aimed at the general public. But what about the Telcan — short for television in a can — in 1963, I hear you say. The £60 kit, made in England, was not a hit. So who knows what is true and what isn't, Skye?'

'That's a very good question, Warren.'

'That was "Message in a Bottle", by The Police. I wonder if corks still go *cloop* when they are pulled out after a long sea journey.'

'Probably not, Skye. Christopher Columbus made some long sea journeys. Luckily, for me and my ancestors, he never found

India. This is why an event from June 2nd, in 1537, caught my attention. Pope Paul III banned enslavement of 'Indians' in the Americas. His declaration stated that they — the so-called Indians — despite being heathens, were fully rational human beings who had rights to freedom and private property. The implications of his decision still impact on the world today. For example, the Spanish, as well as other nations, looked to Africa for its slave labour. And the legacy is complicated. I know that some First Tribes members still prefer to call themselves Indians, rather than Native Americans. And then there's the Washington Redskins, who play in the NFL. So Warren, could you play "Buffalo Soldier" by Bob Marley & The Wailers?'

~

Life Modelling at the Hop Yard #1

'Thank you all for coming,' Angelique said. She looked across at the assembled faces. Gita was resting her left elbow on her right hand, while using her other hand to play with her hair. Skye was looking downwards, but smiling. Marina was looking nervous.

Angelique continued her introduction. 'It was the artist Delacroix who said, "Every time I await a model . . . I am overjoyed . . . and I tremble when I hear the key turning in the door". Now, we are all of a very different artistic standard, compared to Eugene. But I understand what he meant, even though today I am the model. Some years ago, I met a farmer from Dunwich who said I was a bushel bubby. I didn't know then that he meant a woman. A woman with large, full breasts. And I suppose I was that woman then, with the backache to prove it, before my cancer diagnosis. Relief from that pain, following my operation, is a real benefit. So today I am going to model clothed, but *without* my mastectomy bra. For me, it will be like going naked. This is life modelling. It doesn't have to be *nude* modelling. I will instead be what is known as a draped figure. Although if Helen Mirren was here today, I'm sure none of us would object to drawing her in the nude. Something for the future, maybe. But this is our first session, so let's see how it goes.'

Angelique started with some quick poses, each no longer than a minute. These gesture poses were designed to help the artists warm up. First up was a standing pose, quickly followed by a seated one. 'Just quick strokes, ladies. Spirit and mood, not detail,' Angelique said. Next, she reclined on a Pilates mat, before turning over to kneel.

But even though they were swift poses, the mood in the hall was already shifting. Thoughts about Angelique turned to thoughts on how Angelique's form could be represented.

'Now, for a longer pose of ten minutes. Hold out your pencils at arm's length. Use that as a reference point, unless you aren't intending to follow classical proportions, of course.' Angelique stood on an upturned beer crate, her impromptu platform, with one hand on her cheek and the other hanging loosely to her side. She pointed her body towards the artists, but turned her head sideways. And focused on a picture hook. Within a few minutes, all she could hear was the sound of pencil on paper. A pleasing sound, one that reminded her of Geography lessons: "And now shade in the Zuider Zee".

Angelique was brought back to the present a few minutes later. Her left hand was already starting to ache. Her right hand was becoming restless. She was glad this was only a short session. The timer went, and Angelique relaxed. She noticed that the artists were glancing at each other's work, and then glancing at her.

'The next pose will also be ten minutes.' Angelique lay on the mat, with her hands behind her head, supported by a cushion. She raised her left knee and then closed her eyes. She could hear shuffling, as at least one of the artists moved their easel to a new position. Angelique could feel the loose fabric of her t-shirt, so very different to the stretched fabrics she had been used to. There was also a comforting smell of wood and polish, this close to the floor. She almost dozed off.

Once again, Angelique heard the sound of pencils. And then she felt the start of a teardrop in her left eye. She still held her pose though, and felt the tear stop just before it reached her top lip. She could also feel sweat where her hands touched her neck.

The buzz of the timer came as a relief. 'One last pose, and this one will be for twenty minutes. Come and help me find it, if you wish.' Angelique stood up and walked across the room to fetch her water bottle. When she returned, she stood next to a tall lamp. Gita positioned it so there was a clear contrast between shadow and light. Marina gently pushed up Angelique's left hip and raised her right shoulder. 'That's a classical 'S' curve, Marina, but I don't think I could hold it for twenty minutes. I'll use the coat stand for support.'

Marina nodded and placed Angelique's right hand high on the stand's pole. She then placed the other hand on Angelique's waist, forming a triangle.

'That is known as negative space. Before my operation, there'd have been a lot less of it.'

~

'Hey, the Hop Yard is super,' Pippa said. 'And I love this gallery, Is it Art? I totally get it. Just black and white photographs on the walls. And a drawing on each of the three easels. I wonder who modelled for them.'

Angelique peered above her black-rimmed glasses at the couple. The man looked somewhat familiar, but not so his much younger partner.

'I'm Angelique Vonk and the drawings are by members of the Hop Yard life modelling class. They're of me.'

'That's interesting,' Richard said, 'I wouldn't have recognised you. I like them, especially the one where you seem to be crying. You don't look sad though.'

'I wasn't sad,' Angelique said. 'I was caught by the artist, Gita, in a moment of reflection. And her style was *especially* abstract. Do I know you from somewhere?'

Richard hesitated before replying. 'I'm Richard D, and this is Pippa Luscombe. She models too.'

'Actually, I'm an eye and hand model,' Pippa said.'

'That sounds interesting. Quite niche,' Angelique said.

'Yeah,' Pippa replied, 'but there's quite a few of us now. As the advertisers need a range of different eye colours and skin tones.'

Angelique nodded, and then turned back to Richard. 'I didn't catch your surname, could you repeat it?'

'It's Du . . . ,' Richard mumbled again.

'I think there must be paint in my eardrums. One more time, please.'

'It's Duffy, Richard Duffy.'

'There's someone called Zoe who lives here. Her surname used to be Farr-Duffy.'

'I know. She's my daughter.'

'Oh, I see.'

Chapter 04

'Hello Laura, it's really good to see you again.'

'It's good to see you too, Zoe. We were talking last time about how your body, after your transplant, will view your new kidney as an aggressive foreign object. You'll then need to take a selection of drugs for the rest of your life, including immunosuppressants. They're designed to reduce the risk of rejection. I'll give you more details at our next session, but these drugs, combined with exposure to the sun, will make skin tumours more likely. In future, you'll need to stay out of the sun as much as possible, especially between March and October in the Northern Hemisphere. And when you are outside, you'll need to use a high SPF sun cream, of at least 50 plus. Now, and this might seem strange Zoe, you might wish to suspend yourself from the transplant pool for a short time. Maybe for a family celebration, a wedding, or if you wish to go on a special holiday. Do you have any plans?'

'I hadn't really thought about it. I know that Marina, who has become sort of a surrogate mother to me, is planning a coast-to-coast road trip in the States. She has dropped strong hints that I'd be welcome to join her for some, or all, of the trip. She's from Boise, Idaho. Although she first met my mother in Wyoming. And I'd like to see some exotic wildlife in the future, perhaps going somewhere like Costa Rica.'

'I can see a few issues. If you travel to a country where you are at risk from blood-borne infections, such as malaria and yellow fever, you'll be suspended from the transplant pool. Not just for the duration of the trip, but for an extra two months after your return.'

'Why would that be?'

'Any infection would make it unsafe to give you the immunosuppressive drugs before and after your transplant. After having the transplant, you cannot take live vaccines such as yellow fever. And we would strongly advise you not to travel to countries where there's a risk of catching malaria. Oh, sorry. I've upset you again.'

'Thanks for the tissue. As before, it's not you. It just gets a bit much sometimes. Realising that large parts of the world will be no-go zones for me, after my transplant, has been a shock. If I really want to go to the tropics, it will have to be soon. But what if a suitable kidney became available while I was away? Or even worse, when I'd returned to Suffolk, but was still suspended from the pool. Maybe the USA road trip would be a better option.'

'That's a decision for you to make. Though I imagine it would be tricky maintaining a healthy lifestyle during a road trip. I say this, because you can also be suspended from the transplant pool if you put on too much weight. But don't skip lunch today. I'll see you back here in an hour's time.'

'Thanks, Laura. Choices need to be weighed, and decisions have to be made. I'm feeling a lot calmer now. In fact, I feel strangely excited about the future.'

~

'Hi, I'm Skye Hunter and welcome to *Chatter Broth*. It's June 12th and today's guest is George P Salt. Some of you may already know that George runs a shop here at the Hop Yard called

Globe+Artichoke. Can you explain what it's all about?'

'Greetings, Skye. And to you too, Warren. It's almost twelve years since I arrived in Peasenham. I'd rented a cottage near Wicken Fen. There's always been something about wild birds, tall grasses and running water that has captivated me. I'd been intrigued by a photo of the reed beds at Blythburgh, so I cycled over to take a look. En route, by chance, I saw a banner for the Hop Yard's Field Party. I started chatting with an older chap. He recommended I should try the beetroot and shallot falafels. There was a monochrome portrait of him in the window of Is It Art? He turned out to be Colin, the owner of the Hop Yard. Or guardian, as I see him now. One of the units had just been refurbished, and one thing led to another. Within three months, a slightly lost Geography graduate had become a seller of maps.'

'And the vegetables?'

'That was even more unexpected, Skye. The thing I loved best about the Field Party was the communal food kitchen. People brought their surplus crops, stuff which might have otherwise rotted, and created an amazing resource. An army of volunteers then prepared, cooked and served a feast of amazing food. There'd obviously been a lot of pre-planning, as there were also homemade chutneys, jams and cordials. The money raised went towards the cost of running the Hop Yard. So I decided to expand the idea. I encouraged local people to bring in their surplus produce every Wednesday and Saturday. Say they brought in a bag of runner beans. They could then take away a mixed bag from other people's surpluses. Courgettes, rocket and tomatoes, for example. Any food not swapped on those two days was available to anyone who needed it. It's worked well, but I'm thinking of freshening up the system in the autumn.'

'It has worked well. When Warren cooks for us, he almost always includes fresh produce from your shop.'

'I love cooking for all of you, Skye. And thanks George.'

'It seems like a good time to move on, to In This Fortnight.'

'Thanks, Skye. I was moved by what you were talking about with Gita and Warren in the last podcast. About how you lost both your parents and how Colin rescued you. I find it hard to understand how so many children were still with their foster parents, three years after the end of World War Two. You're a strong woman. In a strong community. And all three of us are here of Colin. Which is one reason why we're all rallying around, to help him support Zoe. A positive attitude during a difficult time. But my choices all revolve around conflict. The first V2 was launched in September 1944, but the first V1 was three months earlier on June 13th. The Germans called them *Kirschkern* — cherry stones. Another kind of strange fruit . . . The Falklands War ended on June 14th, 1982. I wasn't born then, but my uncle had made a large scrapbook about the conflict. Which I still have. I remember the images, and how young the soldiers looked. But it wasn't just about military casualties. I'll give you two other names, Kye Ben Kuro and Mary Goodwin. The first was a Hong Kong Chinese merchant seaman on HMS Coventry. The second was a Falklander accidentally killed during British shelling.'

'My mother told me she ate an Easter egg, when she went down to watch the task force sailing out of Portsmouth. Anything else, George?'

'Let's go back to 1898, and the birth of Henry Patch on June 17th. Henry, better known as Harry, was the last fighting Tommy from World War One. My Auntie Amelia drove me up from Bristol to see him speak at the Cheltenham Literature Festival, when I was in my early twenties. Harry Patch spoke about war, but what he really spoke about was peace, and the value of life. I also heard him say, in a later interview, that there were no winners in war. *Everyone* involved was a victim. And I thought of his wise words again, as I stood outside Wells

Cathedral on August 9th, 2009, during his funeral. What I really admired about Harry Patch was his attitude to book royalties. He seemed more interested in cider than cold cash. And the majority of his sizeable royalties were donated to the RNLI. The relief vessel he paid for has saved lives, and has continued to do so since his death. I shall remember him.'

~

George's entry in the Stoker's Cottage Logbook, 2007

Ten Mile Bank, Prickwillow and Stuntney. Cockley Cley, Queen Adelaide and Friday Bridge. They are just some of the villages that I've cycled through this week. An area of meanders and straight lines. And magical Wicken Fen. The whole area has a distinctive smell. A mix of burnt sugar, celeriac and salted greens. A previous visitor wrote in the logbook that he had found the smell, '*strangely intoxicating*' and compared it to the aroma from a '*sticky date and macadamia tart*'. It's not just me that has had their taste buds tangled in the fragrant Fenlands.

Some Fenny Thoughts

1. A fen is a low-lying marshy area, prone to flooding. The Great Level, one of the names for the area, has a base of clay. Water moves slowly towards the sea, cutting through peat and silt.

2. This marshscape made access and transport difficult in the past. Hereward the Wake used this to his advantage when leading resistance to William the Conqueror. Evidence that this was a grim time, is suggested by the fact that Hereward's Saxon sword was known as 'Brainbiter'.

3. Later residents were more likely to use boats than carts. If forced to move on land, stilts were the preferred mode of

transport. One of the novels in the library here is a paperback of CS Lewis's *The Silver Chair*. The depiction of Puddleglum, a marsh-wiggle, was probably based on ancient ideas of how Fen folk lived.

4. The area was seen as a backwater, of little use. But where else could have produced such a commodity as fleggweed, which was used for making fleggeren collars? The mind boggles.

5. Another novel. This time, *Waterland* by Graham Swift. It oozes with atmosphere, the '*tump-tumping*' of drainage pumps, and eels. And eels have always played a part in life around here. The Domesday Book of 1086 records there were 3,250 eels in the nearby Stretham fisheries. Who came up with that number?

6. Shouldn't the nearby city be called Eely, not Ely? And in Ely, I bought a hardback book called *The Last Fighting Tommy*. It's about the life of Harry Patch, and so much more. There are many memorable and thought-provoking passages. The middle paragraph on page 94 is one passage that I've returned to, and will again. If you haven't already got a copy, why not buy or borrow one and see what *you* think?

When I was six, my parents took me to Grand Turk. Even as a young child, I felt there was something desolate about its abandoned salt workings. I would watch the elegant wading birds, and wonder if there were any fish to be caught. I've been back to the Turks & Caicos several times, but that feeling of desolation has never left me.

So being here in the Fens, with its lush grasses and waving reeds, is a refreshing contrast. And then there's this simple house. And I think back to the long abandoned, stark white huts — structures more simple than here, *and* more complicated — near the salt ponds of Grand Turk. For the second time in my life, I've fallen in love. Not with a person, this time, but with a place. This place. A place where the water often flows at a level higher than the surrounding farmland.

When the wonderfully-named Cornelius Vermuyden drained this part of the Fens, he did not realise the full extent of the watery problem. Windmills were used first, to scoop water into the higher channels. But the Stretham engine house next door, with its landmark chimney, took water transfer to another level. The coal-powered engine fed a scoopwheel, which could lift one hundred tons of water every minute. There has always been a lot of water here. Daniel Defoe wrote that the inflow was, '*All the Water, or most part of the Water, of thirteen Counties*'.

I've just returned from a bike ride to The Bluebell at Whaplode St Catherine. I rather enjoyed their home-brewed Ingle Dingle. Which was a good thing, as I was in the wrong pub. I was on the trail of John Clare, the so-called Shepherd's Poet. I should have cycled to The Bluebell at Helpston, to the west of Peterborough. Another time, perhaps. I rode back via Crowland. It has a strange structure, the Trinity Bridge, with three access points. The foundations are dry, but they wouldn't have been in 1947.

That was the year that the local abbey bells rang out a flood warning, after the electric sirens had failed. And it was those same abbey bells, which were reputed to be the first peal heard in England. In 975 AD. And while on the subject of bells, I recommend *The Nine Tailors* by Dorothy L Sayers. And not just because she uses an initial as her middle name. Hers is another ap-peal-ing selection, in the library at Stoker's Cottage.

When I returned to Stoker's Cottage, after another cycle ride of over a hundred miles, I thought of John Clare's poetry again:

> '*Bearing his hook beneath his arm,*
> *The shepherd seeks the cottage warm . . .*
> *And opens the welcome creaking door.*'

To avoid getting a chill, I lit the fire. The logbook has many suggestions on how to do this. But luckily, the previous visitors had left a fire made up for me. All I had to do was set light to it. Thank you, Gemma and Caroline.

Another 'Landmarker' was inspired by a former stoker, who had written, '*I found it was not just a matter of putting together paper, kindling and coal . . . First of all, about four to five hundred weight of coal, in lumps of about one and a half feet by one foot were placed in a horseshoe formation . . . Having laid these lumps of coal, as described, in the furnace, a small fire using faggots of willow wood and small pieces of coal would be lit. This fire was carefully watched and larger pieces of coal were added when it was burning well.*' Impressive.

I think John Clare would have felt at home here, had he had the chance. And he would, surely, have included a small library, for in his *Proposals For Building A Cottage* he wrote:

'*Nor in the corner fail to put*
A cupboard for the books.'

Stoker's Cottage was built as a toll house in 1840. The poet, walking past in 1841, might even have noticed that an old windmill's bricks had been re-used in one of the walls. Noticed, that is, when he walked ninety miles home from the High Beech Asylum in Essex. Because his thoughts and dreams had taken a different turn. A few months later he was re-admitted to an asylum, this time in Northamptonshire. Where he spent the last twenty-three years of his life. His final poem, but the first of his I read, hints at his loneliness:

'*I am — yet what I am none cares or knows,*
My friends forsake me like a memory lost.'

I have often closed in on myself, and suppressed my feelings.

But I've been moved by those heartfelt words. To feel lost and outside the memory of former friends, and to not exist in the thoughts of others. That, for me, would be terrifying.

I think of 1841. Of John Clare's last journey, and of a Spanish shipwreck. Which my ancestors survived.
I raise a glass of rum and ginger beer to his memory.
And to theirs.
Cheers, John Clare.
Cheers, my family.

Today is my last full day at Stoker's Cottage. I've got a temporary job in online advertising, yet I've enjoyed the lack of internet access. There isn't even a television here. I believe that it's a deliberate policy, and one that I now approve of.

I'm going to blow away some more cobwebs today, by riding towards Southwold. I saw a still image, of some reed beds near there, which moved me. I want to see them for real. I'll have to start slowly though. The speed limit outside the cottage is 15mph. How was *that* number chosen? Why not ten or twenty? It's another thread in an unusual tapestry.

I am writing this in the kitchen, home of the original cooking range. Many a kettle will have been boiled on that antique piece of engineering. Another form of steam, the railway locomotive, made the toll house redundant. And so the building became home, after 1845, to the stokers of Stretham. And why did a stoker need to live so close to his place of work? Coal, and great lumps of it.

The boilers used over five tons a day. And the stoker had to feed the flames. Pieces weighing over a hundred pounds would be barrowed up from the river. Then bashed into more manageable chunks, each over a foot wide. And when the stoker wasn't moving coal, there were other barriers to rest and relaxation. Like crawling into the boiler to keep it free of obstructions. While lying in sludge and holding a candle.

I've just re-read *The Wooden Horse* by Eric Williams. I'm still amazed how the PoWs at Stalag-Luft III managed to hide their tunnelling activities from the Germans. Like the Fen stokers, they would have needed to be strong, slim and fit. An article in the library here quotes a former tenant of this cottage. In *The Fen Stoker*, Mr Clarke writes that in his time he '*never encountered a fat stoker*'. I'd find it difficult to understand a life of such hardship. But I know what my ancestors experienced, also in the 1840s. Though that's another story, and I've got a 5am start.

George P Salt, Bristol

~

'What else has caught your eye In This Fortnight, George?'

'I'll move on to an event from June 21st, and another bitter legacy of war. On that day in 1919 German sailors scuttled over fifty of their warships at Scapa Flow, in the Orkney Islands. They were exasperated with the lack of progress at the Paris Peace Conference. Little did they know that the Treaty of Versailles would be signed a week later. And as one of the provisions was a limit of six battleships, perhaps the Allies were secretly relieved about the scuttling. As it was, the German Navy had not actually surrendered and so there were no Royal Navy guards on board. If there had been, they might have seen German sailors casually dropping keys and equipment into the water. A bit like PoWs dropping tunnel sand onto flower beds. But there was some resistance to the scuttling, and nine Germans were shot. One of them, Kuno Eversburg, two days later. He was killed by one of his guards, in what was claimed to be an act of revenge. Those sailors could be seen as being the last casualties of World War

One. There was a peace dividend though. Steel from those pre-atomic era ships is still being salvaged, for use in equipment that's sensitive to radiation. Orkney is a fascinating place, whose history is still being revealed and interpreted. Zoe still talks about you taking her there, Skye'

'And we both want to go back. So much is being revealed. The ceremonial landscape around the Ring of Brodgar pre-dates Stonehenge. And the storm-revealed Neolithic village of Skara Brae always sets the hairs on my arms tingling. That was where Zoe told me she was interested in becoming an archaeologist.'

'My next date is June 23rd. Not the EU Referendum of 2016, but a disaster sixteen years earlier in Queensland. The Childers Youth Hostel fire of 2000 killed fifteen backpackers. A report at said that, "*There weren't many injuries. It seems you either got out alive or you didn't get out at all* ". One of those who escaped was Zoe's father, Richard. He and Zoe have been spending more time together recently, since he heard about her kidney issues. I was chatting to him yesterday, and he mentioned the fire. He was happy for me to discuss it on the show today. He said that he still had nightmares, and unresolved survivor guilt too. His corridor was full of smoke and he couldn't work out where the exit was. His slim frame enabled him to squeeze through the bars of his dorm window and jump. He sprained his ankle, but was otherwise physically fine. Richard shouldn't really have been there, in Australia that is. He admitted that he was running away from his responsibilities as a father-to-be. Zoe was born, a month prematurely, later that summer.'

'Let's take a break there, George. We'll return after Lost Four Words. Last time, we were looking for words beginning with the letter D. Over to you, Warren.'

'Thanks, Skye. The final four are dacker, daggle, docent and dodkin:

Despite being daggled for her career choices,
On balance, she enjoyed being a dacker.
She was a decent docent,
Who saw worth in dodkins.'

'And your thoughts on what meaning there may be, Warren?'
'Well, Skye, does this interpretation make any sense to you?

Despite being dragged through the mud for her career choices,
Overall, she enjoyed her irregular work schedule.
She was a good volunteer guide,
Who saw value in low-value coins.

People can get a lot of grief for their career choices. I was often teased, and worse, for wanting to train for the catering trade. Now, I don't know if I'm ever going to have a career. Maybe that's not such a bad thing. As ever, Skye, who knows?'

'Who indeed? I know I said I wasn't going to select music from my favourite bands, Warren. But what you've said reminds me of one of Prefab Sprout's songs. Paddy McAloon sings about two things that people should be especially wary of: criticising someone's choice of partner, and criticising someone's choice of job. So here's "Jordan: The Comeback".'

'I like that song, Skye. I often have problems sleeping as well. My globe needs to stop spinning so fast. My wordy suggestion, which I wrote down on the poster over at M3, was dobhash. An interpreter. And I've thought of a lively song that has a dobhash, and maybe a docent as well. Can you play "Sharp Darts" by The Streets, please?'

'No problem, George.'

'Thanks for playing that song. I like the sheer arrogance in it. The over-confident police officer and the suggestion that the listener might have no idea what the song is about. And might therefore need a dobhash, an interpreter. Then there's the suggestion that the song will still be played in museums in five hundred years' time. I wonder what a 26th century docent would make of it. And would the museum be on Earth, Mars, or somewhere else?'

'That's a question to ponder, George. Now, I think you had some more thoughts about this fortnight in history.'

'That's right, Warren. Over one thousand passengers disembarked at Tilbury Docks from the *Empire Windrush* on June 22nd, 1948. Nobody really knows how many West Indians were on board, as their landing cards were destroyed in 2010. I don't understand how such an important set of records were treated in that way. Over one hundred of the emigrants had previously been based in Britain, when they had volunteered to serve in the RAF during the war. And sixty-six of the passengers were Polish refugees who had been picked up in Mexico! Anyhow, the tickets cost just over £28. Which is the equivalent of about one thousand pounds in today's money. So it's no wonder that some of the new arrivals had little or no spare money for accommodation. Over two hundred of the Jamaican emigrants were temporarily housed in a former deep-level air-raid shelter in Clapham. It must have been strange, in so many ways. Especially coming from the Caribbean and then starting their new life in a place without any natural light.'

'The shelter was also used as an overflow hotel during the Festival of Britain in 1951.'

'Is that right, Warren? It wasn't quite as grand as the Crystal Palace . . . People still talk about the impact of immigration, and I can understand that. But we're all immigrants, aren't we? What's talked about less is the legacy of slavery. I remember listening to an interview with Michael Johnson, the Olympic

400-metres champion. He was talking about how slavery was indirectly responsible for a concentration of strong genes in a certain area of Jamaica. The area, Trelawny, which produced legends like Veronica Campbell-Brown and Usain Bolt.'

'Many people in Britain made their fortunes from slavery.'

'You're right, Skye. The ancestors of those Jamaicans who arrived here in 1948 hadn't even asked to be shipped to the Caribbean. And compensation after abolition went to the *owners*, not the enslaved. The history of slavery and subsequent emigration has a long tail. And it's still unwinding.'

'The older I get, the more complicated history seems to become. There are so many conflicting views and voices.'

'I agree, Skye. Which is why spaces like *Chatter Broth* are so important . . . There are two linked events from June 25th. The first was a patent for barbed wire in 1867 by an Ohio inventor. There were many such patents in the 1860s. They were all based on creating a metal barrier that was painful to cross. A few, such as the Ohio patent, were focused on deterring livestock. But they also impacted on the migration of the buffalo — aka bison — herds. The railway network also disrupted traditional life on the Plains. The ending of the American Civil War in 1865 was yet another spur to Western expansion, disruption and destruction. Pioneers who had previously passed through the Plains, en route to the West Coast, were now settling there in greater numbers. It was around this time that the Buffalo Soldiers were formed. They were admired by the Plains Indians who gave them their nickname—'

'We played the song last time. How did the nickname come about?'

'You did play it, Warren. As for the nickname, nobody's quite sure, but it was probably to do with the shared characteristic of black, wiry hair. And the respect the tribes had for both the buffalo and the Black US Army soldiers. Which leads on to the linked event, nine years later. The Battle of Little Bighorn. Gold discoveries and treaty violations had been increasing tension in the Black Hills region. Following a battle in 1869, General George Custer smoked a peace pipe with the Cheyenne's Keeper of the Sacred Arrows. Custer promised, "I will never harm the Cheyennes again. I will never point my gun at a Cheyenne again. I will never kill another Cheyenne". The arrow keeper's reply, after pointing to the ash from the peace pipe, was, "If you break your promise, you and your soldiers will go to dust like this. If you are acting treacherously towards us, sometime you and your whole command will be killed". Crazy Horse, leader of the Oglala Sioux later said, "We did not ask you white men to come here. The Great Spirit gave us this country as a home. You had yours". Fast forward to June 25th, 1876. Over 7,000 Indians, mainly from the Lakota and Cheyenne tribes, were camped near the Little Bighorn River. It was possibly the largest such encampment of all time.'

'Even bigger than the Field Party?'

'Just a bit, Warren. The tribes and bands had gathered under the leadership of Sitting Bull, who was chief of the Hunkpapa Sioux. They had rejected a controlled life on designated reservations and were trying to continue their nomadic traditions. The battle that followed consisted of advances and retreats, on hills and in ravines. Ending with the death of Custer, and the last of his men, on what is known as Last Stand Hill. The shock of defeat, just before the centenary of American Independence, was replaced by a renewed call to crush the Indians and their culture. One prong of attack was the destruction of the vast buffalo herds. Sitting Bull said, "A cold wind blew across the prairie when the last buffalo fell . . . a death wind for my people".'

'There are events, markers in the sands of time, which still speak to us from the past.'

'You're right, Skye. For me, Little Bighorn was one of those events. As was the breaking down of the Berlin Wall. Last month I heard you speaking on *Chatter Broth* about seeing *The Wall* performed. June 26th links to two more events in Berlin's history. In 1948, the first planes delivered goods as part of the Berlin Airlift. The codename for the operation was *Operation Vittles*. But even though there *were* vittles — food, mainly potatoes — most of the cargo was coal.'

'Have you read *Great Expectations*, George?'

'I haven't, Warren. But I've seen a few film versions. Why?'

'Pip helps Magwitch in the graveyard, providing an iron file and tasty vittles, or "wittles" as the convict called them. And what a feast it must have been. A pork pie and warming brandy. Even the cheese rind would have tasted good. And Magwitch was someone who actually made something of himself in Australia. Although he never truly broke free of his chains.'

'What was the other Berlin event, George?'

'Sorry, Skye. I got a little lost there. Twenty-five years later JFK spoke to over a million West Berliners. And even though he literally said he was a doughnut, — "Ich bin en Berliner" — his heartfelt meaning was clear.'

'I've never been to the States. JFK was assassinated in Dallas. I remember when India Farr was working in Fort Worth, the city next door to Dallas. India's client was a collector of Western Art who went by the name of Charles Harlakenden Augustus Rochester. He stayed here for three months, well before either of you arrived. He helped Angelique to put on a couple of exhibitions, and bought a couple of her landscapes. Quite a character was CHAR.'

'Can I interrupt, Skye?'

'Of course, Warren. Fire away.'

'It's about India Farr. How does she manage it?'

'Manage what?'

'Manage to get people to let her sort out a house and its contents, while they're out of the country. And then persuade them to spend time here in Suffolk. I mean, it's great. Marina and Angelique live here because of her. Gita too. And I'm looking forward to meeting Hatsu, when she takes over the bookshop. But, how does she manage it? And why doesn't she base herself here, so that she can live with Zoe? Especially now.'

~

'I'm glad you enjoyed your lunch, Zoe. What did you have?'

'Oh, a mixed salad and some garlic bread. It was lovely. I was thinking though, what might happen if a suitable kidney became available?'

'The way things work in the NHS transplant system means you are most likely to be called in late at night. So please keep your contact details up-to-date. At the moment we've got yours, Colin's and Marina's. Let me know if there's anyone else you would like to add. We'll ring the numbers, in the order they are on the list, if there's a possibility of a transplant. The call is made to confirm you are well. And to warn you to stop eating and drinking. It's also to check that you can get to the hospital quickly. Even if you are called in as the priority recipient, you are not guaranteed to have a transplant. There will be further tests to check that you're compatible with the kidney you're going to receive. These will include blood tests, a chest x-ray and an assessment of whether you're fit to have anaesthetic. You should also know, and it's very rare, but diseases can be passed on from the donor. These include cancer, HIV and hepatitis. If your donor is at higher risk of these diseases, you can then decide whether or not to go ahead with the transplant.'

'That's a bridge I hopefully won't have to cross. At least I'm now aware of the possibility. That must be terrible for the donor.

Although I suppose when they got over the shock, they could get treatment earlier than they might have done.'

'The kidney would be from a deceased donor, Zoe. Had you forgotten?'

'I'd sort of pushed it to the back of my mind, Laura. So what happens during the kidney transplant?'

'You'll be put under general anaesthetic. A cut is then made, usually in the left groin. Then the blood vessels from the donor kidney will be skilfully sewn into your blood vessels. A central line tube—'

'I prefer the Piccadilly.'

'Thanks for that, Zoe. I'm glad you're engaging with all this information. Yes, so a tube will be inserted directly into a neck vein. This will allow fluids, including those all-important pain relief ones, to get into your body directly. Then a tube, which takes urine from your kidney, will be sewn into your bladder. The whole operation should take about three hours.'

'What will happen to my kidneys, Laura?'

'They're not usually removed.'

'Oh. That means I'll have three kidneys. Is that right?'

'Yes, Zoe. And some people even have four. If they've had a *double* kidney transplant. But that's a rare procedure. In your case, you'll be in hospital with us for about a week. Mainly, so the medical team can check your new kidney is functioning well. However, you'll probably be able to get out of bed the day after the operation. You'll be given written information about when and how to take your new medication. Another reason we keep you in for a week, is so you can get used to this new regime.'

'What about when I go home?'

'During the first month, you will need to attend the transplant clinic three times a week. Then gradually less for the next three months. Even with a good donor match, there's a one in seven chance that the kidney will be rejected during the first year. Your body's defence system has an excellent memory. It will never forget the kidney is foreign. Therefore, while you're recuperating in hospital, you will be taking your own medication. That will make you more confident when you are managing your medication at home. But don't worry. As I said earlier, you'll also be given written information while you are on the ward, including when and how to take them. I won't go into the full details now, but you'll have to be aware of possible side effects and you'll need to adjust your diet and lifestyle. For instance, one of the immunosuppressant drugs reacts badly with certain fruits. So pomegranate and grapefruit salad will be off the menu. Do you play any contact sports?'

'So that's cage fighting off my schedule. Actually, I play croquet, though outside the realms of *Alice's Adventures in Wonderland* and Jasper Fforde's *Thursday Next* novels, it's not usually a contact sport. I was looking at the Transplant Games website and I was disappointed not to see croquet on there.'

'You have been doing your research, Zoe. Well done. Are you interested in taking part?'

'Definitely. I see that petanque is on the list. Maybe I'll take that up. And virtual triathlon looks interesting too. Warren told me about the competition. He's from Portsmouth, and I think that's where the event first took place.'

'You're correct, Zoe. A transplant consultant called Maurice Slapak was the driving force behind the first event, back in 1978. Now it's a four-day event, with almost 2,000 people competing or spectating. It's mainly about building confidence and raising awareness. However, some contestants are there aiming to be selected to represent Team GB & NI at the World Transplant Games.'

Chapter 05

'Hi, I'm Skye Hunter and welcome to *Chatter Broth*. It's June 26th and today's guest runs M3, our local micropub. Welcome back, Marina.'

'It's good to be back with you and Warren, and our listeners of course. By the way, how many people listen to this podcast?'

'That's a good question, and one for another day. I'll add it to Warren's research tasks though. He's very organised.'

'It's either that or chaos and clutter, Skye. But back to our guest. How's Zoe doing?'

'She's quite *contento* — happy. But nervous too. She's on the national list of patients awaiting a matching donor. All she can do is wait. Unless a living donor comes forward. And that's tricky too.'

'How do you mean, Marina?'

'It would be a huge decision, Warren. And one that needs to be carefully thought through. Though strangely, kidney donors in the UK have a higher life expectancy than the average person. Donors need to have above-average health, both physically and mentally. Kidney donation can also cause stress in families, including guilt at not being able to donate. Or not wanting to donate. Research in Scotland revealed that six out of seven people would consider donating to a family member. But of those that step forward a third fail the tests. And another third decide to withdraw from the process. Though I was interested by one finding from the Scottish survey. One in seven of the respondents said they would consider donating to a stranger.'

'So you don't have to be related to donate?'

'That's right, Warren. People can choose who to donate their kidney to. But two or three people every week anonymously donate a kidney to someone they don't know. In terms of organ donation, Spain leads the world. Forty years ago, it became the first country to introduce a system where organ donation was the presumed choice.'

'What do you mean, Marina?'

'Warren, unless you had registered to opt out, then your body organs could be used. Japan is at the other end of the scale. For cultural reasons, some derived from Shintoism, most Japanese people are extremely reluctant to consider using any organ that came from a dead body. And the kidney has to be retrieved very quickly from the right kind of donor. Just one or two people out of every hundred dies in such a way that their organs can be used. That's another reason why living donors are so important. Iran has taken the concept to another level. It's the only country where it's legal to buy and sell a kidney. Though creating such a market raises even more ethical issues.'

'That's certainly food for thought. Let's move on to In This Fortnight.'

'A good idea, Skye. Neither Colin nor I, for different reasons, are going to donate a kidney to Zoe. She fully supports our decisions, but—'

'You don't need to explain. I can see that it's complex, and I wouldn't wish this situation on anyone. I've known Colin for over seventy years and you for almost fifteen. I trust your judgement.'

'*Es muy amable* — that's very kind. We shall move on. Ninety years ago, on July 2nd, all UK women over the age of twenty-one gained equal suffrage with men. It had been a long struggle. Gita spoke recently about the contribution of Emily Davison. But there have been many necessary protests, and there will be many more. I don't believe in everyone being *mismo* — the same. That would be very dull. But I believe that there should be more opportunities for people to achieve their dreams. And not have to crash through barriers caused by prejudice and ignorance. So my next event happened in 1853, on the Fourth of July, Independence Day. In the 1850s, American suffragists were campaigning for dress reform. Many of them disliked wearing heavy dresses, with constricting whalebone corsets. Amelia Bloomer protested in upstate New York. She delivered a speech in an outfit, which included a pair of loose trousers. Which came to be known as bloomers. It must have been truly liberating. And on July 5th, back in 1888, the employees of the Bryant & May match factory went on strike. They were protesting on behalf of three matchgirls who had been sacked for revealing information about their working conditions. A combination of phosphorous and white sulphur made their hair fall out and ravaged their faces.'

'That was Phossy Jaw. Women working in munitions factories suffered from it as well.'

'That's right, Warren. Your hero, Charles Dickens, wrote about the issue decades earlier, in 1852. I have a quote from his writing. It starts, "*Annie Brown is twenty years of age . . . She went to work at the lucifer-factory when she was nine years old . . . At night, she could see that her clothes were glowing on the chair where she had put them . . . At the side of her mouth are two or three large holes*". I think that people have a right to know the conditions that people work in. Then, and now. Perhaps Winston Churchill under-estimated the British people in 1945. He was surprised when he lost the General Election to Labour on July 5th. Exactly three years later, the NHS was launched. Some of my American friends cannot understand why it exists. The concept of comprehensive healthcare, free at the point of delivery, seems to them to be a bizarre use of public money. But I think it's wonderful. Aneurin Bevan said that it was "the most civilised step that any country had ever taken". Of course, there are problems. However, maybe they stem from treating hospitals as cost centres, rather than as care centres. Nurses, doctors, technicians, porters, cleaners, and all the other people involved, deserve more respect and support.'

'And Zoe is going to need all those people.'

'Yes she is, Skye. Before, during and after her operation. At around £40,000, kidney transplants in the UK are not cheap. And then there are ongoing annual costs of £7,000. But dialysis costs about £30,000 a year. So within two years, a successful transplant saves the NHS money. The situation is completely different in the States. Even if an American has their operation funded by medical insurance, they usually have to pay for the very expensive drugs needed after a transplant. So for financial reasons, they are often forced to stay on dialysis. So once again, hurrah for the NHS.'

~

'So let me get this right, Laura. You led a team which specialised in suitcase design?'

'Indeed I did, Zoe. Not surprisingly, my job involved a lot of flying. And waiting at airport carousels. I needed to depressurise, so I cashed in my shares and moved to East Anglia. A few years ago, I saw this job advertised. And thought, why not? My only regret in leaving, was that my dream project never got off the ground.'

'And your dream project was?'

'The evolution of suitcase design had stalled. From no wheels to eight wheels. From fixed wheels to spinners. But my dream was to actually get rid of the wheels and replace them with mini jet packs. So your luggage would float.'

'That's an amazing idea. You could use it at festivals, on cobbled streets or if you were deep in the—.'

'Were you going to say jungle? We should move on. I need to go into more detail about some of the risks involved. One in twenty-five new kidney transplants don't work. This is known as primary non-function and means the failed kidney will need to be removed. Also, it usually takes several hours for the new kidney to start functioning. If this doesn't happen, and it's known as sleepy kidney, then short-term dialysis will be needed. This happens with about half the kidneys from deceased donors.'

'So it's much better to receive a living donor transplant?'

'Yes it is. But even when the new kidney does start working, infections are common. And one third of patients need a blood transfusion following the surgery. Whatever happens, you'll need to rest to minimise the chance of developing a rupture in the transplant scar. In the longer term, you might be at risk of rejection.'

'Hmm, that would be nothing new for me.'

'What's that, Zoe?'

'Sorry, it's just that I feel my life has been quite complicated. As I've told you before. India's reluctance to be a mother. Richard's accident. Being adopted by Colin. And Marina has been like a mother figure to me. Though it's strange and confusing that she wouldn't be in my life if she hadn't met India, my mother, in the States. I guess I mean that I have mixed emotions. Does that make sense?'

'Of course it does. I think it's amazing how assured and calm you are, or at least appear to be. We could have the next session at your home. Perhaps you would like Colin and Marina to be present.'

'Yes please, that would be super.'

'We could talk about who you might ask to be a living donor. If you find someone, and a transplant date is set, there will be changes in the process. For example, you would be suspended from the national donor pool. That would mean you would not be able to receive a kidney from a deceased donor or an altruistic donor.'

'I'm still amazed that people donate a kidney. And then carry on with their lives.'

'There can be complications. But yes, most people can live a normal life with only one of their two kidneys. And about one in 750 people are born with only one kidney. Although most of them never realise it.'

~

'What else have you spotted, Marina?'

'Something quite local, Skye. We're not far from Pulham St Mary. A village that has an airship on its very unusual sign. Just before World War One, in 1912, the village became the centre of English airship activities. Locals called one of the airships a *Pulham Pig*. Seven years later, on July 6th, 1919, the *R34* became the first airship to cross the Atlantic. When it arrived in New York, after four and a half days, there were no experienced landing crews. So Major Pritchard did a parachute jump, becoming the first person to reach American soil by air from Europe. He was an interesting character. During the war, he had been based at the splendidly named Kite and Balloon School. After the war, he was the Airship Representative at the Peace Conference in Paris.'

'Were the Germans trying to 'scuttle' their zeppelins, Marina?'

'I don't think so, Warren. The flight, from near Edinburgh,

had in itself been interesting. Two stowaways had been discovered on board, a man and a kitten. The commander wrote in his log, "*I cannot help sympathizing with his motive*", but that it was "*bad from a disciplinary point of view*". I presume he was talking about the man, a Mr Ballantyne, rather than the kitten. Ballantyne had been one of the original crew and hadn't accepted his demotion to reserve. He told a journalist, "You see, I'd never been to America, had my heart placed on it, and my mind, too. So, I sneaks out a bit before midnight, about two hours before the *R-34* left Scotland. I hides in the rigging. No-one saw me and we were off". I think I'd have done the same. It was an historic crossing. Buffy's Brewery produced a special *R34* Ale, but I've never tasted it.'

'Were there any other beer-related events In This Fortnight, Marina?'

'Well, Skye, I do have a beery link to Shakespeare. But first, I'll stay in the Atlantic. Iceland sits on the tectonic border of Europe and North America, but I had not known that the USA occupied Iceland in July 1941. The reason given was to free up British forces based there. But it made me think of bananas.'

'A bit of an obscure link there, Marina?'

'*Quizás*, Warren. *Quizás no* — Perhaps, or perhaps not. But I was thinking about what you were talking to Skye and Gita about last month. About the differences between false and fake news. Recently, a customer in M3 told me that Iceland was the biggest exporter of *plátanos* — bananas — in Europe. At first I thought this was a crazy idea, but then I became more convinced. Geothermal energy in Iceland, just like in Boise, is a great resource. Hot water is very cheap. Icelanders have to pay extra to have their water *cooled*. So I imagined that this energy was used to heat giant greenhouses. Indeed, an Icelandic geothermal field hosted a trial at the start of this century. But bananas also need a lot of sunlight, so the two-year growth cycle was uneconomic.

The Agricultural University still produces about a ton of bananas each year. But none of them are sold, let alone exported.'

'So which is the biggest exporter?'

'Good question, Skye. Globally, a quarter of production comes from Ecuador. But the biggest European exporter is Belgium.'

'Belgium?'

'Yes, Warren. Belgians love their bananas, but they *export* most of their banana imports. Spain is the biggest *producer* in Europe, though mainly in the Canary Islands. So it's confusing.'

'I remember bananas appearing again after World War Two. Colin and I saw a Pathé newsreel in Southwold about their arrival at Avonmouth Docks. There were even rumours there was going to be a Banana Day. But I never got one. Neither did Auberon Waugh and his sisters. Auberon later wrote, perhaps tongue in cheek, "*They were put on my father's plate, and before the anguished eyes of his children he poured on cream . . . and sugar, which was heavily rationed, and ate all three. From that moment, I never treated anything he had to say on faith or morals very seriously*". I struggle to believe that story, but perhaps some parents would act like that. What do you think, Warren?'

'Pass. But what was your Shakespeare thought, Marina?'

'*Me acuerdo* — I remember. On June 29th, in 1613, a cannon was fired during a performance of Will's Henry VIII. The straw roof caught fire and the original Globe Theatre burned down. The only injury was to a man whose trousers caught fire. Serious burns were averted when a bottle of ale was poured on him. While on the subject of fire and smoke, there was an interesting announcement on the same day, but seven years later. King James I believed that smoking was hazardous to health. And so he banned the growing of tobacco in Britain. He then spoilt his good work by granting a lucrative monopoly to Virginia. Which earned him a shilling for every pound sold.'

'I think it's time for Lost Four Words. Last time, we were looking for words beginning with the letter E. What are the final four this time, Warren?'

'Thanks, Skye. They are effleurage, everywhither, exaration and eye-service:

The style of exaration,
Reminded her of effleurage.
Being caught performing eye-service,
The waiting staff moved quickly everywhither.'

'And your thoughts on what meaning there may be, Warren?'
'Well, Skye, does this interpretation make any sense to you?

The symbols, carved in stone,
Reminded her of gentle, circular massage strokes.
Shocked into motion,
When they noticed the boss was watching,
The staff suddenly started moving in all directions.'

'My suggestion was to do with something I used to do a lot in Boise. It was elucubrate. To study at night. I also like the link between the last two words. Do people work harder when they're being watched? And is working harder, actually working better? I read an article about supermarket working patterns. It suggested that productivity increased if people worked together *and* were allowed to talk. Rather than just having one worker per aisle. And I love effleurage. Especially on the palms of my hands and the small of my back. It makes me feel tingly just talking about it.'

'I agree, Marina. I've had hundreds of massages, and I prefer gentle strokes to deep tissue pummelling. What about you,

Warren?'

'I've never had a massage. Maybe I'll try one at the Field Party in August. For now, I've got a couple of songs as part of Four Play. The first is "Black Shampoo" by Wu-Tang Clan, linked to effleurage. The assortments of flavours used for massaging, soaking and showering sound wonderful: peppermint, pears and cinnamon. Lavender, coconut and honey. Not at all like the cold showers I had, back at school, in Pompey.'

'And after "Black Shampoo" I played "While We Talk" by Nina Nastasia. I can just imagine eating a moist mouthful of cake — apricot, pear and pistachio would be good — and watching the crumbs shoot off in every direction. Everywhither? Indeed. Polite? Probably not.'

'Talking of food, I've one more event from In This Fortnight. July 3rd, in 1954, marked the end of food rationing in Britain. That was almost nine years after the end of the Second World War. Yes, nine. The legacies of conflict have long and often twisted tails.'

~

'Good afternoon. My name's Warren Wagstaffe and I'd like to donate a kidney to a friend who is a patient at this transplant centre.'

'You've come to the right place, Warren. We can give you some leaflets to take away with you and there's more information available on our website. If you then still want to go ahead with the process, we'll allocate you a living donor coordinator. They'll be your key point of contact and guide you through the complicated, but hopefully very rewarding, process.'

'How long will it all take?'

'The allocation process is quick, but with the rigorous testing regime, including psychological assessments, the pathway to the actual kidney transplant usually takes about three months. Although it can take well over a year.'

'Is that to ensure people really are engaged in the process? To weed out the wavering?'

'We have to make sure that the risks to the donor are acceptably low. Removing a healthy organ is something that goes against the grain. Of medical professionals, that is. And this reluctance continues right up to the day of the transplant. The operating surgeon would even ask you whether you're still sure you wish to proceed.'

Chapter 06

India's entry in the Lynch Lodge Logbook, 2009

Many visitors comment in the logbooks on the peace and simplicity of this Landmark Trust property. And other LT properties are often referred to. Such places are a place to breathe and reflect. Maybe people have too much going on in their lives, or too much 'stuff' in their homes. But even when you strip things down, life does not necessarily become simpler.

The logbooks are fascinating, if not always accurate. They show snapshots of life through our recent decades. Perhaps I should ask the Landmark Trust if I could base a PhD on the logbooks. Just in case, I will jot down lines of enquiry during my stay, starting with:

Why was there lingerie hanging in the kitchen window? (1987)

Wisbech sounds interesting. And how does it sound? Wizbeck? Whizzbeach? Some other way of saying it? Perhaps if I'd visited the place, I'd have a better idea of the pronunciation. But a planned meeting with my daughter, the first since I had handed her over as a baby, didn't work out. I ducked out, which is why I'm only reading about Wisbech, rather than experiencing it.

Anyway, I was fascinated to read about a great feast held there for Queen Victoria's Coronation in 1838. Five thousand people were fed at a cost of just over a shilling per head. The guests each had about a pound of beef, a spoonful of mustard and a slice of plum pudding. This was washed down with a couple of pints of Elgood's ale. In addition, over a thousand guests were given a clay pipe and enough tobacco for a couple of smokes. I wonder what Nigella or Nigel might have come up with as an alternative menu:

How do you flarche for a carrot? (1993);

Did Nigel Slater enjoy cooking a duck in this kitchen? (1999)

Apparently, some of the more characterful locals round here are known as Fen Tigers. I met one, by the name of Priddy, at The Bluebell in Helpston. He told me about the poet John Clare, whose former cottage is up for sale. I wonder how much it will sell for. John was from Northants — it seems that this part of Cambridgeshire used to be in Northamptonshire — in the quirkily-named Soke of Peterborough.

How much is revealed, or concealed, by writers? John Clare lived for over seventy years, but spent the last third of his life locked up in an asylum. Thinking of being out of touch, for so long, makes me sad. Like the feelings expressed in John Betjeman's "The Night Mail". A poem where people wait in hope of a letter, because they cannot bear to think they are forgotten. And John Clare touches on that very theme, in a poem I found in the library here:

'I am — yet what I am none cares or knows,
My friends forsake me like a memory lost . . . '

Then later he goes on to write:

'Even the dearest - that I love the best -
Are strange - nay, rather stranger than the rest.'

I've made decisions in my life, and perhaps I deserve to be forgotten. Especially by those who should be my nearest and dearest. If I was a house, I might be described by others as semi-detached. But I'd suggest that a better description would be at the end of my ~~tether~~ terrace.

Or, perhaps, I don't deserve to be forgotten. People are too often defined by one decision they make. I'm not often this reflective. Maybe it's this place and the poetry. If you're reading this, dig out *The Shepherd's Calendar* and see what *you* think. John Clare was physically trapped in the last decades of his life. Though it allowed him to focus on his writing. I wonder if the best writing is done tucked away, or in the middle of things. There's a puzzle to ponder. And here's another tasty one:

Cryptic clue: GEGS (9, 4) (1997)

Though I prefer omelettes . . .

I'm quite used to moving things into, and out of, houses. Other people's houses*, that is. But the beautiful porch of Lynch Lodge was itself moved. It came from Chesterton, a house belonging to John Dryden. Another John Dryden, the poet, used a diamond to cut a line of poetry onto one of Chesterton's windows. But the great house was demolished in 1807, and the window was smashed. If diamonds are forever, I wonder where that jewel is now.

The porch was transported here, and various rooms and lean-tos were then added on. An earlier owner of the Chesterton estate left an interesting will. His son inherited most of the estate. However, a son from a former marriage was obviously out of favour. The bequest to him was, '*ten shillings and no more, in respect he struck and . . . fought with me. I give unto my wife ten shillings, in respect she took her son's part against me.*' Families. They can be quite complicated, can't they?

A later owner of Chesterton, who would have entered through the porch that's now here, was Robert Piggott. He was regarded as a food and dress reformer. Food, because he was a vegetarian. Dress, because he detested hats. Piggott promoted the use of caps instead, and the brighter the better. Many of his quirky ideas came to him while he was lying on an electric bed. One acquaintance suggested that his ideas were not solidly grounded, but more like "Castles in the Sky" (later to become an Ian van Dahl hit on Ibiza)

Canons Ashby, another Dryden estate, is owned by the National Trust. However, a flat in 'The Tower' is available to rent from the Landmark Trust. I stayed there a few years ago. It's a strange privilege to have the key to the main house at night. You can only walk in certain areas, but it is very atmospheric. During the day, it's quite a thrill to emerge from your private door and sweep down the staircase past a guided tour. And there are mentions of discreet sunbathing in the logbooks:

Is 'The Tower' still suitable for sunbathing? (1986)

Though I wonder what effect the increased use of spy satellites, and even drones, has had on sunbathing. And other outdoor activities. Winston Smith and Julia, in George Orwell's *Nineteen Eighty-Four*, were rightly nervous of being overheard or observed. Even in the countryside. What does a lack of privacy do to us? I think we all need a space to breathe, whether it be a shed, a shingle beach or a sun terrace.

I took the bus to Crowland on Wednesday and saw my first ever wild owl. It flew under a three-legged bridge. A Snowy Owl in the summer heat. On the way back I stopped off at a pub in Castor. I had one drink, so I didn't get castor-*oiled*. I recommend a visit, especially for the toiletries in the restrooms. How often do you see body spray or sun cream in a pub? The pub was one of those things in life, like *Blade Runner*, the songs of Leonard Cohen or Peterborough, whose appeal is not immediately obvious. But then grows on you:

Do birds secretly send messages
across England every morning? (2005)

I walked into Peterborough on Saturday. There was a band called The Blue Penguins busking near the cathedral. The guitarist was good, but the singer could have done with some training. One of their songs, "Roast Potato Dreams", was about replicants — the androids from *Blade Runner*. The theme of the song was to do with reality. In the film, the replicants had been implanted with fake photos instead of real memories. They yearned for real experiences, for a chance to feel. Things like love, hope, and tears in the rain.

The buskers said they were going to be playing at a festival in Dortmund, so I gave them five Euros. They gave me a copy of *The Rotters' Club* by Jonathan Coe and the name of the best place to get falafels in Amsterdam. Trail magic! I found out, later that day, that Jonathan Coe actually stayed in Lynch Lodge while writing one of his novels:

How often do people come across people they know
(or have heard of) in these logbooks? (2008)

India Farr, Bologna and beyond

* My 'career' is based on decluttering. I take on clients, mainly from the States, who entrust me with all the decision-making. My clients actually leave the area while I'm working. Hence the name of my company: IF, only . . .

I'm writing this just after having had tea — coffee and banana cake, actually — with a couple from Ohio. I won't reveal their names, as until recently they engaged in stealing the letter 'M' from every state sign they saw in Michigan. Or 'Itch Again' as they called it. They used to go there to visit their daughter who was on a golf scholarship at Ann Arbor. Two years ago, they discussed hiring me to sort out a relative's estate just outside of Cincinnati.

It didn't work out. They had wanted to stay in the area and discuss progress with me every evening. However, they liked the bespoke UK itinerary that I organised for them. So they're back for their third trip. Based around her interests (Banksy, bookbinding and Jensen 541s) and around his (narrowboats, rose gardens and kippers).

~

Zoe looked up from the deckchair as Warren walked into Bay Six Books. She could see Gita talking to George over by the cash desk, but otherwise the shop was empty. Warren came and sat on the floor next to her.

'Hi Zoe. What's that you're reading?'

'Hey, Warren. It's *A River Sutra* by another Gita. Her name is Gita Mehta. The narrator thinks he has escaped the crowds, by retiring next to a river. But as with *Timon of Athens*, who escaped to the forest, the world follows him.'

'Who was Timon?'

'He was the title character in one of William Shakespeare's plays. The only play not to feature blood relatives or a romantic relationship. There's plenty of cupidity — the fierce greed for wealth and possessions — but Cupid's arrow doesn't even leave his quiver. Although, strangely, it's the only Shakespeare play in which Cupid actually appears and speaks.'

'Sounds a bit confusing.'

'It can be, but for me it works on many levels. One of the characters asks, "What time of day is it?" The reply being, "Time to be honest".'

Warren shifted his position so that he was facing Zoe. 'Time for honesty? Well, I still want to help you. So I've been to the hospital to start the process and—'

'You did what?'

'Zoe, it was just information gathering. I didn't even mention your name. I know you turned down my offer last week. But I still feel very strongly about becoming a donor for you. Warren of Pompey, not Timon of Athens. We're not blood relatives and there's definitely no romance.'

'But the risks, Warren.'

'I'm not going into this lightly. It seems quite a thorough process. Colin and Marina were quite supportive when we all met up to talk it through. Although I think it was a bit awkward for them. You know, them deciding, for different reasons, not to volunteer.'

'I'm fine with that, Warren. In fact, my objections were key to both their decisions. I'm glad you haven't talked to anyone else about it.'

'No, not even Skye. This is my decision. I don't want to talk widely about it, possibly making people feel guilty for not wanting to donate.'

'Are you sure this is what you want to do?'

'At the moment, yes. That might change during the process, but I don't think it will.'

Zoe looked down at Warren's face, and made her decision. 'Hey, why not? Even though a part of my brain is shouting "No, no, no" at me. But let's walk over to M3 and have a chat with Marina and Colin first.'

~

'Good afternoon. My name's Warren Wagstaffe. I'm here to meet my living donor coordinator.'

'Hello Warren, could you confirm your date of birth and also the first line of your home address, plus your postcode. You've been allocated to Harrison Ward. I see from your notes that you've already given blood samples and filled in your medical history questionnaire. That's all part of the initial screening. But it's good to have got that out of the way, so well done. You're quite early, but I see you have a book to read. Just take a seat over there and I'll let you know when he's ready.'

~

'Hi, I'm Skye Hunter and welcome to *Chatter Broth*. It's July 10th and today's guest is Angelique Vonk. It's good to see you. I really enjoyed your life modelling class in May. I see that the drawings are on display in Is It Art? But with no price tags.'

'There'll be another class at the end of the month. And you're right about the price tags. The frames are made by a young chap called Seth up in Laxfield. He uses reclaimed wood and glass. When he has made a dozen, I'll go and meet him at the King's Head, aka the Lowhouse. It's a good excuse to sit on their enormous wooden settle and sample ales drawn straight from the barrel. Let's get a group together next time. Warren can drive the H Van, as he only ever seems to drink water. By the way, where is he today?'

'I'm not sure. He asked to be excused, but didn't want to say why. He said he'd given you all his research notes on Saturday.'

'Yes, we went through them over at M3. Marina's finally found a gin she really likes. It's from Harris in the Outer Hebrides. It was served with a slice of red grapefruit and a drop of seaweed essence. The bottle was a work of art. I'm sure Seth could do something with it.'

'And the invisible price tags, Angelique?'

'Oh yes. So Seth makes the frames for the art works. Rather than "*Hoeveel kost het?*" — "How much is it?", customers at the gallery suggest a price. If I think it's fair, the deal is done.'

'What's fair?'

'Everyone will have a different view. But I like to give Seth at least £50 per frame. And then there are my expenses and a contribution to the Hop Yard running costs. We can't rely on Colin's generosity for ever. So photographs and life drawings normally sell for around £100 to £150, with my paintings going for between £500 and £1500. Though we often get more when we auction them. I still can't believe we got £11,000 for that one last year, Skye.'

'Yes, your portrait of me and Colin dancing on top of the H Van. Complete with a reference photo on the back. I've no idea who bought it. Or how we were persuaded to climb up there. So what did you spot that happened In This Fortnight?'

'My favourite event is from July 10th in 1040. It concerns an Anglo-Saxon lady called Godgifu, which translates as God's gift. We know her better as Godiva. I'd have loved to have seen Lady Godiva riding naked through the streets of Coventry. It would have been a shocking and exciting sight. She was protesting about unfair taxes imposed by her husband Leofric, the Earl of Mercia. But as we know, nakedness is not necessarily nudity. Maybe her long hair only covered her breasts and her upper thighs. A chronicler stated that only her "fair legs" were visible. Maybe she was clothed, but simply, without her rich clothing and jewellery. It might just be a story, but I think that it happened. Perhaps you could play "Lady Godiva and Me" by Grant Lee Buffalo. It's an atmospheric song. Though the lyricist also seems undecided, as to whether Godiva was unclothed, or covered by her hair.'

'Godiva would have known Emma, one of the most amazing women in history. Emma was married to two kings of England, Canute and Ethelred, And two of her sons, Harthacanute and Edward the Confessor, also became kings of England. I'd like to know more about her, Skye.'

'Me too. Back to Godiva, I think the people of Coventry would have been shocked and impressed, Angelique. A strong visual statement was being made. Like the one you made, when you posed for us. I wonder what will be revealed in the next life modelling session.'

'And revealed by whom, Skye? I take it by your shake of the head that it won't be you. I'll move on to another event from Anglo-Saxon England. To the time when St Swithun was the Bishop of Winchester. Since 971 AD, according to legend, if it rains on July 15th it will rain for another forty days. He requested that his coffin be buried outside the cathedral, "*where it might be subject to the feet of passers-by, and drops of rain falling from on high*".'

'We'll have to keep an eye on Hampshire weather reports in five days' time.'

'And perhaps then, for the next forty days. I've got a note from Warren about the number forty. He wrote that it's the only number in the English Language that has all its letters in alphabetical order. Here goes: abcdeF . . . ghijklmnO . . . pqR . . . sT . . . uvwxY . . . and z. Phew, that's made me thirty. Sorry, thirsty! Shall I make some tea, Skye?'

'That would be lovely. Lady Grey for me please, with a slice of lemon. I was a bit confused about Warren's number puzzle, but I've got it now. One is O, then N, but then goes back to E.

Two is T, then W, but then goes back to O. And so on. I wonder why forty isn't spelled f o U r t y. Moving on, Warren also recorded the Lost Four Words section. So I'll play that section now.'

'Hello listeners, it's Warren Wagstaffe here. In a way. We are on the letter F. The four words selected are fango, febrifuge, filibeg and flickermouse:

Sipping a febrifuge,
While covered in fango,
She noticed a flickermouse
Resting on her folded filibeg.

And this is what I've come up with:

Sipping a cooling drink,
While covered in Italian curative mud,
She noticed a bat
Resting on her small kilt.

My favourite word was flubdub, which is nonsense. In more ways than one. Over to you, Skye.'

'I like the thought of being covered in curative mud. Something for the Field Party, perhaps. I know Warren's thinking about getting a massage. It's strange not having him here.'

'I know what you mean, Skye. He has become part of our lives here, and in such a short space of time. He had been thinking of applying to work on a frozen food production line before he came here. We were chatting about it on Saturday. Then he saw the name Peasenham on a map, and just liked the sound of it. So he hitch-hiked up here and the rest is history. Or, his story.'

'And now part of our story as well, Angelique. He listed some songs, so let's listen to two of them while we drink our tea. First up, it's Mos Def with "New World Water". The song links to febrifuge. It's about how refreshing water can be.'

'The second song was "Modern Dance" by Lou Reed. I can imagine him dancing in Edinburgh in a filibeg. A modern dance, for sure.'

'And I liked it when he sang about living by a canal in Amsterdam, Skye. Though I come from the south of the Netherlands, right on the Belgian border. I've got a final event. Apart from kilts and canals, Lou Reed also sang about what it might mean to be a wife. Ninety-five years ago, on July 16th, British women gained equal divorce rights with men. Extramarital sex, by either the husband or the wife, became the sole ground for divorce. Wives no longer needed to prove additional faults against the husband. Just that he was breaking a vow, without permission.'

~

'So you still want to go ahead, Warren. But please remember that it's always your decision.'

'Thank you, Harrison. I'm impressed by the thoroughness of the process and how helpful everyone is. And to assist you, and ultimately Zoe, I'd like you and the transplant team to share any information you consider relevant with my GP and Zoe.'

'Are you sure, Warren? Have you considered all the confidentiality issues? The testing programme can throw up some surprises. For example, and I know it shouldn't be a factor in your case, if a previously unknown genetic link between the donor and the recipient came to be revealed.'

'I did read, at the library, about a donor who turned out to be the recipient's mother, rather than the sister. *That* would create difficulties. But I'm happy to give my written consent, waiving my rights to confidentiality. Especially as I know Zoe. She's part of the Hop Yard family.'

'I noticed that address on the form. It's in Peasenham. I've cycled past, but never been in.'

'You should, it's a special place. And George loves cycling too. He runs one of the shops there. He mainly sells maps, but other stuff as well.'

'The Hop Yard sounds interesting. A bit like that new multi-generational community in Cambridge. Where cars have been relegated to the periphery and there's a weekly communal meal. Now, what's it called? Marshmallow Meadows rings a bell, or was it Mulberry?'

'It's Marmalade Lane. I visited with Colin, who oversees the Hop Yard. We like to check out new ideas and see if they can be adapted to our Hop Yard community.'

'Thanks, Warren. Back to you and Zoe. You'll be donating under the UK Living Kidney Sharing Scheme. Since 1960, this has allowed a family member or friend to donate a kidney to a particular person. Ideally there should be a good match with the blood group and tissue type.'

'What if there isn't a good match, Harrison?'

'That is known as an incompatible or mismatched transplant. A decade ago, it would have stopped the process, but medical advances have made it possible for incompatible transplants to take place. But it's not ideal. For example, there's a higher risk of transplant rejection. This risk can be reduced if the donor is willing to be paired with another patient and donate their kidney to a stranger.'

'Is that what altruistic donation is?'

'Not quite, Warren. For over ten years, since the Human

Tissue Act became law in 2006, people have been able to donate a kidney to a complete stranger. That's altruistic donation. On average, about two people in the UK do it every week. And that's the only time that a person in the national transplant pool receives a kidney from a *living* donor. Pairing is different. You would know that Zoe would receive a kidney, but it would be from an anonymous donor. Sometimes a chain can be formed, and three or more incompatible donors can be linked in what is known as a pooled donation.'

'I couldn't imagine donating a kidney to a complete stranger, if there was no direct benefit to Zoe. But I kind of like the idea of paired donation. It would still be personal, but one step removed. I'd need to think about that and talk to Zoe, Marina and Colin.'

'Whatever you decide, there will be a lot more tests. We need to make sure that your general health is good and that both your kidneys are functioning well. Apart from blood tests — and you will need to give a *lot* of samples — there will be scans, x-rays and urine tests. Another key test will help the surgeon determine which kidney is most suitable to be transplanted. These tests might reveal a medical condition that you were unaware of. So you need to be prepared for that. And even though I'll be your main point of contact, you'll also be assigned to a counsellor who is a trained psychologist. They'll conduct a series of assessments.'

'What kind of assessments, Harrison?'

'They'll include questions about your background, your rationale for donating and any relevant mental health issues. The counsellor will also want to make sure that you fully understand the processes and risks associated with organ donation. For many people, donating a kidney can be an emotional process. Just as the transplant team will focus on reducing medical risk, your counsellor will focus on reducing the risk of psychological harm. In addition, The Human Tissue Authority, which regulates transplants in the UK, has a key role to play. One of their independent assessors, who is completely separate from the transplant team, will have a one-to-one meeting with you. They will ask about your reasons for donating and check that you understand the risks involved in the process. The assessor will need to be confident that you have not been pressured into donating, and especially that there's been no financial reward involved. If everything is in order, you will then need to sign a declaration.'

'What *are* the risk levels?'

'It needs to be said that, while small, there's a risk of you dying in this process, Warren. It's an uncommon outcome, but one in three thousand donors die. That's something you can speak about in more depth with your counsellor. There's also a small chance of damage to organs that are located close to your kidneys. It's more common to experience minor complications such as getting an infection. However, we also need to be aware of the possibility that your emotional well-being or mental health might suffer if things do not work out as expected.'

'In what ways might things not work out, Harrison?'

'There might be complications for you or Zoe. Especially if the transplant does not work and the donated kidney has to be removed.'

'What are the main risks after the operation?'

'It's difficult to predict, Warren. But they might include higher blood pressure. You'll probably need three months of recovery before you return to work. By the way, what do you do?'

'That's a good question. I have a catering qualification. And I still do some cooking, but I also do all kinds of things at the Hop Yard. Restoration work, caretaking, helping out the different businesses, doing research for the *Chatter Broth* podcast.

Whatever's needed really. Until recently, I was sleeping in a van, but I've now got my own bedroom and shower suite. We don't always eat together, but everyone shares the same kitchen. There's an area with sofas and a window seat. Colin, the owner, has said I can have as much time as I need to recover. It's all good.'

Chapter 07

Life Modelling at the Hop Yard #2

Gita rested her right elbow on her left hand, while using her other hand to play with her hair. Her ivory-coloured dress was ruched, but tight. Not the easiest item to slip off for life modelling. Next to her was a washstand and basin. And next to that was a straight-backed wooden chair. She looked over at Angelique, Kenesha and Pippa. 'Thank you so much for coming. And it was delightful to meet you for the first time this morning, Kenesha. Last time, Angelique spoke about what being naked meant. For her, it was revealing that she had had breast surgery.' Gita glanced at Angelique and got a nod in return. 'So I've decided to be naked in my own way as well.' Gita turned her back to the three artists and quickly washed her face. She then flicked her hair in such a way that it covered half her face — a schwoomph — and sat on the chair. Gita then flicked her hair back again, with her chin supported by her fingertips. 'This is me. Naked. No camouflage of gloss, liner or shadow. No mask of foundation or rouge. Just me. Or more of me, at least. Some *real* face time.'

'I work in the fashion business,' Pippa said. 'What you did took a lot of nerve. And there was so much variety in your poses. That surprised me.'

'Yes, it surprised me too. Angelique had told me that that you'd done some specialised modelling.'

'That's right. But never without all my make-up. And only ever my eyes or hands. Never my whole face. I couldn't bear that. By the way, you were terrific.'

'Thanks, Pippa. It was strange though. I was mainly focused on holding my facial poses. I thought I would have had plenty of time to think during the hour.'

'Teaching's a bit like that,' Kenesha said. 'You have a plan, but there are so many questions and interactions. So you have to adapt to the moment. You never get bored though.'

'I could never teach,' Angelique said. 'Not even art. I hope you get back to it.'

'I'd like to.' Kenesha turned to Gita. 'I was impressed with your performance. Starting with make-up on, and then revealing another side of you. Sometimes looking directly at us, sometimes gazing at some object behind us. And I really liked the pose where you had your eyes closed, with your fingertips on your cheeks and throat.'

'Thank you, though I couldn't have held *that* pose for much longer. And you're right, it was a performance. Like being in front of a class, I suppose'

'There is a lot of that. One of my PGCE mentors told me about the importance of *withitness*. That is, being able to stand in front of a new class and project an aura of confidence. Being *with it*. And knowing that while the students were prepared to see you fail, most of them would want you to succeed. So working out how to present yourself, and which props to use, is an important part of teaching, and of life.'

'Another important part of life is food,' Pippa said. 'I wonder what surprises Warren has prepared for us today. Any ideas, Gita?'

'I know that it involves celeriac, shallots and wild garlic. As always, with Warren, you never know what he'll cook up for us. But it will be good, and set me up for the recording later.'

~

'Hi, I'm Skye Hunter and welcome to *Chatter Broth*. It's July 24th and today's guest is Gita Chowdhury. Sorry I missed the life modelling class. Angelique told me it was very revealing. So Gita, this will be your last time on the show. As you will be handing over the bookshop to Hatsu at the end of August. And a big welcome back to Warren, who missed the last show.'

'Thanks, Skye. I've listened to it. I liked the Grant Lee Buffalo song that Angelique chose. Lady Godiva still inspires people, obviously. Who inspires you, Gita?'

'I admire people who move forward in difficult circumstances. Or who come up with different ways of doing things. I'll give you some examples that took place In This Fortnight. I'm not exactly sure what grapeshot is, but it must be dangerous. Horatio Nelson's right arm was shattered by it at the Battle of Santa Cruz on July 25th, 1797. He not only survived the amputation, but also managed to write a letter two days later, with his left hand. His understated letter began with, "*You will excuse my scrawl considering it is my first attempt*". I think that's brilliant. I must also mention a bookish event from July 30th, 1935. Penguin paperbacks went on sale for the first time. The founder, Allen Lane, had found it impossible to find a good book, at an affordable price, while waiting for a train at Exeter St David's. Although he wouldn't have had that problem at an Indian railway station. So he did something about it. First, reprints of so-called classics. Then, later, his own commissions.'

'You have a Penguin section at Bay Six Books. What do you suggest we should buy?'

'Yes, Skye, most of my books are arranged by publisher.

Abacus, Bluemoose, Canongate, and so on. I think you might enjoy *Are You Experienced?* by William Sutcliffe. It's set in India, but not an India that I really recognise. Maybe you could lend it to Zoe, so she'd be aware of some of the pleasures and pitfalls of gap year travelling.'

'I think she'd like to travel. But there's her medical situation and the problems her father had. So maybe not India, at the moment.'

'What about me, Gita?'

'Oh, I think another book with a question mark for you, Warren. It's called *What Is History?* by E. H. Carr. I know how you love researching and editing notes for In This Fortnight. There's a great Jane Austen quote at the start of the book. Catherine Morland, one of the characters in Northanger Abbey, is talking about History. Catherine says, "*I often think it odd that it should be so dull, for a great deal of it must be invention*". Last time I was on *Chatter Broth*, we were talking about the difficulty of working out what was true or false. How do you check your facts, Warren?'

'I use magazines, books and online resources. I visit libraries and archives. I even speak to people. I'm sure that mistakes still slip through, or I'm unaware of new evidence that makes a 'fact' redundant. Are you reading a Penguin at the moment, Gita?'

'I have *Mother Tongue* by Bill Bryson on my desk. It really is a juicy feast of how English came to be such a rich language. It's not just *people* that migrate. And what would language be like without the inventions of Shakespeare? Without his words, we would not be able to describe activities such as having excellent fun. Or enjoy leapfrogging on fragrant summits. Something you and Colin might do for a future painting, Skye?'

'Possibly, but probably not. What else have you spotted, Gita?'

'It's time to get back to books. It's almost three hundred years since *Robinson Crusoe* was published. But its author, Daniel Defoe, had previously had an unusual day on July 31st, 1703. His satirical writing had offended various political and religious groups. His punishment was to be placed in the pillory. Rather than having hard vegetables thrown at him, he had flowers placed around him. Tulips, rather than turnips. People raised their glasses and toasted his good health. Plaudits, rather than punishment.'

'I've never understood the difference between pillories and stocks.'

'You're not the only one, Warren. This is the way it was explained to me. With a pillory, your hands and head would be restrained. So you could be forced to take a pill. With stocks, your feet were restrained. Feet on which you might have worn stock-ings'

'That makes sense. You would be much more vulnerable in the pillory. You wouldn't be able to defend your face.'

'That's right, Warren. The pillory wasn't abolished until 1837, the year Victoria became queen. While we're in that era, I've one more event from history. The British slave trade was abolished in 1807, but slavery itself continued. On August 1st, 1834, the Slavery Abolition Act finally came into force. Almost 800,000 slaves were freed and £20 million was paid in compensation. Not to the slaves, but to their owners. That was a controversial decision. And the legacy of slavery casts a long shadow. Mahatma Gandhi was born, like my parents, in Gujarat. Slavery was *not* abolished in India in 1834. The influence of the East India Company delayed abolition in the sub-continent until 1843. But Gandhi's life took a new turn, in South Africa. Using his London-acquired legal training, he fought for the rights of Indians there. Their working conditions and rights were not far removed from that of a slave. But he also fought for the British, winning medals and forming the Indian Ambulance Corps. But his first protest followed him being ejected from a first-class carriage en route to Pretoria. He soon won the right for 'properly dressed' Indians to be able to travel in first class. A compromise, but a step forward. And without Gandhi, would the British have lost control of India so soon? A long shadow, indeed.'

'Where to next, Gita?'

'Skye, I've heard there were many sad faces in nautical places on July 31st, 1970. Especially in Portsmouth. Warren, your home city turns up rather a lot in the research. Is that a coincidence?'

'I couldn't possibly comment. Which event were you referring to, Gita?'

'It was Black Tot Day, the last time that the official rum ration was given by the Royal Navy. A drop of Nelson's blood, as some of the sailors called it. It was a sad event, but not a tragedy. There were two of those on August 2nd. The first was in 1973 on the Isle of Man. Some people accept that death is an inevitable part of the Manx TT motorcycle races. But the Summerland Amusement Centre fire was an unexpected tragedy. Over fifty people died at the entertainment site in Douglas, the capital. On the same day, seven years later, a bomb exploded at Bologna Station.'

'You were talking about long shadows, Gita. *That* day still impacts on many people.'

'There's one more event I'd like to talk about. The dropping of the first atomic bomb on August 6th, 1945. Hiroshima wasn't even the original target. Kyoto, with all its Zen monasteries and gardens, had been rejected earlier. The flight crew of the *Enola Gay* needed a clear sky so they could film and photograph the damage. And the sky was clear over Hiroshima at 8.15 in the morning. I considered playing the OMD song named after the B-29 bomber that dropped *Little Boy*, but I decided not to.

President Truman justified the deaths and destruction by saying that it saved many more lives. But who knows? Not me, Skye.'

'I wonder what Hatsu would say. She'll be here in a month for the handover.'

'Are you going to let her have your bookshop, Gita?'

'I have to, Warren, and it's time to go back to Florida. As it happens, Mazda are based in Hiroshima. My uncle Kunal had a Mazda Miata soft-top parked underneath his place in Key West. It will be interesting to see what India has done to my uncle's apartment.'

'I think it's time for a bit of romance, Skye.'

'I agree, Warren. One of our irregular features is Slow Dating. It's a chance to put yourself out there on the forecourt. Hopefully resulting in a date, rather than standing outside a petrol station. Your message should be up to fifty words long, and no abbreviations please. If you wish to reply, for courting purposes, please drop me a line at the un-usual address, i.e. *Chatter Broth* c/o M3 aka Marina's Moreish Micropub. So this time, on Slow Dating, it's Haberdasher:

Slightly crazy haberdasher (female, 30ish, East Anglia) seeks lover of cool threads and pan-fried samphire to zip off together for book-sniffing in Boston, cushion sourcing in Cambridge or larking in Lincs. An ideal weekend might include watching Fitzcarraldo, visiting charity shops and feeling tingly.

So if you like cool threads, or watching a Werner Herzog film, why not reply? Please clearly include "Haberdasher" on your envelope or postcard. Ah, Warren has something.'

'Yes, I do. A cushion dance takes place in the John Clare poem, "May-Day Ballad". Here's part of it:

"And then comes the cushion, the girls they all shriek,
And fly to the door from the old fiddler's squeak."

The good old days, Skye?'

'Good research, Warren. I'd have probably been out through a window. I think words and phrases can tell us a lot about the past. Bunting time, when the grass or crops were tall enough to hide young lovers, might sound innocent enough. But dragging time? Referring to events at a country fair, when dusk falls, and young men start grabbing hold of women. That troubles me. Anyway, Warren, do you have any Lost Four Words?'

'Yes, Skye. Listeners might know that we are trying to 'release' underloved words back into common use. My favourite so far is dodkin. What's yours, Gita?'

'Dodkin's good. I wonder what value a coin would need to be, so that someone was not bothered to pick it up. I suppose it depends on where you are and what your needs are. I like cloop, but Skye's story about absquatulating in Austria made me laugh.'

'And yours, Skye?'

'I like buvette, and not just because M3 is just over the yard. Each fortnight Warren and I pin a shortlist of words, with a space for further suggestions, onto our *Chatter Broth* noticeboard in M3. People can then add any words they think should be on the list. Then one of our regular listeners chooses their four favourites. And turns them into a poem. Last time, we were looking for words beginning with the letter G. What are the final four, Warren?'

'Thanks, Skye. They are glimflashy, goluptious, gongoozler and griffonage:

A scrap of griffonage,
Had led to a goluptious afternoon.
Until an unhelpful gongoozler,
Made her glimflashy.'

'And your thoughts, Warren?'

'Well, Skye, does this make any sense to you?

A scrap of scrawled handwriting,
Had led to a wonderful afternoon.
Until an unhelpful watcher of canal-based activity,
Made her angry.'

'I also liked glent, a glance or glimpse. A subtle gesture that can say more than words. Did you find a song for that, Warren?'

'I did, Gita. It's "Tell Me" by Bob Dylan. He suggests that answers can be given non-verbally, with a sideways glance. I'll also play Ian McMillan, reading his poem "Canal Life". He writes about the rhythms, stories and songs of the waterways. And gongoozling, of course.'

'Ian's gongoozling sounds dreamy. But sometimes people just watch on while others are in trouble. Why is that?'

'That's a big question, Gita. Any thoughts, Skye?'

'People might not know how to help or might be afraid of getting into difficulties themselves. If in a group, they might think that someone else would step in. But many people *do* assist, often without working out the risks to themselves. I remember a moral dilemma homework that Zoe did for RE. The class had been watching *Touching the Void*.'

'That's a great, and terrifying, film.'

'It is, Warren. A climber has seconds to make a decision. Whether to cut the rope or to be dragged over the edge by his suspended partner. I won't reveal what happens, but it's gut-wrenching. The class discussed what they would have done. Then Kenesha — she was taking a cover lesson — set the class, including Zoe, *another* dilemma. You, the student, could see a runaway train coming down the track. And you could see your best friend lying on the rails, but did not know if they were unconscious or dead. There was a switch that would send the train onto another line. But there was also a stopped minibus, full of small children, on that line's level crossing. What should you do?'

'You could run and drag her friend from the track.'

'No, Gita. The distance was too far.'

'You could signal to the driver.'

'Sorry, Warren. The train had just come round a bend and the driver wouldn't be able to brake in time.'

'You could divert the train onto an empty track.'

'Again no, Gita. There were only two tracks, and both were blocked.'

'You could just watch and wait. Be a gongoozler. What did Zoe decide?'

'You'll have to ask her, Warren. But she was really upset about the decision she made.'

'She could have just walked away, and avoided making a decision.'

'She could have done, Gita. But that action might have been seen as a decision in itself. Ah, time's almost up. We'll finish with some more Four Play, inspired by scissors. A piece of equipment that a haberdasher might use. Over to you, Warren.'

'That was "Tits on the Radio" by The Scissor Sisters. I wonder what Darkroom Danny is up to now.'

'There might not be tits on the radio, Warren. But there are larks in Haberdasher's Lincolnshire.'

'Unless they were larks of the 'What larks, Pip!' variety, Skye?'

'Thanks for that, Warren. And I wonder about our samphire-munching, tingle-seeking haberdasher, whose Slow Dating request we heard earlier. Was she referring to Boston, Lincolnshire or Boston, Massachusetts?'

'Oh, I thought she was into pan-fried sapphires.'

Chapter 08

**Marina's entry in The Library Logbook, 2010
with additional comments by Zoe
and subsequent comments by India & Henry Zink**

When Zoe and I saw the photos in the handbook, we couldn't resist booking a short holiday in North Devon. To a Landmark Trust property with the potential for two croquet courses. We call them courses, rather than lawns, because our preferred style of croquet is not a manicured version. We like slopes, and bumps, and obstacles. And to play beside the ruins of a Victorian mansion provides extra atmosphere.

Thousands of Basques and Galicians moved to Idaho to escape persecution. That's a story that I know quite well, and is part of my heritage. But there have been other movements of people, most of which still carry a legacy today. English settlers moved to Roanoke, and later Jamestown. Welsh settlers moved to Patagonia, where they allegedly named the penguin after the Welsh words for white and head. Scottish adventurers attempted to settle in what is now Panama. One consequence of which was the Union with England.

Then there were the Devon 'farmers'. They were indentured servants who were shipped by Denys Rolle to East Florida. Denys was the Rolle who probably built this detached library. He liked privacy, hence his preference for long walks and talking with animals. He had an idea to create an agricultural utopia called Peace and Plenty. This was at a time when he was earning a rental income of over £40,000 from his English estates. This was in 1767. Many people in Britain *still* don't earn that amount in a year.

Denys's Devon 'farmers' were not farmers and they were not from Devon. The new residents of Rollestown were mainly desperate and poor people from London. A satirical description, sent to the Governor of Florida in 1767, described them sarcastically as a valuable colony. They included, in the satirist's words, '*bunters, cinder wenches and whores*'. Whatever their former occupations, they didn't adapt well to life in Florida. Few resisted the opportunity to escape from the rigours of picking oranges, raising cattle and tapping trees for turpentine.

And so Rolle brought in African slaves. A report from that era makes for interesting and shocking reading. Each slave looked after 2,500 trees. At the end of the year, each tree would have deep grooves cut into it. The sap (turpentine) would run into a collection box. It would take about a month to fill each box. Rolle provided a guinea per year to clothe each slave, and every three years they got a new blanket.

Highly skilled slaves were valued at £100, field workers at £50 and children (the '*Rising Generation*') at £15. Ten of the kitchen slaves (known as '*Past Labour*') were deemed, in the accounts, to be worthless. And Denys Rolle was viewed, by some, as being a relatively benevolent slave owner. And he was quite unusual in being directly involved, rather than being an absentee landlord.

The Treaty of Versailles (the 1789 version) granted Florida to Spain. Rather than financial compensation from the British government, Rolle was offered land on the Bahamian island of Exuma. His ship, the *Peace and Plenty*, took the slaves on *another*

Atlantic journey. And as he was a Rolle, the two new settlements he founded were called Rollestown and Rolleville.

Such tremendous wealth, which financed many buildings and institutions, and it was all based on the enslavement of people. Something to think about as I sit here in this magnificent former library. A room built with the profits of slavery.

It is strange that Britain fought so hard to develop slavery and *then* to fight against it. And an event in the Bahamas was a milestone in that journey. By 1830, Exuma was owned by John Rolle. He decided that a group of slaves should be moved to another island. One of the slaves, Pompey, led a protest and mass escape.

Although later captured and lashed, Pompey's protest impressed the Governor. He ruled that slaves, although viewed as property, could not be moved away from their families and communities against their will. Although, like most other slaves in the British Empire, the Bahamian slaves were not freed in 1834. They had to serve an 'apprenticeship', not dissimilar to the terms of indentured servants, before they were finally freed in 1838.

But back in 1834, John Rolle was still complaining. He complained in the House of Lords that he had been forced to spend over £1,000 to feed his ex-slaves. A British newspaper at the time lampooned him about his attitude to their '*ungrateful*' behaviour and for choosing a '*victim*' who happened to have been one of the richest slave owners in the world. There was also a suggestion that Lord Rolle avoided further payments by '*discharging the hungry rogues*'.

It is not known whether he formally granted land to the freed slaves, or whether the land was informally taken over. But many people on the island still take the surname of Rolle, and there are still areas of common land outside of present-day Rolle Town. And if you like gridiron, you might be interested to know that

Myron Rolle signed for the Tennessee Titans in the 2010 NFL draft. Ironically, he also received a Rhodes (as in Cecil Rhodes, founder of Rhodesia) Scholarship to Oxford. The impact and legacy of colonisation and of empire-building can be complicated, and it's ongoing.

Lord Rolle died without heirs. A nephew changed his surname from Trefusis to Rolle when he inherited the estates. But he was the nephew of Louisa, Lord Rolle's wife, rather than Lord Rolle himself. This did not amuse Aunt Stevens and Aunt Moore (as a poem they wrote reveals). Here is part of it:

> '*Hungry Louisa, forced to wed,*
> *Took stale Rolle*
> *Instead of bread,*
> *And (not?) forgetting all her store*
> *Cut out Stevens, cut out Moore.*'

I'm not sure if the 'not' makes sense, but the two aunts were definitely not 'Rolle'-ing with laughter. Another descendant, Mark Rolle, was known for his parties and estate improvements. And he must have still been wealthy. How many people can move to another mansion for three months every year, with a special train laid on to ease the process? I didn't know there was so much money in turpentine. In fact, I didn't even know what it was. I had to look it up in the dictionary.

Thank you, Landmark Trust, for rescuing yet another treasure. And thank you to whoever chose the books in the library. And final thanks to the housekeeper. *El florero* (the vase) of flowers was a lovely touch.

Marina Rueda, Idaho and Suffolk

PS Apart from croquet, we have also made a few excursions. We enjoyed paddling at Instow, followed by a delicious Hockings ice cream. And I enjoyed some refreshing drinks: local Winkleigh cider at Rosemoor Gardens and a chilled freshly-squeezed orange juice at the Duke of York in Iddesleigh. The 'Duke' is a place that could have become a time capsule, but also seems quite at home in the second decade of the twenty-first century. *¡Salud!* — Cheers!

Thanks, so much, to Marina and Colin for renting this place for my tenth birthday. Walking up the swirly stairs is great, and then there are the two views. First, you look out the back, over a smoothish lawn. This is good for trying out long shots, but it's a bit too flat. At the far end of the lawn is an EnOrMoUs BeDrOoM with big glass windows. It looks chilly, so I'm glad *we're* not sleeping in there. Colin stayed there on the first night. Then went down to Exeter to stay with friends and buy some more colourful clothes from Lugets. Someone else stayed in the room across the lawn last night. Though I didn't meet her or him.

Out the front is the second lawn. Humans can reach it by using the stone steps. But croquet balls can use the steep slope. You place your ball at the top of the slope, and then give it a little tap. If you've aimed well, the ball will shoot through the hoop. Or maybe get stuck in the jaws. One night (we had candles lit to see where the hoops were), Marina somehow managed to get her ball through two of the hoops. With just the one shot.

It's fun to roll the balls where the Rolles once lived. Oh, and Marina says I could stay in a tower one day with really swirly stairs. That would be fun. Marina says the proper name for swirly stairs is a spiral staircase. But I'm keeping my name for them.

ZoE, aGeD tEn

I usually enjoy reading the suggestions and comments in these logbooks. But the most recent one was too close to home. Or rather not my home. Colin arrived in his H Van, at 9.59am, to collect Marina Rueda and Zoe. Marina had invited me to arrive a day early. I think she wanted me to meet Zoe, who I haven't seen for almost ten years. Although I've met people who, in turn, have met her. And who then enrich her life with art, or drama, or words. I'll be staying this week in the 'EnOrMoUs' bedroom.

My client will be staying in The Library. Next week, he'll head over to Suffolk, which will be his base for the next four months. I'll head over to Lake Tahoe in Nevada and start to declutter his recently inherited home. Henry's a sculptor, so I'm sure he and Angelique can work on some projects with Zoe. And he's also got a vineyard in Washington State, so I'm sure he'll have plenty to chitchat about with Marina.

I may not be a 'mother' but I'm looking out for my child. Trying to provide rich experiences for her, despite rejecting more accepted norms of motherhood. And yes, I am still running away. But I'm sure other mothers have considered doing the same. I've been asked why I even bothered having a child. And I don't really know why I did. Or why I'm still watching from a distance.

There's no 'eau' and no loo in the Orangery. Last night, I considered walking across the lawn to use the one at The Library. But I found I was still not ready to meet and speak with my daughter. And who knows what her reaction might have been?

I was interested to read Marina's thoughts on movement and legacy. There are some similarities between indentured 'servants' and slaves. While the servants had more choice, they were often desperate to escape poverty. They gave up their freedom, and their right to earn money for seven years, in return for passage to a new home. The inability of many of them to survive the harsh conditions led many estate owners to look elsewhere for cheap labour. And so the growth of the African slave trade was given another tragic boost.

India Farr (from here, there, and soon somewhere else)

My, oh my. What a tremendous place. While the export of buildings to the States is less common of late, I would love to own — or even lease — a building such as this. Not because of its history, but because of its magnificence. A detached library is such a luxury. And, if the roof had originally been made of straw or reed, a detached *and* de-thatched one. Ho, ho?

Now I know some Americans say there's a short and thin history in the States, but I disagree. The Acoma Pueblo in New Mexico has been continuously inhabited for over a thousand years. Maybe it's a different kind of history my compatriots are thinking of. Yet, even our colonial history is longer and more complex than the '*Mayflower* 1620' founding story. I too was interested to read Marina Rueda's comments, especially those about slavery.

The year before the *Mayflower* arrived in Massachusetts, another ship had arrived near the colonial port of Jamestown in Virginia. John Rolfe noted that the Dutch-English crew traded food for around twenty 'Negroes'. Whether they became slaves is not known, but Africans were being traded before the freedom-loving Pilgrims arrived Stateside. And three years before 1620, John Rolfe's wife died on the Thames, near Gravesend.

And her name? Rebecca Rolfe aka Matoaka aka Pocahontas. Seeing the statue of her at Jamestown, during a summer vacation, inspired me to become a sculptor. I also saw the Wright Brothers sculpture on that trip, down at Kill Devil, OBX (the Outer Banks). Apparently, Orville got into a huff with the Smithsonian in the 1920s. As a result, the *Wright Flyer* ended up in London for a couple of decades. It wasn't on quite the same scale as Picasso's *Guernica* being exiled to the USA until after the death of Franco. But surely almost unimaginable today?

I took a little persuading to make this trip, but it seems India is on to something. I heard about her from Ana Logan, who lives near my vacation home in Buxton. That's the Buxton near Cape Hatteras, OBX. Not Buxton, Derbyshire.

There are a few things I would tweak with IF, only . . . But India provides an important service. And a great chance for people like me to explore Britain and beyond. We're going to drive to St Ives tomorrow and chase the spirit of Barbara Hepworth. Those forms. What imagination. Simply classic.

My parents bought two 'Hepworths' back in the fifties — which arrived at their place by seaplane — but they kept them in the guesthouse. I'm hoping to get to Coventry as well, to see what rose there out of the ashes of war. And I hear you have a few standing stones on these islands, so I'm sure I will not be lacking inspiration

Henry Zink III (Henry the Third)

(Hey, am I royalty over here?)

Walla Walla, WA

~

'Hi, I'm Skye Hunter and welcome to *Chatter Broth*. It's August 7th and today's guest runs M3, our local moreish micropub. Welcome back, Marina.'

'It's good to be with you and Warren again. There have been lots of suggested words written on the *Chatter Broth* poster. My favourite was honey-fuggle, to deceive. Did it make it to the final four?'

'Warren?'

'Thanks, Skye. And sorry, Marina. Yours wasn't chosen this

time. The final four 'H' words are haaf, hakama, half-mourner and hibakusha:

Heading for the haaf,
She was surprised to see a half-mourner,
Flying above a hibakusha,
Who was dressed just in a hakama.'

'And your thoughts on what our mystery poet meant, Warren?'

'Well, Skye, does this make any sense to you?

Heading for the deep sea,
She was surprised to see a marbled white butterfly,
Flying above an atomic bomb survivor,
Who was wearing just a pair of Japanese
multi-pleated baggy trousers.

I'm quite taken with that butterfly's name. Like someone at a funeral who's sad, but didn't really know the person. And August 9th was when the hydrogen bomb was dropped on Nagasaki. One other thing that's sad is that the Japanese had to invent a name for the survivors. I can imagine a hibakusha wandering around in a daze, for days, wearing just a pair of trousers . . . What have you spotted In This Fortnight, Marina?'

'I know Angelique has visited Nagasaki. The Dutch had a lot of influence there. I'll start with sport. It's just over 150 years since the first croquet Open Championship was played, at Evesham. Zoe and I love playing it together.'

'Isn't it dull and a bit, well, posh? Not the kind of sport for a mush like me?'

'Not at all, Warren. Not the way we like to play it anyway. It's strategic and fun. It's a bit like bar billiards, but on *la herbia* — grass.'

'Colin and I enjoy playing too, Warren. Maybe Zoe could set up a demo at the Field Party.'

'It would definitely be more fun than being a child labourer. On August 7th, 1840, parliament banned the use of climbing boys as chimney sweeps. And thirty years later, on August 9th, the 1870 Education Act was passed. It provided free and compulsory education for all children between the ages of five and thirteen. Though some families would have seen it as an intrusion into their working lives.'

'What about home education? Wealthy families would have had governesses and tutors. And tens of thousands of children are still educated at home. Are they covered by legislation?'

'I don't think so, Warren. I don't think the government even knows how many children are being home educated.'

'I'll add something, Marina and Warren. Local authority schools are very tightly controlled, including having to follow the national curriculum. But academies, private schools and home educators have much more freedom and flexibility. Perhaps the government doesn't want education provision to be accountable to local voters. I know that Kenesha was not impressed when her school became an academy. What do you think, Marina?'

'That's a tricky issue, Skye. Now, as in the past, not all reforms are necessarily improvements. In 1834, on August 8th, parishes lost their responsibility for providing poor relief. This system, flawed though it was, was replaced by the workhouse. And Charles Dickens definitely had some views on that. *Verdadero* — true, Warren?'

'He did, Marina. *Oliver Twist* was not a book that was talked about in our house. My great-grandmother, on my mother's side, was born in a workhouse. In Nottinghamshire. I still haven't even read *Oliver Twist* or watched the film. It still seems a bit too close to home.'

'Family histories can be complicated, and you often find twists. Even in the most recent generations. Skye and Colin know all about that.'

'You're right, Marina. And some of my wartime experiences feel like they were in another lifetime. Perhaps, in some way, they were. Do you have any other thoughts?'

'*Desde luego* — certainly. It's almost two hundred years since the Peterloo Massacre of 1819. An event, on August 16th, which inspired the first publication of the *Manchester Guardian*. A crowd, similar in size to one you would now get at Old Trafford, was hearing speeches about the urgent need for parliamentary reform. The government's response was to authorise a horseback charge. A charge which was executed by Hussars armed with drawn sabres. Fifteen people were killed and hundreds injured. It was named for its location, St Peter's Field, and an ironic reference to the Battle of Waterloo. It's difficult to imagine anything like that happening now.'

'It was before Warren's time, but those who witnessed the Battle of Orgreave during the miners' strike in the '80s might disagree. No sabres, but plenty of batons used with intent.'

'I know a little about that time. The film *Billy Elliot* is set against that backdrop of miners versus the police. In earlier generations, the miners would probably have been convicted of riotous assembly and then been transported to the colonies. Which reminds me of a hearty sea shanty by the Fishermen's Friends. Which also links in with haaf, the deep sea. So heave-ho and we'll listen to "South Australia".'

'That was a rousing song, Warren. I remember, back in May, I was talking with you and Skye about why Britain needed a new place to transport its convicts. So my final comment relates to the birth of colonial expansion, in what is now the USA. On August 18th, 1587, an English expedition of 117 colonists landed at what is now called Roanoke Island. It was the third voyage organised by Sir Walter Raleigh. A fourth voyage, three years later found no evidence of the settlers. Just an enigmatic carved message. The Virginia colony had become a *lost* colony. And strangely, Raleigh never visited North America. Sir Francis Drake did though. In fact, he visited Roanoke in 1585. Perhaps the capital of North Carolina should change its name from Raleigh to Drake. One last thing, for now. Two of the missing colonists were the parents of Virginia Dare. She was the first child of English parents to be born in mainland North America. But not the first European child. That honour belongs to Snorri. A Viking child, born over half a millennium earlier, in Vinland. As for the name of the first 'native' North American, we'll probably never know. Maybe someone whose name translated to something like She Who Crossed The Ice.'

Chapter 09

'Hello. My name's Dr Dangerfield, but please call me Jerry. Is it all right if I call you Warren?'

'That's fine, Jerry. So how will this process work?'

'Sometimes I'll ask you questions. At other times I'll let you talk at length and just take notes.'

'But things settled down with my stepfather after that.'

'Can you give me an example, Warren?'

'Rather than insisting I go with him to watch Pompey at Fratton Park, he asked me more about my hobbies and interests. This resulted in us spending a lot of time in the Royal Dockyards, especially on *HMS Victory*. Have you been, Jerry?'

'No, but I saw its masts and rigging when I was on a ferry to the Isle of Wight a few years ago. I can see, from your enthusiasm, that I should perhaps add it to my list of things to do.'

'And I was doing really well on my catering course, Jerry. The lecturers were really switched on. They'd got us thinking about things like sustainability, seasonality and foraging. I loved the sourcing of ingredients and finding interesting ways to prepare and cook them. There were also interesting placements at pubs and restaurants.'

'Which was your favourite, Warren?'

'There was a great bistro in Horndean, near the old Gales

Brewery, where I helped to develop a new small plates menu. And it was really exciting when I helped to prepare a celebration meal on the mess deck of *HMS Victory*. But, my favourite? You now know Portsmouth is the only city built on an island in England. Well, I did one of my work placements in a pub-restaurant, in the middle of Hampshire, that felt like an island. Its garden spilled down to the River Itchen, but it was the atmosphere, not just the water, that gave it that island feeling. That's one of the main reasons I moved to Suffolk. I like that watery feeling, even though I don't like to get my feet wet. I'd have made a rubbish marsh-wiggle. Puddleglum? I'd have been Puddle-very-glum.'

'Nice Narnia knowledge there, Warren. So why didn't you pursue a career in catering?'

'I began to dislike the actual service, rushing to get plates to the pass, the late nights. I finished the course though, with distinction. Then things got even more complicated at home. But I'm organising the catering at the Field Party in August.'

'That sounds good, Warren. Now let's focus on the donation process. Having spoken with Harrison, it appears that you made the decision quite easily.'

'That's right. It just seems like the natural thing to do.'

'That's fine. But many potential donors find their decision stirs up emotions and unexpected feelings. Some try to hide the fact that they're actually donating out of guilt, or because they lack self-worth. And whatever you feel now, remember you can change your mind at any time. About a third of potential donors do. And another third drop out due to medical issues.'

'Yes, I remember Marina telling me about that. And I respect the fact that Marina and Colin are not joining the donor scheme. They've both done more than enough for Zoe already. And Zoe doesn't want to involve her birth parents. So here I am, Jerry.'

'How would you feel if the transplant failed, and Zoe had to go on dialysis? Or if the kidney didn't last long and Zoe had to wait for another operation?'

'I don't know exactly, but I'd be sad. But not as sad as if I'd done nothing. There will always be risks, but the medical tests are pretty thorough.'

'Yes they are. I'm now going to ask you lots of questions based on a series of tests. We'll start with a health literacy test. Are you ready?'

'Yes, Jerry. Fire away. I'll do my best.'

'I'm going to show you eighteen cards with three words on them. First, I'd like you to read out the top word. Next, I'll read the two words underneath. Then I'd like you to tell me which of the two words is more similar to, or has a closer match with, the top word. If you don't know, please say "I don't know". Don't guess. Does that make sense?'

'Sounds good to me. Shall we start?'

'Yes, I believe you're ready. Here is the first card. Please read the top word out loud.'

'Kidney.'

'Which of the urine or fever is most similar to the top word?'

'That would be urine.'

'Occupation'

   'Work or education?

   'Work, definitely.'

'Nutrition.'

   'Healthy or soda?'

   'Healthy, surely.'

'Infection.'

   'Plant or virus?'

   'Well, plants get infected, so plant.'

'Alcolism.'

'Addiction or recreation?'

'Both, from what I've seen. But if I had to choose, addiction.'

'Dose.'

'Sleep or amount?'

'Amount. Why's sleep there? Oh, I suppose if it had a Z, that would make sense.'

'Syphilis'

'This is the last one, Warren. Contraception or condom?'

'Condom, I think.'

'Well done, Warren. You got almost all of them right. Plants can be infected, but 'virus' is closer. And it' alco-hol-ism. We'll also explore your response to that word later in the interview. The next test is written. Please read the instructions and then pass the sheet back to me'

Warren scanned the sheet and then spent a couple of minutes underlining his answers. The questions were focused on his ability to bounce back after setbacks and stressful events. 'They seemed quite straightforward.'

Jerry took the sheet and did a quick mental calculation. 'Yes, you're fine there on those questions about resilience. I've now got two questions about your recent mood. For both of them there are four options. Not at all, several days, more than half the days or nearly every day. So firstly, and over the last two weeks, how often have you been bothered by having little pleasure in doing things?'

'Not at all. A few years ago, the answer would have been different. But leaving home has been very positive in many ways.'

'Secondly, how often have you been bothered by feeling down, depressed or hopeless?'

'Feeling down, a little. Let's say on two or three days. But not depressed, and definitely not hopeless.'

'Well done, Warren. I won't need to ask more detailed questions on that theme. The next two questions have the same four options as before, and also are about how you've felt in the last fortnight. Firstly, how often have you been bothered by feeling nervous, anxious or on edge?'

'Several days, maybe more. But I don't dwell on things as much as I used to. I'm so much busier now and I've got people around me who really seem to care about me.'

'What about not being able to stop, or control, worrying?'

'I'm worried about Zoe, but I feel as if I'm doing something, so I'll go for the several days option again, Jerry'

'Based on your answers, I'm going to ask you five more questions, and then we'll take a short break. Over the last two weeks, how often have you been bothered by the following problems? And you can answer using the same four options. Do you want me to remind you, Warren?'

'No, that's fine.' Warren shifted in his chair and gave a small yawn.

Jerry smiled. 'You're doing really well. So have you worried too much about different things?'

'I've thought about things, such as finding my own flat and getting a longer-term job. But worrying, no. So not at all.'

'Have you had trouble relaxing?'

'There's not much time for relaxing at the Hop Yard, but again, not at all.'

'And finally, have you felt afraid, as if something awful might happen?'

'Most days. Often when I've just woken up, I suppose. But that's one of the reasons I'm here. To do something about it. To try and help Zoe.'

'Let's continue, Warren.'

'I'm actually quite enjoying the process, Jerry. It's making me think deeply about who I am and what motivates me. It goes beyond my decision to put myself forward as a donor.'

Jerry smiled and then looked down at her notes. 'I've now got a series of eight questions. If you're not sure how to respond, think about what your answer would be most of the time. And you don't need to explain your answers. A "yes" or a "no" is fine. Here goes. In general, Warren, do you have difficulty making and keeping friends?'

'At school, yes. In the last year, no.'

'As I suggested, just give your 'most of the time' answer. We'll talk about some of your answers in more detail later, if we need to. I'm sorry if I sound a bit harsh, but do you have difficulty making and keeping friends?'

'No. And it's fine, Jerry.'

'That's good, Warren. Would you normally describe yourself as a loner?'

'No.'

'In general, do you trust other people?'

'Er, yes.'

'Are you normally an impulsive sort of person?'

'What do you mean, Jerry?'

'Do you normally do things on the spur of the moment, without thinking of the consequences?'

'No.'

'And the last question, Warren. In general, are you a perfectionist?'

'No. But I like to do things well. Sorry, there I go again.'

'Now the next questions have five options. None of the time, a little, some, most or all of the time.'

'Aren't "a little of the time" and "some of the time" the same thing, Jerry?'

'I see your point. Just imagine that 'Little' is smaller than 'Some'. And don't worry about adding *some* explanation. I'm not a strict machine.'

'Okay, Deckard.'

'Deckard? My surname's Dangerfield.'

'I know, Jerry. Deckard was the character who ran the empathy tests in *Blade Runner*. What's the first question?'

'Ah yes, Roy Batty's tears in the rain. I can see how you made the connection. Also, I once went to a festival dressed as Pris, so I hope you don't *actually* suspect that I'm a replicant in disguise. So question one. Is there someone you can count on to listen to you when you need to talk?'

'Most of the time, and more than one person. Skye, George and Angelique are all good listeners.'

'Is there someone available to you to give you good advice about a problem?'

'It depends what you call good advice, Jerry, but once again I'd say most of the time.'

'Is there someone who shows you love and affection, Warren?'

'Love? I don't think so. Affection? I've got people who I feel are my friends, but I don't really know how much affection there is. I'll go with a little.'

'Finally, are you currently married or living with a partner in a romantic relationship?'

'No. That's something that doesn't interest me at the moment. But, in the future, who knows?'

'Just one more set of questions, Warren. With the same five options as the last set.'

'I'm ready when you are, Jerry.'

There were over a dozen questions and Warren went into a kind of daze as he answered them. He was there, but he also felt separated from the moment. It was almost like he was looking down on a new version of himself.

'Is there someone you can count on to listen to you when you need to talk?'

'Is there someone who hugs you?'

'And finally, is there someone to do things with, to help you get your mind off things?'

'There are lots of people, actually. Skye is unbelievable, and so calm. Colin always has time for me. Gita and I chat, about all kinds of things, while we are sorting through new stock at Bay Six Books. I like spending time with George, and it looks like I might get more involved on the food side. Angelique likes me to help get the gallery set up for a new exhibition. I like to hang out with Marina at M3. She's found a few low-alcohol beers for me like BrewDog's Raspberry Blitz, or their Nanny State. But I usually stick to a glass of water or my fruit and veg smoothies. It's all good.'

'Have there been problems with alcohol in your family life, Warren? I'm thinking back to one of your responses from the first part of the interview.'

'My father couldn't handle alcohol, or money. That's why my mother kicked him out. My step-father doesn't drink. Not that I know of anyway.'

'Do you still see your father?'

'Not often. Just once, actually. He's got a new family, down the coast near Hastings.'

'And your grand-parents?'

'They're all still with us. Granny and Grandad live in

sheltered housing near my Mum, who's their daughter. And Nan and Grandpa Wagstaffe are just a short ferry ride over the Solent in Ryde. Have you been there?'

'No, I was based in Cowes.'

'For the yachting, Jerry? Messing about in boats. That sort of stuff?'

'No, I was doing some prison-based work at the Albany and Parkhurst sites there. We might need to talk again, but I'm satisfied that your responses make you a suitable candidate going forward.'

'But I didn't get them all right and I struggled with some of them.'

'That's entirely natural. I'd have been more worried if you *had* sailed through with no difficulties. If you'd admitted no concerns. I was impressed with your honesty and awareness of the complexity of the process.'

'Thanks, Jerry. Though you wouldn't believe how different my answers would have been before I moved to Suffolk. It's almost like I've found a new family.'

~

'Hi, I'm Skye Hunter and welcome to *Chatter Broth*. It's August 21st and today's guest is Colin Pargeter.'

'Hello, Skylark. And hello, Warren. You look a bit tired. Working too hard on the preparations, p'raps?'

'I'm fine Colin. Getting my en-suite room ready took a lot of effort. But it was well worth it. Thank you so much for thinking of that. I was grateful to sleep in the H Van, but brick walls are much better than a metal box. Which I parked, at first, under the horse chestnut tree. That was pretty stupid of me. All the local kids clambering up on the roof last autumn, looking for that elusive monster conker. And now we're all busy getting ready for the Field Party. I've been helping Zoe prepare her croquet course. Lots of digging and making mounds. It's a bit different, but I think the visitors will like it. Extreme croquet. Who'd have thought a mush from Pompey would enjoy playing such an exotic sport?'

'The Hop Yard does that to people, and I'm glad you've settled in. We'll talk more about the Field Party later, but let's start with In This Fortnight. Over to you, Colin.'

'Right-o. Its twenty-nine years tomorrow since British Telecom held the public launch of the world's first mobile phones. Though the owners had to be within 100 yards of each other. And it's almost five years since BT closed its dial-up internet service. Even though the telecoms regulator had said almost a million people were still using it. It was just going to be broadband or mobile access from then on. A bit of a disconnect there, I think. Can you imagine if they turned off the radio signal and forced everyone to listen online? Or got rid of the text-based services on the BBC's Red Button? There'd be a *not so silent* revolution. Now, I know Skye that you've always been up to date with technology. And that this podcast is accessed by people in over forty countries. Just look around this studio. It's state of the art. But the lad here doesn't even own a phone. Why is that, Warren?'

'A mobile phone was more trouble than it was worth at school. I don't know why they aren't banned in classrooms and playgrounds. Things can get out of hand too quickly. But Zoe's new phone doesn't even have apps or internet access. I might get one like hers.'

'Oh yes, her *burner* phone. Why not, indeed, if that's your kind of thing? What's next, Colin?'

'Britain banned the slave trade in 1807, but it wasn't until August 28th, 1833, that the Abolition Act was passed. Though it did not apply immediately in some places, such as East India

Company territories. It took almost another year to come into force. Marina did some research about it when she was staying at The Library a few years ago. It seems that, even after abolition, the ex-slaves had to serve a kind of forced apprenticeship until 1838. And then there was the £20 million compensation. Which was given to the former owners, *not* the former slaves. I've heard it said on this podcast that life can be complex, with the lines of history having a long tail. In five days, it'll be two years since Colin Kaepernick made his protest.'

'He was the quarterback for the San Francisco 49ers, Colin.'

'That's right, Warren. He took a knee, as they call it, before the national anthem at a pre-season game. He said, "I am not going to stand up to show pride in a flag for a country that oppresses black people and people of colour". As it happens, I've always felt uneasy about the labels used for people, like black and white, coloured and mixed race. That sort of thing. I think Steve Biko got it right, when he ridiculed the Afrikaans establishment at his trial. Telling the judge that he, Steve Biko, was not black. But brown. And telling the judge that he, the judge, was pink. Not white. Life, and history, is definitely not black and white. Peter Gabriel might have sung that the man is dead, but Steve Biko's legacy lives on.'

'Colin has always looked out for other people. And he—'

'Ah, I notice that the Ordnance Survey was founded in 1791. On August 30th. And George has such a good stock of maps, both historic and contemporary. Did I hear that you might be getting more involved with the food side, Warren?'

'Yes, Colin. I was talking to him and Marina about it over at M3 recently. George was quite impressed with my celery, nettle and tomato smoothie. Though not enough to persuade him to order it instead of a dark rum. He's had Globe+Artichoke for a good few years. I think George now wants to concentrate more on the map side. I didn't know he used to focus on maps *and* wine though.'

'That was another good business. Colin will remember that it took a while for Marina to find her feet. She was more interested in brewing, than running a micropub. So George wasn't treading on her funky wellies by selling wine.'

'It's as you said, Skye. George would match maps to wines. Argentina with Malbec. Lebanon with its rich Chateau Musar. Rome with Frascati. That sort of thing. What was it called, Skye?'

'It was called Compass Rosé. It was a bit obscure, but some people got it. A bit like Marina's barley sideline.'

'What was that?'

'You don't like most beers, Warren. But I know that Colin, when he's not on the cocktails, has always liked a pint or two. Even when he was an evacuee. But until quite recently, flat beer was common in pubs. So Marina sold these little wooden boxes of roasted barley seeds. Seth was just a boy when he made them for her up in Laxfield. Though they were fiddly to fill. The idea was you'd pop a few of the seeds in your pint. The chemical reaction would send a steady stream of gas, and hey presto, a foamy beer. It never made any money. They'd have liked her, but laughed at her 'business' plan, on *Dragon's Den*.'

'What was it called, Skye?'

'It was called Lovely Head.'

'Is this story just a way for you to get in one of your favourite Goldfrapp songs?'

'Not at all, Warren. When Gita found an old sample, she came up with Uttar Froth.'

'Utter?'

'Utt-ar, Warren. A play on her Indian heritage. I'm sure George has a map of Uttar Pradesh in his shop. Although the shop's closed while he's in Edinburgh.'

'Oh, I heard he was up there. Selling maps, p'raps?'

'Sort of. It's part of his plan to hand over responsibility for food to me. I'm not exactly sure what he's doing. Did he speak to you, Skye?'

'No, but I heard from Marina that he was performing at the Edinburgh Fringe. A sort of one-man show, involving a giant fabric map of Edinburgh. It was going to be called *Get Lost With GPS*, but I think he changed the title. I'm sure we'll hear more when he's back next week for the Field Party. And if not, he might talk about it when he's our guest next month. I think it's time for a brew. What song have you got for us while I'm making the drinks, Warren?'

'That was "Perfect Skin" by Lloyd Cole and The Commotions.'

'A song linked to Lost Four Words, I think. Last time, we were looking for words beginning with the letter I. And what are the final four?'

'Thanks, Skye. They are immure, insolated, interdigitated and irrorate:

Not wishing to be immured,
She interdigitated behind her head,
Exposed her irrorate skin,
And insolated, slowly.'

'And your thoughts on the meaning, Warren?'
'Well, Skye, do these lines make any sense to you?

Not wishing to be confined within walls,
She interlocked her fingers behind her head,
Exposed her dew-wet skin,
And dried in the sun, slowly.'

'That's a powerful image. Someone going outside at dawn,

perhaps naked, and then drying off in the sun. What do you think, Colin?'

'Not the sort of thing you would normally see in Suffolk. Though, p'raps if you were listening to Lloyd Cole by the lake at Latitude. I suggested ignify, to set on fire. Could you play "Beds Are Burning" by Midnight Oil, Warren? A song that seems to become more relevant as each year passes.

'I'll get it set up, though I half expected you to choose Firestarter or something by Fire In The Pack.'

'I'm not surprised those Australian cockatoos were so scared. The bloodwood tree doesn't sound like a friendly perch, especially in forty-five degrees of heat. Wildfires must be terrifying for creatures, as well as for humans. Good choice, Colin.'

'Thanks, Warren. And forgive me, Skylark, but I'm going to finish with the war. That war. Our war, I suppose, even though we were just children.'

'Go ahead. It's fine.'

'At the end of August, I was about to go back to school. The older kids still had, or would have had, another fortnight on holiday. Our school was one of those chosen for a full-scale rehearsal. It was quite exciting, but there was an accident that delayed things, quite near Pershore Place, as it happens. A chap was hit by a car while he was painting a kerb. That was sad, and there was a lot more sadness to come. The white paint was meant to help in a blackout. There were all kinds of new regulations. That's why the Citizen's Advice Bureau was set up — on the very day that Neville Chamberlain declared war on Germany — to help people cope with all the new rules. Pity the council couldn't have done something about the Regents Canal though. Loads of people walked into that during the war, and many of them drowned. And there was strange stuff going on a few days later, at the zoo near that canal. Some of the animals were being evacuated and they were looking for sponsors. Mother laughed when I said that I wanted to help a penguin. She told me the cost would have been thirty bob a week. But in her first postcard to my new foster parents, she wrote that she gave a sixpence for a dormouse. Just for a week. I hope it survived and slept through most of the bombing.'

'So that rehearsal was the first of four evacuations for you?'

'That's right, Warren. After the rehearsal, the first *real* evacuation happened. *Operation Pied Piper,* they called it, and off we went. On September 1st. The government also switched off the television signal. For seven years as it turned out. We've spoken about that before, but there are a couple of things I didn't tell you. The Ally Pally's transmitter was only meant to send its signal 25 miles. But I heard that they received it up here in Suffolk. My family in London didn't have a television, but I found a copy of the *Radio Times*. There was an advertisement in there inviting anyone to go up to Alexandra Palace. It was all part of something called Radiolympia. The gist of it was you had to find this chap called Harold Cox. You could suggest to him what kind of demonstration or musical turn you would like to perform. If selected, you would appear on *Come and Be Televised!* And that programme wasn't just going to be broadcasted. The BBC announced it was going to be *radiated*.'

'So you were on the telly?'

'No, Warren. The bloomin' war was loomin' and I got evacuated to avoid the expected boomin'.'

'And the second thing?'

'It might be difficult to believe, young Wagstaffe, but there were only about twenty thousand televisions in Great Britain at that time. And my adoptive parents had two of them. Yes, two. One in London and the other at Peasenham Hall. Can you imagine that? Not that I got to watch them during the war. The one at Peasenham Hall became a temporary plant stand. And I hardly watch any TV now. Just *First Dates*, *Grand Designs* and *Only Connect*, really.'

'And anything with Brenda Blethyn in it. Eh, Colin?'

'S'pose so, Skylark. She knows her way around a scene.'

Chapter 10

Zoe's entry in The Mackintosh Building Logbook, 2012 with additional comments by Skye & Colin

Hurrah for the Mac Flat! It's been kind of fun sharing a room with Skye. She makes funny noises at night. Some are snuffly and some are much louder! This is the first time I've left England. Some of my friends go abroad every year, but I don't mind. Daddy had problems in Australia and my Mummy is all over the place. But things happen everywhere, I suppose. Even here in Comrie.

I thought it was a bit silly that we were going to a place famous for earthquacks, as I like to call them. But I'm glad we're here. I love the corner turret in the living room. With its three tall windows, each with a different view. My windows on the world. 'Earn' is a funny word for a river. I wonder what it means. I can think of three rivers that sound like letters: the Dee, the Exe and the Wye. I wish there was a River Zed.

Zoe F-D, Suffolk

There are some delightful walks to be had in and around Comrie. And some of the 'pensioners' round here are like mountain goats. Moving past us at speed, often with the aid of two high-tech walking poles. And there are lots of interesting metal fence posts to be seen. One of them reminded me of the title character from the film *WALL·E*. Maybe you suspect I'm under the influence. Perhaps, but the bar next to the hotel is a grand place to recover after a long walk. Or better still, a short walk.

Locally, we liked Crieff. But we loved Aberfeldy. There's a cracking bookshop there in a converted watermill. It's definitely a Top Six contender, along with Barter Books (Alnwick), Laurence Oxley (Alresford), The Open Book (Wigtown) and Scrivener's (Buxton). Not forgetting the wonderful Book Barge (location currently unknown, though it could be almost anywhere on the canal system, with its hoard of books and delicious homemade cakes).

Talking of cakes, let's get back to Aberfeldy. Colin tested the local specialities, while Zoe and I scooted around for a couple of hours. I bought a book called *The Thought Gang* by Tibor Fischer, because I liked the colours on the cover. Is that a good method, or reason, for buying a book? It certainly 'helped' me to find *Miss Smilla's Feeling For Snow*, *Morvern Callar* and *Portrait of an Unknown Woman*. I'm sure most people have their own buying quirks.

Skye 'Queen of The Snorers' Hunter (Suffolk)

I cannot quite believe this. The delight of staying in one of the most beautiful 'flats' in Britain. It's simply wonderful. Climb the creaky stairs and, after a turn or two, you come to an elegant hall with five handmade doors. If you're out of puff, you can rest on a chair designed by Charles Rennie Mackintosh. Each panelled door is painted in a muted green. The doors lead, in clockwise order, to the 'double', the kitchen, the 'twin', the living room and the bathroom (whose fittings are a lively shade of avocado green).

The town is famous for its frequent tremors and earthquake research. Indeed, a seismic observatory used to stand on top of this very building. The local enthusiasts became known as the Comrie Pioneers and commissioned the world's first seismometer, in 1841.

I remember a friend of mine taking me to see a film called *Electric Dreams* in the 1980s. There was a daft plot about a computer taking over the life of its owner. Surely that could never happen? The computer's owner, based in San Francisco, was designing an earthquake-proof brick. Perhaps he was channelling the spirit of those Comrie trailblazers.

Thanks to the Housekeeper for presenting the property so beautifully and for the vase of heather left on the kitchen table. Can we come again? It's my first time over the border, but it hopefully won't be the last.

Colin Pargeter, The Hop Yard, Suffolk

PS Charles Rennie Mackintosh was well aware of the contribution made by his wife, Margaret Macdonald. He thought that he had talent, but that *she* was the genius. CRM once said of her, "Remember you are half, if not three-quarters, in all my architectural work". Margaret was very talented. Her 1902 work, *The Red Rose and the White Rose*, sold six years ago for not far short of two million pounds.

~

'Hi, I'm Skye Hunter and welcome to *Chatter Broth*. It's September 4th and today's guest is Angelique Vonk.'

'Skye, it's great to be invited back. And it's nice to do a show with Warren this time. Hey, what a great feast you organised for our Field Party. I loved your falafel wraps with celeriac and mint. And getting Southwold paddleboarders to forage ready-salted seaweed for your tempura-style green 'spaghetti'. That was an inspired idea. Oh, and I loved the comforting *havermoutpap* — porridge, that you served at dawn the next day. A real lifesaver.'

'Thanks, Angelique. Everyone was so generous with their

food donations and it all came together.'

'And then there was Zoe's unusual croquet competition. People having to aim their ball *away* from the hoop because of the bumps and curves on the course. Very amusing.'

'Zoe was inspired by the wonderful Himalayas putting course at St Andrew's. Colin and I took her there a few years ago, after we'd stayed at the Mackintosh Building in Perthshire.'

'That must have been thrilling, Skye. I love all of the furniture and designs created by Margaret Macdonald and her husband Charles Rennie Mackintosh. I know that Seth lives in hope that he might spot a forgotten 'CRM' chair at a yard sale. That, or one of those big landscape panels by David Blackburn. Seth's a dreamer. There's studio space for him here at the Hop Yard, but he's quite happy up in Laxfield. Though he really enjoyed the festivities last week.'

'He made me some chopping boards, using half a dozen types of salvaged wood. He says I can pay him back with soup, when the autumn chill comes on.'

'That's great, Warren. Any new recipes in the pipeline?'

'A few, Angelique. I'm obsessed with celeriac at the moment. So maybe that as a base, with carrots, ginger and sour cream.'

'That sounds delicious, and links nicely to Lost Four Words. Last time, we were looking for words beginning with the letter J and the final four are—'

'Oh, I hope one of them was jiffle. To fidget.'

'Let's find out, Angelique. Over to you, Warren.'

'Thanks, Skye. No jiffling, I'm afraid. The final four are jabble, jargle, jimswinger and jussulent:

Listening to her guests jargling,
And admiring the wearer of a jimswinger,
She jabbled the ingredients,
Knowing that they would all soon be jussulent.'

'And your thoughts on the meaning, Warren?'

'Well, Skye, I hope this makes sense to you and our listeners.

Listening to her guests chattering,
And admiring the wearer of a swallow-tailed coat,
She shook up the liquid ingredients,
Knowing they would all soon be full of soup.

Hmmm, jussulent. Full of soup. Like Seth's going to be this autumn, and *The Clangers*. Those crazy space puppets. They'd be jussulent. Especially after "Nine Bowls of Soup".'

'Nine?'

'Yes, Skye. It's a song by They Might Be Giants, and it's up next.'

'That's a funny song, Warren. It would be strange if we received a message from aliens. Saying they'd like to pop down to earth for a spot of lunch. Maybe they don't have celeriac on their planet.'

'Very amusing, Skye. An Unbelievably Funny Outburst, indeed. Moving on, Angelique, what has caught your eye In This Fortnight?'

'I'm a bit confused. But what if the aliens put on napkins to avoid soup stains? Then requested that the food be, "*Neet te heet, alstublieft*" — "Not too spicy, please". That would be funny. Talking of heat, Canterbury Cathedral burned down on September 5th, 1174. On the same date, but in 1646, Oliver Cromwell abolished the position of Archbishop of Canterbury. So in one hundred years' time, I'd probably not advise anyone to be in that part of Kent.'

'Oh, I see. You just added on another 472 years from 1646. And staying with the Canterbury theme, I'd love to visit its Beaney Museum. Mainly to see its quirky collection of soup-slurping Clangers.'

'Good knowledge and research, Warren. You were definitely the right choice to be Skye's apprentice. But thinking about fire again, you played that song by Midnight Oil last time. I've been getting to know Richard, and Pippa, in the last few months. Zoe's illness has brought things into focus, and Richard wants to do more than he did in the past. That song, even though it's about sleepwalking to an environmental catastrophe, still stirs up memories for Richard. Of the hostel fire. And beds which were actually burning. He still has feelings of guilt. But he's not sure whether they're mainly from surviving the fire, or from his neglect of Zoe. He said he'd like to be a guest on a future *Chatter Broth*. Is there any chance of that, Skye?'

'I'm sure there would be, Angelique. What's the diary looking like, Warren?'

'There are a few spare slots next spring. I'll see if one of them suits him. If he's still around.'

'Oh, I'm sure he will be. Anyway, back to my thoughts about In This Fortnight. There are several events linked to war, and the consequences of war. Over 300 soldiers were executed for desertion during World War One. It was an interesting decision by your government to 'pardon' them all, twelve years ago. But I'm thinking about the first soldier who was executed, on September 8th, just over a century ago. His name was Thomas Highgate. His pals probably called him Tommy. Or they did until they were all killed. Private Highgate survived, but was arrested. You could argue about the unfairness of his lack of legal representation, or that there were no witnesses for the defence. But what shocked me was learning that an officer argued that Private Highgate should be executed "at once, (and) as publicly as possible". That doesn't fit in with my image of fair play.'

'I agree, Angelique. And forty years later, to the day, the first

V2 fly bomb fell. It fell on Chiswick, and changed my world forever.'

'I wonder what your birthday present was. The one you left behind on the front step. Maybe something knitted, like a scarf or mittens.'

'Possibly something like that, Warren. Though it felt quite heavy. Maybe it was runner bean jam. Or even a cake made with real eggs. And it was another six years, again on September 8th, before soap rationing ended in 1950. It feels like several lifetimes ago.'

'And I have another example of time lag. Or long shadows, as Gita called them. Now, as you know, I think the best Dutch art is on another level. But, hey, I accept that other countries have produced great artists. So I am looking back to the return of Picasso's *Guernica* to Madrid in 1981. What a powerful work of art it was, and is. It had been displayed in New York while General Franco was still in power. I wonder if something can become more powerful because of its absence. What do you think, Skye?'

'In some cases, yes. I remember seeing a talk four years ago by Rick Gekoski, up at the Wigtown Book Festival. It was based on his book *Lost, Stolen or Shredded*. One of the chapters focuses on the theft of the *Mona Lisa* in 1911. Huge crowds queued to see the space where Leonardo's painting had hung. In fact, Picasso was one of the key suspects in the police investigation.'

'That's interesting, Skye. I wonder why some things are valued more than others are. Back in 1847, Shakespeare's birthplace became the first property in Britain to be officially preserved. The United Shakespeare Company bought it for £3,000. But other buildings are neglected or deliberately demolished.'

'That's why the Landmark Trust was founded, Angelique, back in 1965. One of Thomas Telford's canal buildings, the

Junction House in Cheshire, was "*needlessly*" demolished. So John and Christian Smith set up the charity to rescue "*quirkier*" buildings which were in danger of falling "*through the holes in the net*".'

'But, are works of art or interesting properties valued more than people? Do people react more to events like the fire at the Glasgow School of Art, than they do to the victims of natural disasters or acts of violence? Who knows? Perhaps they do, if they can put a name to a face. I say this because I'm thinking about Steve Biko. Colin was talking about his trial on the last *Chatter Broth*. Forty-one years ago, on September 12th, Steve Biko died in police custody. His *self-inflicted* death followed five days of interrogation. And a 750-mile drive, on often bumpy roads. While he was handcuffed. And naked. And unable to stop his head from banging on the metal seat. But *he* had a name, and he left a legacy. Try and make time to see the film *Biko*. One more thing, this country is going through some political difficulties at the moment.'

'That's one way of putting it, Angelique.'

'I'm sure there are others, Warren. My point is that Britain has a complicated history with Europe. But we Dutch, generally, have a soft spot for your country. And I don't see recent events as bringing a *zonsondergang* — a sundown, on our relationship. So it amused me to find an event from 1759 in your quirky notes. In that year, on September 14th, the first board game was sold in England. One of its names was "*A Journey Through Little England*". Sorry, I'm joking with you. It was actually called "*A Journey Through Europe*". I don't know what my residence status will be in the future, but I find some comfort in the name of that game.'

'There's plenty to think about there. And sometimes events do leave me lost for words.'

'Was that a subtle link, Skye?'

'Not really, Warren. But, go ahead.'

'Next time, we're looking for words beginning with the letter K. Remember, listeners, to write your suggestions on the board over at M3. I think I could whip up an interesting dish with kimchi and kumara. Served on warm kwanga with a knubble of butter.'

'Go on, Warren. I've heard of kimchi, but the rest? Enlighten us, so our taste buds have the chance to tingle.'

'Thanks, Skye. My dish would be made with Korean pickled cabbage and sweet potato. And served with a small knob of butter on warm manioc bread.'

'Not celeriac bread?'

'That's an interesting idea, but George loves his manioc—'

'Hey, Warren, you might not have seen the film. Maybe you did, Skye. Was it Irene Cara or Laura Branigan who sang about that root vegetable in *Flashdance*? "He's a manioc", or something like that.'

Chapter 11

'Hi, I'm Skye Hunter and welcome to *Chatter Broth*. It's September 18th and today's guest is George P Salt. A lot has happened since you were last on the show, back in June. Where do you want to start?'

'Thanks for the welcome, and hello to you as well, Warren. To start, I'm intrigued about what's happening next door at Bay Six Books. Lots of books have come *out*. I've also seen pallets, and what looked like futon mattresses, going *in*. It's been closed for almost three weeks and the windows are now covered with tissue paper. I'm making changes too. I'll speak more on that later, Skye.'

'Change is happening, but I'm excited. What do you think, Warren?'

'It was strange at the Field Party. A sort of "Goodbye Gita" and "Hello Hatsu". And meeting Zoe's transplant co-ordinator was good. Laura was very chirpy, and positive about future possibilities.'

'She certainly was. I'd just got back from Edinburgh and we were talking about luggage design. We came up with some ideas about cases with pop-outs and compression compartments. And I also came up with an idea to make wooden globes. Seth was certainly up for it when I mentioned the idea to him. Actually, he's coming over later to see Hatsu, and he said he'd drop in to Globe+Artichoke to design my new signage. And you're going to be involved, Warren.'

'Sounds exciting, George. What's the plan?'

'I've been really impressed with your food ideas. Cooking us meals, organising the donations, running the Field Party kitchen. Those sort of things.'

'It's been great. I feel like I'm earning my place here. It's tricky to describe, but the Hop Yard is more than a place for me.'

'I think that's true for all of us. I've been here, on and off, for over seventy years. George, I hope your plan doesn't mean me losing Warren.'

'Not at all, Skye. Globe+Artichoke will be no more. I never sold a globe, and there was rarely an artichoke to be seen. So I'm handing over the food side to Warren. And focusing on selling maps, and maybe even a few globes. GPS Maps will be up and running at the beginning of next year.'

'Are you sure about handing over the food side?'

'I am, Warren. And I need to go away for a while later in the year to explore some of my family history. So the food side would have been neglected.'

'I've also got something I need to do, for a friend. But I'm sure I can manage that, and develop the food side. I've got some ideas about the H Van, now that I'm not living in it. Maybe take it out on the road, to collect and deliver food. Perhaps cook meals for people who struggle with day-to-day living. This is a great opportunity. While I think about things, and thanks again George, what are your thoughts In This Fortnight?'

'Angelique was talking about how and what and *who* we value. And that led to her talking more about the life of Steve Biko. That certainly made me think . . . Getting back to what we value, Angelique mentioned Shakespeare's birthplace. So it was interesting to note another heritage purchase. This one happened later, during World War One, but the structure was much older. A Mr Chubb was looking to buy an interesting present for his wife. So on September 21st, just over a century ago, he attended an auction. And what did he get for £6,600? Stonehenge.'

'I'm still amazed at that, and I did the research for you. What do you think, Skye?'

'It was an unusual present bought during an unusual conflict. What did Mrs Chubb think of it, George?'

'She didn't like it. So she was happy when it was given to the nation three years later, at the end of the war. Of course, it can be difficult buying presents. Especially for the person you're closest to.'

'I've always struggled to find the right present for Colin.'

'Relationships, romantic or *otherwise*, can be tricky. Which is why an event from 1650 caught my eye. A lot of people now meet through online dating, but on September 29th of that year, Henry Robinson opened the first marriage bureau. This was during a time of national turmoil. Yes, there have been other ones. It was in the year following the execution of Charles I. But the search for love isn't bounded by timing considerations. So Robinson's Office of Addresses & Encounters was launched. Although who knows what makes for a successful relationship? I like the idea though. It was more *tender*, than Tinder.'

'Which reminds me of Slow Dating. It was great to meet Haberdasher at the Field Party. Though I won't mention her real name on air. She even brought me some samphire for my stir-fry. And her new partner was lovely, too. They bought dozens of books from Gita, including a signed copy of the *Withnail and I* screenplay. Which is a good excuse to play Procul Harum's "Whiter Shade of Pale".'

'I remember buying that song when it came out. Thanks for playing it, Warren. I still find it exhilarating and kind of upsetting. I think Bruce Robinson, who wrote the screenplay, got it right when he wrote about the song being so sweet, *and* sour. It makes me feel tingly, *and* tearful. And there'll be more Slow Dating next month. But for now, back to you, George.'

'I agree about that song, Skye. And Presuming Ed and Ralph Brown's Danny are two of my favourite characters in film history. Here's another event that surprised me. In a week's time, on September 25th, it will be the 200th anniversary of the first human blood transfusion. It took place at Guy's Hospital in London. Yes, two hundred years ago. Hopefully medical advances will continue to develop. I'm sure Zoe is taking a keen interest in kidney research.'

'And she's not the only one. I feel a little helpless. But the whole idea of always pushing for medical advances is tricky. Obviously, Zoe fully deserves every opportunity to lead a full life. But I'll be eighty in a few years. My health is quite good, but would I want to live well into my hundreds? I don't think so. Maybe people should focus on giving more people a good start in life, rather than focusing on prolonging life. What do you think, Warren?'

'I'm sure it will become an issue, as more young people struggle to get a decent job or a place they can call home. Maybe a national body like the National Trust could help. Release some of their land for a multi-generational building project. Young people could be trained in sustainable construction skills. They could then live in the homes they had built, say for five years. They could also build flats for older people. It could be like an expanded Hop Yard. The National Trust property would then have a host of potential volunteers on its doorstep. And they could do so much with food and estate management. There'd be so many health benefits, and a reduction in loneliness and isolation. It could be a rich experience, and one that could be rolled out wherever there was a need.'

'You've been thinking things through, Warren. I'm even

more convinced I'm right to hand over the food side to you. And you're both right about the value of a good start to life. So I'm going back to 1672 and the founding of the RAC.'

'The Royal Automobile Club surely isn't that old?'

'Not that RAC, Skye. I'm talking about the Royal Africa Company. It was founded on September 27th after being granted a trade monopoly. A monopoly to sell African slaves in the Americas. The company even gave *discounts* to those who bought a full shipload. And a slave who survived the voyage could be bought for just £20. It was over 150 years later in 1833, on August 28th, that the House of Commons passed the Abolition Act that abolished slavery in the British Empire. I was talking to Marina about this back in August. She was telling me about what she had found out while staying in Devon some years ago. The place she rented had been formerly owned by a slave-owning family.'

'That was The Library near the town of Great Torrington. The Landmark Trust property where Zoe began to develop her unique croquet style.'

'Her croquet course was brilliant at the Field Party. During a break from cooking, I had a go. I really liked the bit where you had to play towards a hoop you couldn't see. The tunnel made the shot even trickier. And as for the hoop on a see-saw . . . '

'You're right, Warren. I loved the hoops that you had to play away from. You had to work out the slopes and contours. Did you have a go, George?'

'I watched Zoe go round with Laura and Kenesha. It was definitely a new spin, so to say, on a traditional sport. But back to my chat with Marina. She told me about one of the exceptions to the Abolition Act. The Kandyan chiefs of Ceylon, now Sri Lanka, asked for 60 years to fully abolish slavery. And that emancipated female ex-slaves should still be submissive. Really? The British government compromised with an agreed offer of an extra ten years. The Victorian era was a complex mix of repression and reform. Although it did produce my favourite building in the world. The Midland Railway opened St Pancras station on October 1st, 1868. Pershore Place Mews is lovely. But a flat at St. Pancras, even a tiny one, would be my dream London home.'

'I'm not sure what Colin's plans in Marylebone are. It's still a link back to his foster parents, and Abigail died only a few years ago. Perhaps, if India turns up again, things will become clearer. Shall we move on to Lost Four Words, Warren? Last time, we were looking for words beginning with the letter K. Warren has the final four.'

'Thanks, Skye. They are ket, killick, knitch and kreng:

Lacking even a killick,
She gathered a knitch,
And having removed the ket,
Found a strange warmth
Within a kreng.'

'And your thoughts on what meaning there may be, Warren?'
'Well, Skye, this one's a bit weird. Who does write them? But here goes:

Lacking even a small anchor,
She gathered a bundle of wood,
And having removed the carrion,
Found a strange warmth
Within a blubberless whale carcass.'

'I agree that it's a bit weird, Warren, but I like killick. I think we *all* need a small anchor. Not to weigh us down, but to stop us drifting. That's what the Hop Yard and Peasenham has always meant to me. Since I first came here, all those decades ago. The little urban skylark, lost in the countryside. And then found. Of course, I've been away, so I'm not tied down. I can breathe. I can soar and sing.'

'Here's a song for you, Skye, that I think fits your ideas.'

'That was "The Anchor Song" by Björk. I hope she had breathing gear, for her nocturnal visits to the ocean floor.'

'And I hope she didn't get the dreaded bends — no, Warren, you don't need to play Radiohead — on the way up. While we're in music mode, I'm thinking again about live performance. There are some bands that I like listening to on the radio. But there are some who come into their own when they're playing live, especially at festivals. Because festivals have flows and rhythms, and if a singer or band can catch the moment, then that's when the magic happens. Acts like Skunk Anansie, Cruising Julie and the Kaiser Chiefs come into their own on a festival stage. A group of us used to go to the Rhythm Festival in Bedfordshire. It was sited, for five years, next to the airfield where Glenn Miller flew from in World War Two. There was so much energy: Geno Washington, the Three Daft Monkeys, the Saw Doctors. And of course, the Grand Slambovians aka Gandalf Murphy and the Slambovian Circus of Dreams. Ooh, I'm getting carried away. What were some of those K-words you were hoping for, Warren?'

'I was hoping for a bit of kumara or kwanga. But kreng is an interesting word, as we get quite a few whales washed up on the coast. But I don't fancy using them for food. Maybe Hatsu has a view on that. She told me she was brought up near the sea in Japan. Any thoughts, George?'

'Not on whales. I was listening to your K-word kitchen ideas in the last podcast. Thanks for mentioning manioc. We called it cassava, when my family visited Grand Turk. One of our relatives, who still lives on Grand Cayman, came over to visit with us. She used cassava as a key ingredient in her Heavy Cake. Along with nutmeg and cinnamon from Grenada. And coconut milk fresh from a tree. Yum. So I laughed when you were talking about manioc and the song "Maniac". I actually watched *Flashdance* again last week. What a feeling, indeed. Angelique had an old copy on video. There's a lot of tension in that film. And sometimes tension should remain more clothed, perhaps. Irene Cara sang the theme song, but it was Laura Branigan who sang "Maniac". Though I prefer her song "Self Control". I say this because Angelique went over to M3 and suggested the word karezza—'

'That sounds a bit like caress, George.'

'You're in the ballpark, Warren. Although it's more intimate than a caress. Karezza means prolonged sex, and without ejaculation.'

'My goodness, George. What a thought. Thanks, I think, for that. Now, I remember a certain afternoon in Potsdam. It was soon after *The Wall* concert in Berlin. I'd just come back from eating ripe figs at the Sanssouci Palace. And then I 'bumped' into an old friend, and we—'

'I think it's time for that song by Laura Branigan.'

'I've calmed down now, Warren. Before we go, George, can you tell us a bit more about your time in Edinburgh?'

'Of course I can. And a lot of it's down to you.'

'In what way?'

'You gave me that gorgeous cotton scarf with a huge map of Edinburgh printed on it. Where did you find it?'

'I'd been up to see the Hepworth Museum in Wakefield. On the way back I stopped at the Yorkshire Sculpture Park. I was smitten as soon as I saw their display of fabric city maps. And when I saw the Auld Reekie one, I knew I had to buy one for you.'

'The city is still 'Auld', but it doesn't reek as much as it used to. I used the scarf as a prop for my Fringe walking tours. I was going to call my 'show' *Get Lost*, but I decided on *Get Found* instead.'

'I'm a bit confused, George.'

'And so were some of my customers, at first, Warren. I stood in the Royal Mile, on my reinforced purple top hat. My t-shirt said, *Get Found* on the front. And, *With GPS & His Amazing Map* on the back.'

'I still don't get it.'

'So people would ask me what the t-shirt meant. I told them that I'd give them a walking tour of Edinburgh, and together we would find things.'

'Did people *pay* for this?'

'They did, Warren. One couple gave me a Scottish £100 note. Which I still have. The tours kind of developed. Whenever we stopped to look at the map, people would gather round. The map is big and unusual, and it feels lovely. Locals would try and find where they lived on it. Tourists would ask for directions. It became a walking-talking point. And my customers usually realised that they were actually a part of a mobile performance. After the first few days I had so many people coming up to me — sometimes over five a day — that I had to start a bookings diary. It was magical, and made me think about what I wanted to do with the shop.'

'The Sheffield-based company, that makes the scarves, also makes pyjamas.'

'I'm glad you chose the scarf, Skye.'

~

India's entry
in the Queen Anne's Summerhouse Logbook, 2013

It's probably normally quite peaceful here in Old Warden Park, save for the sound of historic aircraft taking off from the nearby Shuttleworth Collection. But definitely not *this* weekend. This Bedfordshire site has been taken over by the Rhythm Festival, and it's rocking. I like camping, but what a luxury it is to stay in this magnificent red-bricked building. With its deep bath, comfy sofas and handy viewing platform.

In fact, I've invited a few people up — just two at a time, I know the rules — to share the experience. And try out my Warden pies, which were made using Warden pears. I found the recipe in Act IV of Shakespeare's *The Winter's Tale*, of all places. The Clown, talking to Autolycus about a forthcoming feast, says "I must have saffron to colour the warden pies . . . Nutmegs, seven; a race or two of ginger . . . four pounds of prunes and as many raisins o' the sun".

I had to guess what 'race' meant, and work out that the raisins were sun-dried. Then I reduced the quantities, as four pounds of prunes seemed rather excessive to me. And I added the unmentioned pears. Other ingredients, such as mace, were mentioned. That they were then luxury items, was hinted at by Shakespeare. Autolycus, later in the scene, said to the so-called Clown, "Your purse is not hot enough to purchase your spice".

This rather practical folly, sited rather daringly on top of a rabbit warren, was probably commissioned by Samuel Ongley. And he rather extravagantly selected 'gauged' (aka 'rubbed') bricks for the construction. These are bricks whose final shape comes from being rubbed by hand. Nearby are a set of horse graves. Local lore suggests the horses were buried standing up. I'm not sure whether to 'bridle' at that theory.

Samuel kept a kind of expanded diary, called a commonplace

book. Entries include a list of 'essential' items to be used in fitting out one of his ships, the *Anna*. I can understand the need for colanders, ladles and a pepper box. But a speaking trumpet? He also gives advice, perhaps to his younger self, on how to deal with trading in hotter climates. Including that those ignoring his warnings about drunkenness or over-eating will '*fall into the bloody flux and die*'.

Samuel Ongley had been a director of the East India Company, but in 1711 became involved with the South Sea Trading Company. This was at a time when lotteries were very popular. It was quite a gamble to invest in South America, a continent mainly controlled by Spain. A country Britain was at war with. The spectacular collapse of the company, the South Sea Bubble of 1720, resulted in lost investments and protests. The Chancellor of the Exchequer was sent to prison. Can you imagine *that* happening now? However, Samuel managed to ride out the financial storm. Maybe he benefitted from insider trading. Or maybe he was just lucky.

His jottings suggest a settled life at Old Warden. In one recipe, for Stilton cheese, he offers the options of using marigold petals or sage for colouring. Later ill health caused him to exclude vegetables from his diet, '*they being very windy*'. He planted hundreds of oak saplings, partly to satisfy his desire for wood, '*for the good of the Kingdom in General and for my own use in particular*'. In his role as a magistrate, he enforced laws against '*wandering paupers*'. But he did pay out thirty old pence a quarter towards the education of an '*intelligent*' village child.

His varying attitudes to young people, perhaps, explain a note which he sent to his chosen heir (a great-nephew, for Ongley was a bachelor). It read, '*I have not yet mentioned your inclination to Drunkenness and Creating a great acquaintance of new Companions. All these things are the forerunner of destroying an Estate . . .*

and unless remedied . . . will very much lessen my esteem of you and will have a fatal consequence which you will have the whole time of your life to repent '.

We all make decisions in life. It's not necessarily the decisions themselves, but how you adapt to them. And how other people react to them. But now I need to get my gear on. Ready to leave this beautiful folly and hop over the fence to the festival site. To listen to The Men They Couldn't Hang, Hazel O'Connor and The Animals. Perhaps Ongley's heir was familiar with the sort of establishment sung about in "The House of the Rising Sun".

What a great festival. My favourite band was Macavity's Cat. What an energetic performance they gave last night. At one point there were over thirty people on stage. The band owns a pub down in Kent. I bet they have some foot-stompin' nights there too.

I'm just getting ready to meet my next client, Leah Williams. She used to be a mermaid, in Montana. That's where I met her, when she was performing, in a pool, at a bar in Great Falls. Now she's inherited a lakeside property, just west of Glacier National Park. I'll be going over there, by myself. I always work alone to 'declutter' an estate. And she, Leah, will live in Suffolk while I do it. At a place called the Hop Yard. Where my daughter lives.

I wonder what tricks and skills Zoe will be taught in Suffolk by Leah. It will be another part of my ongoing programme to provide enrichment for my daughter. A daughter who is hopefully having a better life than I could provide if I was actually with her.

India Farr, Marylebone
and (soon) Montana, and then Elsewhere.
Wherever I lay my hat, and all that . . .

~

'It's great to see you again, Harrison'

'Likewise, Warren. And thanks for inviting me to the Field Party. I knew Laura already, but I was made to feel so welcome. I bought a lovely framed photograph from Angelique, and Gita found me a great set of books by Tim Cahill.'

'The Australian footballer?'

'No, the American travel writer. I wouldn't like to be *Pecked to Death by Ducks*, but I enjoyed his take on travel. And it was good to talk to you and Zoe together. Although I was confused by her croquet course. Earlier that day, I'd been at your case meeting. Jerry could see no reason why you wouldn't make a good donor.'

'That was an intense series of questions. I didn't answer them all as I'd have liked to.'

'Jerry would have been more worried if all your answers had been perfect.'

'So when do I go through and have the next series of tests?'

'That's the thing, Warren. There's a problem, but it's physiological, rather than psychological. I'm going to ask Jerry to sit in though, if you don't mind.'

'So I've only got one kidney, Harrison?'

'That's correct. It's relatively rare, but there are tens of thousands of people in Britain who share your situation. And most of them never find out.'

'That's right, Warren. You can lead a perfectly normal life with only one kidney. Otherwise, living donor kidney donations wouldn't happen. How do you feel about this new information?'

'I'm shocked, Jerry. I can see why Harrison wanted you here. This could take a bit of getting used to.'

'That's a normal reaction. Remember we talked about possible feelings of guilt if the transplant process failed?'

'I do. But this is so unexpected. I'm a very confused mush. And what will Zoe say when I tell her? She's going to have to find another living donor. Or go back and wait again in the deep end of the national pool.'

Chapter 12

'Hi, I'm Skye Hunter and welcome to *Chatter Broth*. It's October 2nd and today's guest is Marina Rueda. Have you packed yet?'

'Just about. Although Zoe is ready and raring to go.'

'Hello, Marina. Is Zoe okay?'

'She is, Warren. It was a shock when she lost her donor. And had to go back into the national pool. Then she decided to suspend herself from that transplant pool, while she decided what to do next. It was a big decision, but she talked it through at length with me and Colin. And my trip to the States is going to be shorter, with a focus more on apples than on hops.'

'What will happen at M3 while you're away?'

'Kenesha has offered to run it, Skye. With Colin's help. Like he did *la última vez* — the last time.'

'That's good, and I hope it works out for Zoe. Just as I hope it works out for Digs Disco. Over to you, Warren.'

'Thanks, Skye. It's time for more Slow Dating. A chance for people to find someone. Got lost? Get found, so to speak. If listeners wish to apply, your message should be up to fifty words long. And as always, no abbreviations please. Skye just can't get used to them. Please post your message to the same *un*-usual address. Thanks, Marina, for letting us use M3. We don't have a letterbox at the studio because it would cause audio issues.'

'You're welcome, Warren. Who's the lucky person today?'

'This time, it's Digs Disco on the Slow Dating forecourt:

Hopeful detectorist (male, 50-ish, North Suffolk/South Norfolk) seeks gold-digger to love, to hold and to search for The Trove. A love of Eurovision isn't absolutely necessary, but it would be good if you could throw some dance floor moves. Maybe even the Gold Dance. Do you dig?'

'That's quite funny. I'm almost tempted to reply to him myself. Even if he is a little too young for me.'

'How much *does* age matter in a relationship, Skye?'

'That's a good question. I'll put a brew on while I think about it. A good time for In This Fortnight, Warren?'

'More than you know, Skye. Listeners might know that I research a fortnight in history, and then pass on my notes to our guest.'

'Thanks Warren. And I did spot the tea reference, Skye. On October 3rd, 1952, after a dozen years, tea rationing ended in Britain. Yes, twelve years. How did you cope?'

'Marina, I wasn't born until 1941. So it wasn't quite as bad for me as for others.'

'So you almost missed hearing the then Princess Elizabeth making her first radio broadcast.'

'Was she announcing the beginning of tea rationing, Marina?'

'Haha, Warren. That would have been strange. Using a 14-year-old to announce a drugs ban. No, she was sending a message of support to child evacuees.'

'Colin might remember it. Maybe she was asked to do it. The government was worried about evacuees drifting back during the *Phoney War*. And the impact that would have had on the war effort.'

'I think you're right, Skye. And another country that loves tea is Japan. And they love wrestling. It's 27 years since the first Sumo tournament was held outside of Japan.'

'I remember that. Colin walked across Hyde Park and queued up to get tickets at the Royal Albert Hall. But they had sold out.

I wonder if Hatsu has ever seen any Sumo wrestling.'

'She's our guest next time. I took her the research notes yesterday. At what's now called Book Bathing @ Bay Six Books. It's really interesting what she's doing there. I said I'd keep it a secret though. She's opening on October 17th, the day after she's with us on *Chatter Broth*. I like how Colin is open to change. Letting people develop our community here at the Hop Yard. He's like a parent taking the stabilisers off a bike. Supporting us as we become more independent. Letting us make mistakes, and giving us a hand up if we fall.'

'Well spoken, Warren. I was a confused and scared fledgling before he helped me become a skylark.'

'*También estoy de acuerdo con Warren* — I also agree with Warren. I wouldn't be here either if he hadn't helped Abigail in Bologna and got her to hospital quickly. Swift action that saved India's life. Who I first met in Yellowstone, all those years ago. Life is about threads, and how they connect. We were talking about that here back in May. I believe some threads have combined, to form a Hop Yard tapestry. And it's still being woven. I suppose we're also all artists, in our different ways. So I was amused — or should that be not amused? — to find a letter sent to Queen Victoria. King Leopold wrote to her, in this fortnight, in 1845. The letter warned her to beware of artists, because they mix with all classes of society and are therefore most dangerous. He should have visited a place like this. I'm not sure of the exact quote, but research can be tricky. You'd agree, Warren?'

'One hundred per cent. Sometimes you find good-looking sources, but they conflict. Whether in books or on the web. Though I like this joke I found the other day. It went, "*The problem with quotes on the Internet is that it is hard to verify their authenticity. As said by that internet pioneer, Abraham Lincoln, in 1938*".'

'That's a good one, Warren. I think I'll finish with three events from October 11th. Firstly, back in 1216, King John lost his crown and most of his jewels in The Wash. Up near Wisbech, where Zoe and I first hit balls through the hoops. But did he really lose the crown jewels? *Hierba mala nunca muere* — even a bad penny always turns up. So why was no treasure ever recovered? Maybe he had already sold the precious items. As it happens, a week later he was dead. His idea of self-medicating, with ripe peaches and cider, failed to arrest a sudden illness. Now, King John had previously been excommunicated. He had quite a record of winding up rich and powerful men, didn't he? And before that, the Pope had ordered that all church doors be locked. An order, or interdict, which lasted for over six years. That meant no official baptisms, marriages or burials for over seventy months. People not being able to celebrate or mourn with their family members. Can you imagine that?'

'I can't. And take care with your cider tasting in the States, please.'

'I will, Skye. And maybe I'll get rid of a bit of baggage too. My second event happened three centuries later. Another pope, Leo X, was in communication with Henry VIII—'

'Shouldn't that be excommunication?'

'Not in 1521, Skye. The pope was actually impressed with the young king. So impressed that he named him *Fidei Defensor* — Defender of the Faith. The Catholic faith. Which is kind of ironic? Given what happened later. And you've spoken on *Chatter Broth* about time lags and consequences. There's a long tail here, too. Or more of a head. I've brought eight coins with me to demonstrate . . . Now these four — the 1p, 2p, 10p and pound coins — have F D on them. The other four have FID DEF on them. Which is short for—'

'*Fidei Defensor.*'

'Exactly, Warren. Or spot on, as Gita liked to say. Actually, I'll be seeing her next week. She's driving all the way up to New York State from Key West. Zoe and I'll spend a few days in

Brooklyn, then take a Metro-North train up the Hudson River to Beacon. We'll meet up with Gita there. There's also someone I need to see in Beacon before we head into Vermont. Things might be coming together. But I'll hold off talking more, until I get back at the beginning of November.'

'*Fidei Defensor*?'

'Oh yes, and thanks Skye. It's strange that the title still appears on British coins. After all these centuries. And on coins which show the head of the Church of *England*, not Rome. *Extraña* — strange, indeed. Another thing that's strange, and my final link to October 11th, is Magdalene College, Cambridge. Not the pronunciation, though that's tricky enough. But an event in 1988. The first female undergraduates were admitted. Yes, only thirty years ago. Many of the male students wore black armbands, and one of the porters flew a black flag.'

'I went to an all-boys school, and would have loved to have had girls there. I didn't really talk to females, apart from my mother, until I moved to Suffolk.'

'And I went to an all-girls sixth-form college in 1957. I quite enjoyed it, especially the science lessons. They were much calmer than the boy-dominated ones I'd had at school. So I don't support the 'mourning' Magdelenes with their funereal imagery. But I can understand why some people might prefer single-sex establishments. Though it's ironic that a college with that name would protest against females, especially if one or more of them was called Mary.'

'I was talking to Kenesha about this subject at the Field Party. Just after she'd kindly agreed to look after M3 for me. She said that girls, typically, seem two or three years more mature than boys. At least, once they've got over their tricky Year 9 friendship fallouts. But that there would also always be some boys who were real role models. So you never can tell. I think she misses helping students learn. If a job comes up, I've told her to go for it. And it would be amusing if Colin ran the micropub, for a time. You wouldn't be able to move for cocktail equipment. He's not a mover, on the dance floor, but he's a great shaker.'

'And if he did that, maybe some mocktails for Warren.'

'Sounds refreshing, Skye. A good time for Lost Four Words?'

'I think so. Last time, we were looking for words beginning with the letter L.'

'Thanks, Skye. The final four, and these ones are really weird, are lagan, lammervanger, loblolly and locofoco:

She observed the lammervanger,
Buoyantly perched above the lagan.
And was surprised to find a locofoco,
In the loblolly box.'

'And your thoughts on what meaning there may be, Warren?'

'Well, Skye, does this interpretation make any sense to you?

She watched the lamb-snatching eagle,
Perched on the buoy that marked the seabed wreckage.
And was surprised to find a self-igniting cigar,
In the ship's medicine box.'

'That one's quite atmospheric. What do you think, Marina?'

'My suggestion was logodaedalist, a wordsmith. Though I can't recall a suggestion made by one of your guests being included. It's a bit odd, Skye. Who makes the final decision?'

'Good question. And while Skye thinks about that, I'll put on a couple of songs by Alanis Morissette. "Ironic", because that word's been mentioned a few times today. And because I love her voice. I disagree with some of her lyrics, though. Why *shouldn't* someone, two years short of their hundredth birthday, win the lottery?'

'Maybe because the shock might kill them.'

'Possibly, Skye. Although living here's a bit like winning the lottery. And I'll also play "Knees of My Bees". Alanis sings about a caring wordsmith who has had quite an effect on her. However, I've no idea what "knees of my bees" actually means.'

~

The Hudson Valley, 2018

Marina had other favourite places along the Hudson River, but she never tired of Beacon. Perhaps because it had seemed so down on its knees, and was now getting back on its new feet. The old foundries and warehouses given new leases. Signed by people looking for space and community. The legends of *Sleepy Hollow*, allowed to breathe and become more than a background whisper. The enduring spirit of Pete Seeger and his red-sailed sloop, which hinted at a different way forward. And then there was India. Farr, far away, but based in a place not so dissimilar to the Hop Yard. Marina and Zoe continued walking up the sloping part of Main Street. They'd had an early start from the light-filled transport cathedral that was Grand Central Station. But, going against the inward commuter flow, they'd had almost a whole carriage to themselves. The train had slipped north, towards upstate New York. An advertising sign, for a storage company, on the side of a factory read, '*Raising a baby in NYC is like growing an oak tree in a thimble*.' Marina had smiled at that, but Zoe hadn't seemed to have noticed. They'd had a good couple of hours in Dia, the giant artspace reclaiming a place abandoned when the Nabisco factory closed. And Beacon's art pioneers were not afraid of scale. Or reviving the ghosts of Americana. Saying, "It's *Not* Alright". It was ten years since the Starn brothers had taken over the old Tallix foundry. On a previous visit to Beacon, Marina and India had climbed inside the monumental *Big Bambú* — a cantilevered bamboo tower which felt, despite its scale, intimately organic. A kind of forest bathing. Away from its bamboo grove, but still connected with nature. Marina usually struggled to speak honestly with India, but climbing inside *Big Bambú* had released something in her. She had been a lass in space, and although high, she had understood that she wouldn't fall. And so despite the tension at the heart of *their* relationship — the relationship each had with Zoe — she had felt more able to reach out to India. To nurture the link that stretched back to the Hop Yard. Back to decisions made. Back to Zoe—

'Hey, Marina. You've got to see this.' Zoe was standing outside the window of a shop called Remade. 'I'd never thought about hand-poured soy before and never heard of a company called Weird Beard. But I think I've seen the perfect present for Colin.'

'The wood and glass chandelier?'

'That's great, and Colin would love it, but it's a bit impractical. No, there, in the window display.' Zoe pointed to the Lumbersexual candle and smiled at Marina. She was about to enter the shop when Marina called her back.

'That's a great idea, but we need to pop into a place just up the street first.'

Zoe hesitated, but sensed a firmness in what Marina had said. They walked a little further up Main Street to the door of a gallery. A red Mazda convertible pulled away from the kerb and the driver seemed to be waving at her. But then she was gone . . . Zoe turned and saw someone putting up a framed map on the far wall. There was something familiar about the way her hair and body moved. 'It's Gita!'

Marina stood aside as Zoe rushed into the gallery. And then

followed, closing the glass door behind her.

The three of them enjoyed the walk along Main Street. As it levelled out, Zoe pointed to the large mural on the side of the RiverWinds gallery. At the strong woman looking down, with her protecting arms, over the town and the river. And at how the red-sailed boat navigated the strong currents of the Hudson. They continued east, and passed the Towne Crier. A poster by the front door listed the October programme.

'Oh, the Grand Slambovians played last night,' Marina said. 'We just missed them.'

'Who?' Zoe asked.

'The Grand Slambovians,' Gita replied.

'Though they were called Gandalf Murphy and the Slambovian Circus of Dreams,' Marina said, 'when they played in Suffolk a few years ago.'

'Oh, I remember them,' Zoe said. 'Half-folky, half-rocky and half-something else.'

'That's right, and I kind of understand the maths. Or math as most Americans would say. But I'm feeling half-empty, so shall we get a bite to eat. To the Hop, Gita?'

'Oh, that place moved, and then closed. Let's go down to the Dogwood and try some of their lunchtime menu.'

The trio crossed over the river and soon found what they were after.

'Hello there, my name's Jay. I'll be waiting your table today. It looks like you folks are good and ready to order.'

'Spot on,' Gita said, 'and thanks, Jay. I'll have the goat's cheese, red kale and pickled cauliflower salad. With the avocado oil, lime juice and roasted garlic dressing'.

'Sounds good,' Zoe said, 'and like something a friend of ours would rustle up. I'll have the same, please.'

'And I'll have the Mac 'n' Cheese,' Marina said. 'As it comes. No toppings, please.'

'And would you like to order any drinks?'

'I'm fine with the iced water, and I'm eighteen. So I'm too young to drink in the States anyway.'

'You're the expert, Marina. What do you think?'

'Thanks Gita, but a lot of these beers are new to me. A lot's changed since I batch brewed in Portland.'

'Portland, Oregon? Or Portland, Maine?'

'Oregon, Jay. What do you recommend? Especially any beers that are brewed locally.'

'I think your meal choice would pair well with Two Way Heart of Darkness Stout. It's brewed right here in Beacon. And for your friend, I suggest Rushing Duck's Divided By Zero.' Jay then glanced over at Zoe. 'And if you come back in three years, I'd be happy to pour you an Old Speckled Hen. We've got it on Nitro.'

'Ducks and Hens. Any chance of a Kingfisher?' Gita asked.

'They're very elusive. A whoosh of blue, a little spark of light. But, you . . . oh, I get what you did there. With your Indian beer reference. That's amusing. In the spring, we serve an Indian Pale Lager. Anyway, let me go and get your orders in.'

'So Gita, what are you doing in Beacon?'

Gita glanced over at Marina, and got an affirming nod, before responding. 'I'm finishing tidying up Uncle Kunal's estate.'

'But he lived in Key West. What are you doing up here?'

'It's to do with how India operates. Your mother, not the country.'

'My mother. Is she here in Beacon?'

'She is. We drove up from Florida, hauling a dinky trailer, in my uncle's Mazda. And stopped off at interesting places that began with A: Apalachicola, Athens, Asheville, Appomattox,

'Arpers Ferry — we weren't too serious about doing things to the letter — Arlington, Allentown. We were in India's gallery earlier. The one she's rented for two days, anyway.'

'In Beacon? Did you know about this Marina? Is this why—'

'Ladies, here are your drinks. Your food will be out in about ten minutes.'

Zoe and Marina zig-zagged along the Main Street sidewalk.

'It's a lot busier than yesterday,' Zoe said.

'It is,' Marina replied. 'A lot of people come to Beacon for Second Saturday. It's a monthly event with lots going on.'

'So India rents a short-term space to sell the art and furniture that she clears from people's houses.'

'Yes, she sends a catalogue to her client, and they decide which items she can sell. Your mother used to have a similar set-up in Old City, Philadelphia. But then Zeb's lease ran out and the new rent was too expensive for her. So she came here. Whenever she finishes a contract in the States, this is where she completes the process.'

'Zeb was so funny. He also taught me origami and how to look at things in different ways. But I still find it strange that people let India sort out houses by herself. What if she missed something or threw away something that was valuable?'

'That's the thing, Zoe. A lot of people don't have the time or motivation to do it themselves. And your mother has got a good reputation.'

'For sorting out *other* people's lives, at least.'

'Remember, I was India's first client. She found things that my brothers and me had forgotten, or didn't even know about. India also made three copies of a photo book for us, highlighting the treasures she had found. She captured the essence of our family home, and some of the moments we had shared. And India did it very sensitively. For instance, she shipped all the valuable stuff to an out-of-town storage facility. So it wasn't picked over by people from Boise. You know, friends and neighbours of my parents. They didn't need to see that part of things. Though they certainly used all kinds of excuses to try and get in. But India was having none of it. As for me, I couldn't have done that work, especially with well-meaning people popping by all the time. Picking over things as our family home was being boxed up. I didn't want to see it *como una tienda de segunda mano* — becoming like a thrift store. Your mother has made some difficult choices, but she helps other people. Just not her daughter. At least, not in the traditional sense.'

Zoe pretended to study the sidewalk.

Marina noticed a slight flushing of the skin below Zoe's ears. But she also noticed a sense of some new understanding. Or if not understanding, perhaps a realisation that her mother meant different things to different people.

'I'd like to meet my mother. Not today, and not here. Somewhere neither of us has been before. Neutral ground. Maybe at the apple farm, up in Vermont, where we're staying next week.'

Zoe walked by herself up the steps to the start of the pedestrian bridge. She'd left Marina at Poughkeepsie Station. The '*Watch The Gap*' sign at the edge of the platform had been quite funny. But her thoughts were more focused on information gaps, rather than physical ones. She knew that Marina, and Colin, kept in touch with India. And that many of the Hop Yard community had first come to Suffolk because of India. But all the same . . .

The sound of a freight train brought her back to the present. On the west bank of the Hudson, dozens of freight cars snaked south. And here she was, walking where trains had once steamed. She had enjoyed the High Line in New York, but the Walkway On The Hudson was something else. And not just because it was the longest pedestrian bridge in the world. The autumnal colours and the watery reflections of a faraway bridge gave her a boost. There were so many other people on the elevated walkway. More than the number that lived in Peasenham. Zoe decided to make the walk into a loop. Marina had suggested visiting another bridge. The FDR Mid-Hudson Bridge. And listening to it. The bridge that she now saw both above the mighty Hudson, and reflected on it.

'What did you think, Zoe?'

'I'm thinking about quite a lot at the moment, Marina.'

'I'd be surprised if you weren't.'

'There's the operation I need. And the fact that I have no memory of ever meeting the woman who gave birth to me. But apart from those kinds of things, I also enjoyed the walk. And the bridge music was certainly different. I like that Joseph Bertolozzi came up with the idea that a bridge could become a musical instrument. I also liked the fact that the designer of the bridge had also been a musician. Maybe he had always intended his structure to hit a high note. All those amazing sounds made by 'playing' the bridge. It was a bit strange though, being at a Listening Station, with all those big eight-wheelers thundering by. Not your typical music venue at all. And I was thinking about that red-sailed boat. What's the story there?'

'Pete Seeger, the folk singer, was part of a group that wanted to raise awareness of water pollution. They used a sloop called *Clearwater* as part of their campaign. The current sloop is a replica called *Woody Guthrie*—'

'Another folk singer, right?'

'That's right, Zoe. Pete and Woody were close. And they made more than music. Good folk, in more ways than one. When we caught the bus up to Beacon from the station yesterday, we passed Riverfront Park. That used to be a derelict, sewage-spoiled area before the tide turned. Now the area is a great place to breathe, right next to the mighty Hudson.'

'So people *can* make a difference.'

'They can. I was thinking of heading up to Hyde Park, to see FDR's childhood home. And Val-Kill, Eleanor Roosevelt's place, is nearby too. But maybe we should catch the train back. The Beacon Sloop Club are putting on their Annual Pumpkin Festival Day, and it doesn't finish until 5pm.'

'Sounds good. Though I'd like to visit those two sites another time. Franklin Delano Roosevelt had to deal with serious health issues. And look what he achieved. As for Eleanor, she was more influential than many actual presidents were. What would the world be like now, if *she* had run for president after FDR died in 1945?'

Chapter 13

'Hi, I'm Skye Hunter and welcome to *Chatter Broth*. It's October 16th and today's guest is Akahoshi Hatsu. She's taken over Bay Six Books from Gita. Here at the Hop Yard in Peasenham. We'd love to hear about how you came to be in Suffolk, and what your plans are. But first, what did you think about the In This Fortnight notes that Warren gave you?'

'Firstly, please call me Hatsu. In Japan, people normally have their *family* name first. The notes? I liked them, and I bought a book, *Under Storm's Wing*, about one of the poets he referred to. You can sometimes start off in one place and end up somewhere unexpected. Oh, and hello Warren.'

'Hi, Hatsu. My full name is Warren Wagstaffe.'

'Warren Wagstaffe. I like your name. It sounds jolly, and a bit like my favourite bird, the *sekirei* - the wagtail. What influence do our names have on our lives? Are our names a more important part of our identity than we realise? Do people think about us differently because of our names? What do your names mean, Warren?'

'A warren's a place where rabbits live. Wagstaffe? I've no idea. What about yours?'

'*Hatsu* means 'first' or 'beginning'. And *aka* means 'red' and *hoshi* means 'star'.'

'So in Japan, that famous Serbian football team would be known as Aka Hoshi Belgrade.'

'Thanks, Warren. But I doubt if Hatsu is interested in East European football.'

'I don't know too much about that area, but I love football. My favourite players are Saki Kumagai and Shinji Kagawa. It's a pity that I missed seeing Matt Le Tissier play. He was the best.'

'He wasn't quite so popular in Portsmouth.'

'Back to sport, well kind of. It was fifty years ago, tomorrow, that Tommie Smith and John Carlos gave a salute at the Olympics in Mexico City. Tommie later called it a Human Rights, not a Black Power, salute. This is backed up by the fact the badges that they wore — and also worn by the other medallist, Peter Norman — read, "Olympic Project For Human Rights". Peaceful protests can be more effective than violent ones. Such as Picasso keeping *Guernica* out of Spain, until some form of democracy was restored. And one date really struck me, October 21st. How random life, or death, can be. In 1805, Nelson was shot and killed at the Battle of Trafalgar. Why was he up on deck in his full uniform? Did he have a death wish? And there's 1988. When a cruise ship, full of British schoolchildren and their teachers, sank in the Mediterranean. And they all survived. But the third event from that day really shocked me. Now, in Japan, many children have safety helmets attached to their desks. And we're all trained in evacuation procedures. But not for events like the one centred on Pantglas Junior School in 1966. Where one hundred and forty-four people died, and over one hundred of them were children.'

'I remember that time, Hatsu. It was just after my twenty-fifth birthday. Colin drove down to Wales straight away, to see if he could help. He filled a van with fruit and veg. He was exhausted when he came back from Aberfan, three or four days later.'

'I'm not surprised that Colin did a thing like that . . . These are not just dates and events. They are things that matter. In some cases, just to a few people. But they still matter. In other cases, ideas and events resonate on a larger scale. Like Japanese people visiting a disconnected phone box in a town called Otsuchi, which is in Awate Prefecture.'

'Why would they do that, Hatsu?'

'This is my understanding, Warren. It was set up by Itaru Sasaki, with a view of the sea, as a way of coming to terms with the death of a cousin. He called it *Kaze no Denwa* — the phone of the wind. But other people then started to visit it, after the 2011 Tōhoku earthquake and tsunami.'

'I remember learning about that in Geography in Year Nine. There was a man trapped in his car. He was taking a video, as he was swept down a street. It looked terrifying. Unreal, almost.'

'That part of Japan is still dealing with the aftermath. In Otsuchi, over one thousand people died. Many of the bodies were never recovered. The phone box, with its old-style phone, gave relatives the chance to 'dial up' and then 'speak' to their missing loved ones. Their messages would be carried on the breeze. There was also a notebook available, so people could write messages. In an interview *Sasaki-san* — Mr Sasaki, said that, "thoughts such as these cannot be relayed over a regular phone line. They must be carried on the wind".'

'That phone box became an outlet for grief. A place where people could start to come to terms with their loss.'

'And it still is, Skye. Tens of thousands have visited, many hoping that their thoughts and messages will be somehow carried on the wind.'

'I'd like to visit it myself. Or a place like it. To say goodbye to *my* mother and father . . .'

'I think I'll finish with two events from another date, October 25th. In 1839, it was the publication date of the first railway timetable, *Bradshaw's*. I love reading railway timetables and planning out unlikely routes. Like Takamatsu to Matsue, via

Aomori and Kanazawa. Or Albuquerque to Salt Lake City via Charleston. Or Penzance to Hastings via Mallaig. Oh, and four years later, also on October 25th, the first telegram was sent. From Paddington Station to—'

'To a marmalade-loving bear in Peru?'

'That's amusing, Warren. But no, to a place called Slough. Many people see Britain as a place of pilgrimage for its invention of the steam train. They certainly do in Japan. And it was a major news item when a specially-made vessel was used to ship a *shinkansen*, a bullet train, to the National Rail Museum in York. Which I'd like to visit. For the trains, but also for the KitKats.'

'York City changed the name of their ground for a few years to KitKat Crescent. What do you like about KitKats?'

'They come in ever so many exciting flavours, Warren. My two favourite ones are Plum Wine and Banana. Here's a list. Do you see any interesting varieties?'

'Cherry and Sake both look interesting, but I'd love to taste some of the more unusual ones. European Cheese or Miso Soup. Wasabi or Baked Potato. What about you, Skye?'

'You're definitely more adventurous than me, in terms of food at least. But the Crème Brûlée sounds nice. Although I wonder how different it would be to Bakeable Custard. It's interesting why a certain variety becomes popular or falls out of favour. You can still buy a Chocolate Orange in the UK, but I remember when Terry's of York produced a Chocolate *Apple*. That was a lovely treat, so I can understand why some variety is good. But too many choices can be overwhelming. So why are KitKats so popular in Japan, Hatsu?'

'One reason is that you could buy and post them at any Japan Post branch. But I think the main reason is the name. It sounds quite like *Kitto Katsu*, which means, "You will surely win". So it's a popular gift to give to students before they sit important exams.'

'Last time, we were looking for words beginning with the letter M. What are the final four, Warren?'

'Thanks, Skye. They are maffle, mazard, moorpunky and mulligrubs:

She did not wish to maffle,
So she hired a moorpunky.
And set out in search of mazard blossom,
As a cure for her mulligrubs.'

'And your take on what meaning there may be, Warren?'
'Well, Skye, does this version make any sense to you?

She did not wish to waste time,
So she hired a peacock-sterned Indian pleasure boat.
And set out in search of wild cherry blossom,
As a tonic to top up her low spirits.

What do you think, Hatsu?'

'I like the poem, and your version too, Warren. And I love blossom. But why didn't she set out in search of a mohoohoo. That was my suggestion.'

'A what, Hatsu?'

'A mo-hooooo-hoo. A type of white rhino.'

'It's a great-sounding word. I can't think of a relevant song, so here's one about maffling.'

'That was "Turn" by Feeder. A song which definitely comes with a warning against wasting time.'

'Where would you turn the clocks back to if you could, Warren?'

'Oh, I think 1851, Skye. So that I could visit the Great Exhibition in Hyde Park, on its May 1st opening day. And I'd probably have bought a season ticket as well.'

'Not back to any time in your lifetime?'

'No, Skye, I quite liked the challenge of looking for a place where I could be me. Not a hero and not a zero. And, until further notice, Peasenham suits me.'

'I'm happy for you, Warren. Now, as regular listeners might know, our Four Play selections are normally based around well-known songs.'

'That's right, Skye. I listened to your advice from the first show. But today, I've included a couple of poems. They are both linked to mazard, the wild sweet cherry. First, and suggesting to me that the past can be a foreign country, is a section from *A Shropshire Lad* by A. E. Housman:

"*Loveliest of trees, the cherry now*
Is hung with bloom along the bough,
And stands about the woodland ride
Wearing white for Eastertide."

Ah, I think today's guest wants to make a point.'

'Thanks Warren. First, I was thinking about *sakura* — cherry blossom. Even though I secretly prefer *ume* — plum blossom. But what got me thinking, was what you were saying about the past. When will the future, or imagined futures, become a foreign country, and for whom?'

'That's deep, Hatsu. I can see that I'm going to have to raise my game with you here. The other poem, "The Cherry Trees", is by Edward Thomas. He volunteered for the *Artists Rifles* in World War One. Although he died at Arras, on Easter Monday in 1917, I don't see him as a war poet. I see him as a poet who died in the war:

"The cherry trees bend over and are shedding,
On the old road where all that passed are dead,
Their petals, strewing the grass as for a wedding
This early May morn when there is none to wed."

That's a poem that looks at the past, present *and* future. And it seems more poignant because of Edward's early death, aged 39. He had lived near Petersfield with Helen, and his children Bronwen, Merfyn, and Myfanwy. She was the youngest daughter who assembled all the parts of the book you bought. Their home was just up the road from Portsmouth, where I was born.'

'Oh, Portsmouth. The home of Dickens and Isambard Kingdom Brunel. We learned about both of them at school. Brunel was such an innovative engineer. I come from the city of Takamatsu, which is on the island of Shikoku. It's a beautiful place, just off the main Japanese island of Honshu. There's a lot of engineering and manufacturing in Takamatsu. Many of my family have worked for Tadano, a company that specialises in heavy lifting. In fact, the company slogan is "Lifting Your Dreams". I like that idea. Because sometimes your dreams can weigh you down. Or lift you up, of course. Now, I'm thinking back to what I said earlier about names. Like India Farr. We first met, far away from our homes, on Easter Island. That was six years ago, but the story really started back in 1988. I was four then and had some health problems. I'm better now. Well, sort of. We were watching TV and saw images of these strange stone figures. My family was captivated, trying to work out how the statues would have been moved. There was even some tea spilled on the tatami mats. That's how excited they were. Then there was a message from a Mr Rapu, a former Governor of Easter Island. He said something like, "It would be a dream, but if we had a crane, we could raise the Moai statues back on their feet".'

'You mean the Easter Island heads?'

'That's right, Warren. Though some call the island Rapa Nui, or even Isla da Pascua. That suggestion on TV led to many discussions and plans within the company. Within three years a *fukesei* — a replica, had been made. It was full-size and weighed over eleven tons. This meant heavy-lifting tests could be carried out. If you ever visit my home city, we could take a ferry over to Megijima Island and see the replica.'

'I don't have a passport, but when I get one I'd love to visit you in Japan. What happened after the replica was made?'

'The following year, following scientific and archaeological discussions, the first machines arrived on the island from Takamatsu. The main focus was a large platform of moai, the Ahu Tongariki. It had been almost destroyed by a tsunami back in 1960. By 1996, eight years after the initial idea, the project was completed. And those fifteen moai, stood facing inland from their ceremonial platform, are one of the most iconic sights on the island. If not the whole world. I visited with my father and younger sister, back in 2012. And that's where I first met India.'

'How did she come into the picture?'

'Actually, she crashed into it really, Skye. I found her, dazed, sitting next to a fallen branch.'

'That's ironic, on an island that's famous for having destroyed all its trees.'

'It is, Warren. But there are now a lot more trees on the island than there were a couple of centuries ago.'

~

Rapa Nui / Easter Island, 2012

India paused next to a storm drain to let another Mini Cooper past. She still couldn't get over how many of those iconic cars had made it to the island. An island that lacked a port or modern docking facilities. She had seen the delivery process on her last visit to the island. Outriggers headed out to a cargo ship beyond the surf. She had watched as a car was lowered down and strapped to a pair of the wooden boats. And then been amazed at the sight of a course being steered through the surf. Before the car was safely unloaded on Pea Beach. Not that it was much of a beach. Anakena in the north, with its wild horses, was the best, of very few options, for most beach activities. Though Pea Beach had one key advantage. It was near the Toruku disco. After a final sip of *ron y cola con hielo* — rum and cola with ice — and a final blast of Rapa Nuian ukulele hoedown, anyone who had made it to 6am would head over to the beach. And strip off down to shorts or bikinis. Before taking a dawn dip in the Pacific Ocean. As India had done five hours earlier.

India stepped over a piece of broken pavement and continued along *Te Pito o Te Henua* — The Navel of the World. Even some of the street names here aroused her. Over to the right, the *Artesenal Mercado* was quiet. The craftspeople at that market would be much busier tomorrow when the cruise ship arrived. When the Mini Coopers would be hidden away, to be replaced with more authentic horses.

Heading downhill on *Avenida Policarpo Toro* (another great name, but not a tingler) India considered getting another tattoo. Her first *takona* was usually hidden by the watch face on the inside of her left wrist. Tiare, the ink artist, must have sensed her hesitation.

'*Iorana* — hello, India. *Peke koe?* — How are you?'

'I'm good, Tiare. Though my head's a little fuzzy. I should

have stuck to papaya juice. But, wow, you Rapa Nuians can dance. If disco dancing was an Olympic sport, one of you would have been on the Olympic podium in London earlier this year. Something for the future, perhaps. Though my daughter would also be pushing for croquet to be re-admitted.'

'I didn't know you had a daughter, India.'

'Didn't you? Hey, where do you think I should go for lunch?'

'You could try Hakehonu. Perhaps eat out on the terrace and feel the sea breezes. The smashed sweet potato with shrimp sauce is good, though you might find the sweet potato too sweet.'

'*Mauru uru* — thank you, Tiare. I'll see you in a couple of days, when the island quietens down again.'

'I know some people don't like the influx of cruise ship tourists, calling them *los gentes del barco* — the boat people. But I think that tourism can provide a good future for our island. Perhaps making us less dependent on Chile. As Easter Island, we had a reputation for environmental degradation. Perhaps, as Rapa Nui, we can forge a new identity. But a more positive one, based on green tourism. Let's meet up later to watch Colo-Colo vs O'Higgins. It's a big cup match, and most of the national park rangers here support Colo-Colo. So there should be a good atmosphere in the Topatangi pub.'

It had been a stiff climb up to Orongo, the ceremonial village, but the effort was worth it. What a place. A raw place. Like at the Grand Canyon or Yellowstone, there were no barriers. A sign read, '*No hay garantias para su seguriad*' — 'There is no guarantee for your safety.' India wondered whether this was just a site-specific warning, or directed at life in general.

Ahead of her were low buildings, covered in grass. Each had a small doorway, close to the ground. India felt drawn to the stone huts in the village. They reminded her of sketches Skye had shown her of Skara Brae. She would have liked to stay in one overnight, but her attention was drawn to another one of the many signs: '*No se permite acampar ni pernoctar en el Parque Nacional*' — 'It is not allowed to camp in the park or spend the night in caves.' The sign didn't actually forbid her, but India knew that staying would go against the spirit of the advice.

Something had gone terribly wrong with the moai culture, and Orongo was developed to create an alternative tradition. India walked up to the cliff edge, and looked down at several small islands, one shaped like a shark's tooth. She edged closer, resting her hand near one of the many stone carvings. A tour group was listening to their guide.

'Each year people would gather here in July for the competition. The different clans would put aside their differences and engage in a series of rituals and festivities. Each candidate for chiefdom would then select a contestant to represent them. These *hopu* would then swim during August to Moto Nui — *Isla de los hombres* — and wait for the seabirds to nest. The winner would be the first one to return with an unbroken egg. This is why it became known as the birdman cult. The winning candidate was known as *Tangata Manu*. He would spend most of the next year in isolation. Do you have any questions?'

'How did the *hopu* survive? The cliffs here are really steep. And the islands look like bare rocks.'

'Many didn't. It was a dangerous task. The *hopu* had to go down into the volcanic crater of Rano Kau to collect reeds. They used these to weave a *pora* — a sort of bag — for their supplies. Death came in many forms. Not just the obvious risk of drowning, but also from cliff falls, shark attacks and starvation. They had to wait out there until the first birds arrived back. It could take days, or even weeks.'

India was impressed by the bravery of the *hopu*. Though

another of the warning signs made the revival of the birdman cult unlikely: '*Observe los islotes (motu) desde el mar, no disembarque en ellos ni perturbe la avifauna nativa*' — 'Watch islets (motu) from the sea, do not disembark there or alter the native bird fauna.' She continued to listen in on the questions and answers.

'Why didn't the candidates to be chief perform the task?'

'Good question. People who seek power often rely on the efforts and sacrifices of others.'

'Did the new cult start after all the moai had been toppled?'

'We're not sure. There may have been some overlap. The moai which is in the British Museum was taken from this site. It has birdman carvings on its back, but these might have been added later. That museum has a petroglyph, a design carved in stone, also from this site. It shows a birdman with a huge hand, in which is nestled an egg.'

'Did the birdman cult reduce inter-clan tension and violence?'

'While the clans were in Orongo, yes. But maybe not so much during the rest of the year. Visitors who arrived during those times often commented on the absence of women on the island. Many of the visitors were slave traders. So Rapa Nuians, especially women, became skilled at hiding themselves in *karava* and *ana* — rock shelters and caves. The moai might have looked inwards, but observation towers — *tupa* — were manned to look *out*, to scan the horizon. To see which new trouble blew in on the *tokerau* — the wind. So there was a lot of stress on the island. With internal and external roots.'

India was moved by what had happened on this island. Another message on the board seemed more like a poem than mere information: '*Es un testimonio único de una civilización que se ha vuelto vulnerable*' — 'It is a unique testimony of a civilisation which has become vulnerable.'

'How could the new chief rule in isolation?'

'His clan would carry out his wishes. These were relayed by the only person who could visit him, a priest. It must have been strange, though. The new chief would have all the hair on his head cut off, including his eyelashes. Then, after a final feast, he would lead a procession down the slope to where the airport is now situated. Following a victory tour of all the important island sites, he chose a secluded place to live for the next year. The quarry at Rano Raraku was often chosen, as it was no longer used for making moai. It must have been quite a ghostly place, haunted by the remains of half-carved moai. And finished ones that never made it to their planned final resting place. We'll visit the site tomorrow. It's very popular, but it's a site that gives me strange sensations.'

The group moved off and India peered into the crater of the Rano Kau volcano. She could see plants, maybe reeds, growing at the base. It was the kind of place you wouldn't be that surprised to see a dinosaur. The south-west face, the one nearest to the ocean, looked very vulnerable. Maybe that part of the crater would collapse, and salt water would flood in.

India started the long walk back. She could see Hanga Roa, laid out far below. On the ground were thousands of black obsidian chips. These pieces of glassy lava, shiny and tiny, had been one of the main tools used on the island. As India continued her walk, she failed to notice one last warning sign: '*Esté alerta a la posible caida de ramas de árboles y de cocos*' — 'Beware the branches and coconuts that may possibly fall from trees'.

India was amazed at the spread, and lushness, of the vegetation. A red-soil track snaked its way down the tree-covered hill. Huge seed pods hung from some of the bushes. India stepped back, then waved, as a group of riders trotted past her. She started walking again, looking back towards where the horses had gone. It was like being on another island. She smiled, then—

'Oh, good. Can you hear me?'

India could just about make out the blurred face above her.

'Don't move. I have some water for you. I think you got hit by a falling eucalyptus branch. Your head is grazed, but there's no *shukketsu* — bleeding.'

India came to at least some of her senses. 'How long have I been here?'

'Just a few minutes. I saw you fall over.' India's rescuer pointed towards some raised stone structures. 'I was looking at the *manavai*. They're like micro fields, and their circular walls were designed to reduce soil erosion and improve water retention. They're *kakushinteki* — innovative. My name is Hatsu. What is your name?'

India couldn't immediately respond. But then it came to her. 'My name's In-di-ia.'

'Indoa? That means indoors.'

'No, India. As in the country.'

'Ah, in Japan we call it Indo. Were you born there?'

'No, Hatsu.'

'So why are you called it?'

'It's a long story.'

India waved to the advancing figure. She had agreed the previous day to meet up with Hatsu. 'It's lovely to see you. Thank you again for everything you did yesterday.'

'I was happy to help.'

The pair were surrounded by moai on the slopes of Rano Raraku. Each, whether upright or slanted, had its own character.

'I want to hug them,' said Hatsu. 'But I know I shouldn't. That notice says, "*Mire, no toque*" — "Look, do not touch". The signs are helpful. Even if you didn't understand the words, the picture clues are clear. It's the same for that one too, "*No recoja piedras ni otros objetos*" — "Do not pick up any stones or other objects".'

'I agree,' India said. 'Sometimes people need a reminder about how to act.' She pointed to a trio of tourists recreating one of the signs with their bodies. One of them was lying on the ground while the other two pretended they were about to stand on her. 'They're creating a visual version of, "*No suba ni camine sobre la arqueología*" — "Do not climb or walk on the stone structures". You can tell they want to get more interactive with the moai. But the signs, and the people around them, are controlling their behaviour. Shall we walk down to the bay to get a closer look?'

'Tsunami,' Hatsu said, 'are so much more than just harbour waves. I think the fact that the moai were damaged by a tsunami was significant to the Japanese involvement. When we meet up later with my little sister Yuriko and my father, he can tell you more.'

Hatsu and India stood in front of the fifteen moai of Ahu Tongariki. It was difficult for both of them to imagine the water force needed to move these giants hundreds of metres.

'We, that is Japanese people, are very aware of risks from natural hazards. But the 1960 tsunami caused death and destruction all around the Pacific region. Easter Island escaped relatively lightly, as the ten-metre-high tsunami hit here on the eastern side. Hanga Roa, where most people live, was protected. The people of Hilo, in Hawaii, were not so lucky. That city was destroyed.'

'I've met people who believe that the tsunami was a catalyst for change here.'

'I've heard that as well, India. Before the destruction, all the moai were toppled and face down.'

'On the way here, I stopped at Akahanga. The moai there is

still toppled. With its head supported by its nose, and its deep eyeless eye sockets. It made me feel sad, and almost tearful.'

'I feel *aichaku* — a love — for the moai. It's not romantic, but it is powerful. Maybe they will leave some of the moai toppled, as a reminder . . . The tsunami revealed some of their faces once again. It also revealed human remains that had been buried under the massive ceremonial platform, the *ahu*. In the same year, at Ahu Akivi, seven moai were raised up. The first ones of the modern era. Later excavations here at Tongariki produced more surprises. Part of the *ahu* was made up of seventeen older, broken moai.'

'You must be very proud of the contribution that Japan made.'

'I am, and more so for my island, Shikoku. It has a reputation as being something of a backwater. But a company from *there* was a key ingredient *here*. Shikoku is also famous for its pilgrimage circuit. For me, this place has made me feel a *henro* — a pilgrim. It's not such a difficult journey as the 88-temple circuit on my home island, but it has helped me to think clearly.'

'This place has been more of an escape for me. I've used it to avoid making important decisions, especially those to do with my responsibilities in England.'

'Maybe you will now follow a different path. I would love to visit England. To experience the land that inspired Beatrix Potter and Harry Potter. I love pottery.'

'That's funny, Hatsu. I have contacts in a place, which like Shikoku, is seen as being away from the centre of things. Perhaps you'll be able to visit one day.'

~

'Talking of trees, and wood products, what's going on at Bay Six Books? Warren has visited a few times, I know, but he hasn't revealed much.'

'The new shop opens tomorrow, Skye. In Japan, we are famous for our capsule hotels, and also quite well known for a holistic approach to healing. For example, many people spend time in the woods. Scientists don't really know why, but a lot of people feel better after being amongst, and touching, the trees. We call it *shinrin-yoku*, or forest bathing. So I've come up with Book Bathing. People can dip into books, and then, if they wish, spend a night surrounded by books. Seth has been so helpful, creating the platforms and shelves. During the day, people can sit on them. But at night they turn into beds.'

'Will you have enough space to sell books?'

'*Tabun* — maybe, Skye. Although I'm changing that side of things as well. Concentrating on books from smaller publishers that might not have such a wide distribution. But the shop will also make money when people donate books . . . I see you both look a bit confused. Say someone has a book that I think might sell for £8. If they agree with my valuation, then they hand over £2. A quarter of the price. If the book sells within a month, they get £6. So overall, they would gain £4 and so would our shop.'

'What if the book doesn't sell?'

'That's a possibility. In the example I gave, Warren, the person will have made a £2 donation to our community. Although I think most of the books will sell. It will make people think more about the books they hand over. And they can write a card explaining why they think people might enjoy the book, or books.'

'Books?'

'Yes, Skye. For example, if it was me donating, I might start with a book of haiku poetry by Matsuo Basho. Then a book about someone following in Basho's footsteps. Say, Lesley

Downer's *The Narrow Road to the Deep North*. And finish the set with a copy of Will Ferguson's *Hokkaido Highway Blues*. It briefly mentions Takamatsu, my home city, but not as I recognise it. More as a city of ghosts . . . Kenesha said she'd pin up some of the book cards, over at M3. She was sure Marina wouldn't mind. I hope she's enjoying leaf-peeping with Zoe in Vermont.'

~

Vermont, 2018

'How y'all doing. Welcome to Whetstone Station. My name's Neilanie and I'll be looking after you today.'

'Hi Neilanie,' Marina said. Do you have any local beers?'

'We certainly do. And some of them are made right here. We make experimental batches behind the glass doors over there. But we brew most of our range over at Frost Street. That's a really chilled place to work . . . What are you looking for today?'

'Do you do a tasting flight?'

'You could try three of our eight percent Third Rail Double IPAs. They're made with the same hops, but use different yeasts: Burlington, Coastal Haze and London Fog.'

'They sound really interesting, but a bit strong for lunchtime. Even though I'm not driving today.'

'No problem at all. I'll set you up a lighter trio. How about our Whetstoner IPA, Bumpy Ryed Pale Ale and Penguin Porter?'

'Those sound better. What about you, Zoe?'

'I'm not sure. Perhaps a Maine Soda root beer or a—'

'That's so funny, as we have a Red Ale called Zoe. I guess you're not legal for drinking, but when you are, come back. It's delicious. Think dark chocolate and raisin cookies, with a citrus twist. It would go really well with carrot cake. Sorry, I'm getting carried away. I'll get the flight and a root beer. Or would you prefer the seasonal Pumpkin Pie soda. That's great with Harvest Pumpkin Swirl Cake. Oops, there I go again.'

'I'll try the pumpkin soda, please. And thank you, we feel very welcome.'

Neilanie scooted back to the bar. Marina and Zoe looked out over where the Whetstone Brook joined the Connecticut River. A large green 'coat-hanger' bridge was reflected in the slow-moving water. As was the autumnal foliage of the riverside trees.

'Rudyard Kipling loved this time of year,' Marina said. She opened her journal and found the right page. 'He once wrote that, "*A little maple began it, flaming blood-red of a sudden*". But he knew that the show would be brief. The leaves would all fall. Leaving, "*bare boughs, and one could see into the most private heart of the woods*". Maybe he was sat near this spot when he wrote it.'

'I prefer spring to autumn, but I understand his passion. Was Brattleboro his nearest town?'

'It was, Zoe. The river was a main trade route and the town had a railroad station. Some people thought Kipling could be a bit distant. But he liked to listen, rather than talk. A station employee remembered that Kipling listened out for, "queer turns of speech that he could use. I never saw a man so hungry for information". Some of those conversational snippets were later recycled into Kipling's stories.'

'So he was a magpie. And words were his sparkling treasure. Which he hoarded until they were needed.'

'*En cueros vivos* — he was stark naked without them. I think he was on to something when he said, "Words are, of course, the most powerful drug used by mankind".'

'Here's your order.' Neilanie set the drinks down and also passed over a folded card. 'If you need to go to the restroom, you can pop one of these *"Please keep your hands off my beer: Gone to Pee"* cards on your drink. Have you thought about food?'

'We have, Neilanie. You first, Zoe.'

'I'm almost there. And I hope those cards work for soda as well as beer. Oh, what's in the Buddha Bowl?'

'There's a base of polenta and quinoa cakes. They're topped with sautéed carrot, ginger and bok choy. And some seriously smoky roasted sunflower seeds.'

'I'll have that, please, but just a starter portion.'

'And I'll have the vegan burger, please. With some hop mayo. That sounds interesting.'

'That's also a good choice. Would you like any extra toppings, for 99 cents each? The record's nine.'

'I will, but just three please: roasted red peppers, maple smoked bacon and the orange mango slaw. Oh, and can I upgrade my fries to the sweet potato ones?'

'Sure thing. Though you're the first customer to order the vegan burger *and* the bacon. Was that right?'

'I like a lot of vegan food, but I eat meat too.'

'You're certainly living up to our unofficial "Keep Brattleboro Weird" motto. I'll get your order out to the kitchen.'

Chapter 14

**Marina's entry in The Carriage House Guest Book, 2018
with additional comments by Zoe & India**

Two buildings seem to float above a tree-lined meadow in Dummerston, Vermont. Both clad in green, with a mix of boards and vertical shingle tiles. Behind them is Kipling Hill (follow the trail downstream and you might come across an interesting college called 'World Learning'. When I first saw the sign, I thought it said World *Leaning*). The larger of the two buildings here is Naulakha, Rudyard and Carrie Kipling's Vermont home.

The second is the Carriage House, where we are staying. It had been a carriage house, with Nip and Tuck stabled in a nearby barn, but was later extended to become the Kipling staff house. Although it probably didn't have a ping-pong table in the basement at that time.

Upstairs, the pine interior glows in the late afternoon sunshine. And the heavily glazed kitchen looks out over the most magnificent woodshed I have ever seen. Jack Kerouac — who chopped up many cords of winter wood, while a fire watcher in *Desolation Angels* — would have been impressed. And then probably would have had a glass of red wine, while sat in one of the Adirondack chairs. Although if he was here now, a glass of Angry Orchard hard cider might be more appropriate.

Zoe and I had a great game of tennis this morning. Though it was difficult to see the lines due to the fallen 'fall' leaves. A family from Okracoke in the Outer Banks* have rented Naulakha. They all work in publishing, and gave Zoe a copy of Christopher Benfey's *If: The Untold Story of Kipling's American Years*. They also invited us to visit the Big House.

We were invited to spend time in Kipling's study. The study of a writer who was awarded the first Nobel Prize in Literature for a work in English. I sat at the desk where he wrote, near to a sculpture of a black panther. Shere Khan, sheer magic. We also saw the passage that connected the study to his 'escape hatch'. Which was a set of stairs leading upwards. Kipling would use these when unexpected visitors arrived. But he had 'form' himself.

As part of his shortened honeymoon — his funds were suspended while he and Carrie were in Japan — Kipling had planned to just 'pop in' on Robert Louis Stevenson. In Samoa! And en route to Vermont, Rudyard Kipling had met Mark Twain in New York State. Despite Kipling's dislike of unexpected visitors, he turned up without warning at the front door of Huckleberry Finn's author. Kipling later wrote about one of the issues fans face when they meet their heroines or heroes. He wrote, '*It occurred to me for the first time that Mark Twain might possibly have other engagements other than the entertainment of escaped lunatics from India, be they ever so full of admiration.*'

Naulakha was where Rudyard Kipling and Carrie Balestier settled in the 1890s. They'd first rented Bliss Cottage, where their first child, Josephine, was born. She came into the world in 1892, on December 29th. This was very well-timed, as Rudyard's birthday was on the 30th and Carrie's on New Year's Eve. And there was more cause for celebration. The site and setting inspired Kipling to recall scenes and stories from his Indian childhood. Including the tale of a forest boy raised by wolves.

Kipling wrote, '*the pen took charge, and I watched it begin to write stories about Mowgli and animals, which later grew into the two Jungle Books.*' Their growing family persuaded the Kiplings to build their own home, Naulakha. Kipling thought of it as a land-based ship. A sunny ship to shelter him from the gathering storms. But those storms were in the future . . .

Kipling had many visitors, one of whom was Arthur Conan Doyle (I wonder if *he* just turned up without giving any notice). Sherlock's creator gave Ruddy, as Rudyard's friends called him, the first set of skis ever seen in Vermont. They exchanged shots on Vermont's first ever tennis court. And with donated clubs (aka sticks), Conan Doyle taught Ruddy golf. But Kipling preferred the red-ball snow version that he had invented (even though a shot could skid and skip for over a mile).

Dummerston was a place of firsts and indeed it still is. Later this week, a young adult will meet her mother for the first time. But I must pause my writing for now. It's 'Apple Day' down at Scott Farm, and we're hoping to find some great local produce.

What a place. All of the buildings at Scott Farm are listed on the National Register of Historic Places. My favourite was the Hog Barn. It sits on a slope above a reflecting pond. And it has an extra layer of history, as a film set. It stood in as the dormitory (of the migrant apple pickers) in the award-winning film of John Irving's *The Cider House Rules*.

Peering through a window, I noticed a scrap of paper on a wooden pillar. Perhaps the last remnant of the 'rules'. Rules that were deliberately broken. For example, by migrant pickers sitting on the roof at night. For why should people follow rules, if they're made by people who don't respect the people the rules are made for? And the Landmark Trust broke the 'rule', of monoculture, when it took over Scott Farm in 1995.

The orchards had been growing just one variety. The apple? McIntosh. Now, under the guidance of the magnificently whiskered Ezekiel Goodband, over one hundred heirloom varieties are grown. My favourites were Blue Pearmain, Orleans Reinette and the Lady Apple. The 'Lady' was known in the Roman era, but had its heyday during the Renaissance. Apparently, women would tuck one or two into their bosom. Ready to pluck out, should a chance meeting require a fruity breath freshener. A good job that *pineapples* weren't all the rage.

Marina Rueda, Suffolk, England

* Our 'new' friends from the Outer Banks (often known as OBX) know Ana Logan, an 'old' friend of ours. I asked them to pass on our best wishes. That's one of the things about smaller communities. You know more people than you would do if you lived in a city. That's been my experience, anyway. Ana's now working for the NPS, at their Fort Raleigh site in Roanoke. To finish, some thoughts:

1. Was the Hokey Cokey invented in Ocracoke?

2. Iain Banks wrote fiction. His 'Inner' Banks?

His alter ego, Iain M. Banks, wrote science fiction.

His 'Outer' Banks?

3. Some of Iain's ashes were mixed in with explosives to make fireworks. And launched, by his friends, at their and his favourite places. Way to go?

I'm a bit nervous. Does it show in my writing? A red sports car is approaching along Kipling Lane . . .

PS Kipling had been great friends with Wolcott Balestier, one of Carrie's brothers. Naulakha was named for a book that Ruddy and Wolcott had written together. But it was her other brother, Beatty ("I'll blow your soul out of you . . . ") who caused Kipling to flee back to England. To Torquay. A pending court case for the alleged assault by Beatty (Kipling stated that, "I have a distinct aversion to being shot at . . . ") and strained Anglo-American relations (Kipling thought it was like being, "aimed at with a decanter across a friendly dinner table") combined to hasten his escape.

I can assure future readers of this Guest Book that no glassware was flung here this week. Although the ping-pong matches have been a bit lively.

Some rules are made to be broken. But not all of them, surely? But let's start at the beginning. Before this trip, I'd never been out of Britain. Though some of the places round here seem familiar. Sort of. I loved the Medieval Fair(e) up the road at Putney. Seeing Marina whizz down a zipline on a 'knightly' horse was hilarious. On the same day we visited Woodstock (no, not *that* Woodstock). Marina and I did the Civil War Home Front walking tour. It's the only US National Park Site that focuses on the impact of that war on the civilian population. It's a lovely town, and Pleasant Street is well-named. But the chill in the air seemed more than just autumnal.

On the way back we stopped for cheese sampling at Grafton Village. Delicious, and staffed by such lovely people. Who even warned us to watch out in the woods, as it was bow-hunting season. We also stopped off at some of the covered bridges. The early evening light was just right for photography. Next to one of the bridges was an interesting rules sign. You may be relieved to read that we didn't engage in any blocking of roadways, destruction or nude bathing. And we were out of the area by the directed time of 9pm. Failure to follow those rules could have cost us $360.

Apart from our 'Woodstock' tour, we have stayed within five miles of Dummerston. I like Brattleboro, the local town. It has been described as a '*little gem*', but I see it more as an '*iceberg*'. Yes, there are lots of indie stores and pop-ups, but I reckon its hinterland is even weirder. Having said that, I loved Mocha Joe's. What a place to drink great coffee and watch the world go by.

I heard some people in there talking about a 'Win a Kidney' website. Marina tried to edge me out of there, but I stayed to listen. Americans can 'advertise' for a kidney. A kind of medical popularity contest. Feeling a bit shaky, I headed off. And found comfort in touching the wonderful fabrics at Delectable Mountain Cloth. I didn't buy any, but I did get some vintage buttons. They'll make lovely presents for my friends back in Suffolk. I also visited a shop, which a friend of mine (Seth) would have loved. It had some great pre-loved furniture, and hit the nail on the head with its name: Experienced Goods.

If you like large orange 'fruit', head for the Whetstone Station in Brattleboro. Neilanie, our server, made some great pumpkin-based menu suggestions. I also enjoyed chatting with her about her plans for the future. She's training to be an emergency motorcycle courier, delivering blood or organs wherever, and whenever, they're needed. Now, that sounds like a very useful and rewarding career.

She also told us to check out the listings for the New England Center for Circus Arts (NECCA). We did, and signed up for the intriguingly-named 'German Wheel Jam'. Marina and I didn't really know what to expect from a wheel-gymnastics class. But it was really good. The 'German' part refers to the nationality of Otto, its inventor. The 'wheel' consists of two large (and connected) circular tubes. The 'jam' part is creating freestyle moves and enjoying yourself.

We managed some straight-line moves, but some of the 'jammers' were doing 'coin' spins. And one of them even managed to stand on top of their wheel — that looked tricky enough by itself — and then did a backflip. Very impressive, but I think I'll stick to croquet. Which would be quite fun in the snow, which I understand they get a lot of here. The croquet balls would not need painting, though the hoops (Americans call them wickets) might need to be hundreds of metres apart.

It's difficult to sum up this week. I've loved walking through the woods and orchards with Marina. And it's been great listening to Zeke's apple stories. I've also loved being able to buy 'cider'. That's what they call the apple juice here. They sell it — the 'it' being Heirloom Apple Cider — in 64oz glass jars from the bustling farm market at 707 Kipling Road. There's no escaping Mr Kipling here! If you want 'real' cider in the States, you have to ask for hard cider.

Then my mother arrived, in a MX-5 (called a Mazda Miata over here).

We didn't talk much, but we played lots of ping-pong. Each game was not just up to the old school '21' points, but had to be *won* by 21 points. I was down in one game 29-10, but came back to win 285-264. That game finished at 4.44am. And just what *do* you talk about with someone who gave birth to you, but who you had never met?

Zoe, 18 (Peasenham, Suffolk, England)

My daughter, with very little traditional support from me, has grown up to become a lovely young woman. A woman who has not let life's problems drag her down. A woman who not surprisingly does not want help, of any kind, from me.

But I saw glimpses and overheard snippets, which suggested that Zoe and I do have more of a shared future. More, at least, than that suggested by a quote from a book I found in the library here. Rudyard Kipling, in *The Light That Failed*, wrote, '*We're all islands shouting lies to each other across seas of misunderstanding*'. There was no shouting this week, and our separation has not been based on lies. As for misunderstandings, I can hardly blame my daughter for those. I don't really understand some of the life decisions I've made myself.

India Farr, 38 (from all over the place)

~

'Hi, I'm Skye Hunter and welcome to *Chatter Broth*. It's October 30th and today's guest is Colin Pargeter.'

'Hello, Skylark. And hello, Warren. You look perky. Got a few ideas whizzing around in your noddle, p'raps?'

'A few, it's an exciting time.'

'I agree. And we can't let Zoe's health issues stop everything else from happening. I know it's autumn, but the change feels stronger this year. I just need some time to get *my* noddle round it. I don't mind. In fact, I revel in it. You know, what Hatsu's doing with the bookshop. And your food and housing ideas, Warren. I loved the ideas you came up with on the show last month. That stuff about multi-generational living, on a larger scale to what we have here. The National Trust would be good, but it might also work on Ministry of Defence land. So not just for the old and the young, but maybe also a way to help military folk bridge the gap to civilian life. Maybe to help ex-prisoners, too. It could develop organically, under the radar. A silent evolution. And it'll be people like you and Zoe and Kenesha, who'll end up leading it. Skye and I will take more of a backseat. We might even borrow your H Van and drive to the end of the world. If not *that* far, to the coast at least.'

'I'd like that. You and me racing along at 35mph. Feeling safe, but also out on the edge. But looking back, what have you spotted In This Fortnight? Back to you, Colin.'

'Right-o. I'm thinking about age and responsibility. I know from Warren's expression that he's a bit overwhelmed, and excited, by the changes. He had a big disappointment recently, but he's really getting stuck in with other things. Young people have so much talent and they need to be able to express it. Look at Ethan Ampadu. Kenesha and I saw him play for Chelsea earlier this year. They signed him from Exeter City, where he'd made his debut while still a schoolboy. And he's already made his full debut for Wales.'

'And this links to what?'

'Right you are, Warren. On November 6th, 1429, Henry VI was crowned. He was seven years old, and had actually been king since he was a baby. Now, that's probably too young, but you never know. Sometimes, in life, you need to get a good run-up. Enough time to make mistakes. Then move on, because it's not the end of the world. Young people just need to be given a chance. Like Tommy Brown. He was a canteen assistant on *HMS Petard*, and as a sixteen-year-old he shouldn't even have been at sea. That didn't stop him volunteering to join a small team that boarded the sinking U-559. The documents and equipment he retrieved — tragically, the other two volunteers drowned — were a key part of Bletchley Park's code-cracking success. And Tommy became the youngest person to ever receive the George Cross.'

'I've walked through a submarine. It was the *HMS Alliance*, which is laid up across Portsmouth Harbour in Gosport. That was a tight experience. Everywhere you looked, there were food supplies. Loaves of bread wedged in the ceiling. Big tins of custard in empty torpedo racks. Tins of sardines stacked like tins of . . . '

'I see what you did there. Very amusing, Warren. As you were.'

'Thanks, Colin. Our guide explained it was difficult enough getting out of a sinking sub. But can you imagine volunteering to go *in* to one? That's bravery.'

'So is facing an enemy. Though technological advances can

have unexpected consequences. On October 31st, 1915, British Army troops wore steel helmets for the first time. And what happened? They popped their heads up more often, with the inevitable consequences.'

'I hope they learned soon, Colin. I remember, it must be decades ago, reading about George Orwell's lucky escape in Catalonia. He was a very tall man. So he should have been even more cautious when he stood on a sandbag, to peer at the enemy. A sniper's bullet went cleanly through his throat, just missing an artery. Medical staff told him how lucky he was, but he thought he'd have been luckier not to have been hit at all. Now, I think it's time to explore Lost Four Words. Last time, we were looking for words beginning with the letter N. What are the final four this time, Warren?'

'Thanks, Skye. They are nabbie, naevus, nipperkin and nobbins:

The naevus on her neck,
Resembled a nabbie.
After performing, she used most of the nobbins,
To buy a nipperkin.'

'And your thoughts on what meaning there may be, Warren?'
'Well, Skye, does this make any sense to you?'

The birthmark on her neck,
Looked like a Scottish herring boat.
After busking, she used most of the hat money,
To buy a half-pint of ale.'

'I suggested nipperkin. Though I'd shorten it to nip, over at M3. My other idea was noctiflorous. That is, bloomin' at night.

And not just plants. People too.'

'I agree, Colin. I'm not a nightbird. Although it can be exhilarating to see the sun rise, to do some dawn treading. Now, I remember a certain early morning in San Sebastian. I'd bumped into an old friend the night before in Bar Nagusia. We were just going to have a few *pinxtos* — local tapas— washed down with a chilled glass of Txakoli. And then someone — was it me? — suggested trying out another place. Then another. And so it was that, some hours later, we walked down to the bay. The beach there, *La Concha*, is shaped like a scallop shell. There was no-one around, so we—'

'I've got a Four Play link for noctiflorous. It's "Night Owls Early Birds" by Foxes. That's the band, not the animals. There's a line in the song that suggests the writer is turned on by words. But maybe I'm getting carried away as well.'

'And that second song was "First We'll Take Manhattan" by Leonard Cohen. He was guided by many things in that song. Including a naevus, a birthmark, on his skin. And after taking that New York island, he wanted Berlin. I don't understand why.'

'Nor do I, Warren. But Berlin was in the news in this fortnight. The Wall was breached on October 9th, 1989. I'm sure that Skye would agree that Berlin is one of the most interesting cities in the world.'

'I would. And it's also haunting. Atmospheric. Dynamic. Shocking.'

'I've got three more dates, two of which are linked. 115 years ago, on November 2nd, the first issue of the *Daily Mirror* was printed. It was designed for female readers. Maybe the recent death of Queen Victoria was a catalyst for change. Although it wasn't until 1942, that the Church of England dropped the rule that women had to wear hats in church. Headwear probably wasn't at the top of people's wartime priorities.'

'I was only one at the time, so hand-knitted woollen bonnets were more my thing.'

'I'm sure you'd still look lovely in one, Skylark. My last event though, takes us to South Africa. November 12th, 1928 was the date of birth of Bob Holness. Now, I loved listening to him on the radio. But who can forget *Blockbusters*? I was chatting to Laura, Zoe's transplant co-ordinator, at the Field Party. She won four out of five Gold Runs. Including two hundred pounds worth of record vouchers. Can you imagine that? Laura had some very happy memories of filming at *Central TV* up in Nottingham. She loved Bob, and admitted to shedding a few tears when he died in 2012. In fact, I think I'll pop over to M3 to see how Kenesha's getting on. And raise a new cocktail, a "B, please Bob", to his memory. And to Zoe and Marina's safe return.'

Chapter 15

'Hi, I'm Skye Hunter and welcome to *Chatter Broth*. It's November 13th and today's guest is Angelique Vonk.'

'Thanks for inviting me again. It's lovely to be in this cosy space, as the days become cooler. And it's lovely to have Zoe and Marina back. Zoe was telling me about some epic table tennis games she had contested in Vermont. So I'll head straight to November 19th. Not Lincoln's Gettysburg Address, but an event twenty-six years later, in 1889. James Gibbs and his family were using cigar box lids, to hit champagne corks back and forth across a table. But two years later, Jacques of London patented the name Gossima, and introduced their own version. They were looking to boost income that was falling due to tennis taking over from croquet at Wimbledon Croquet Club. But early sales were slow. Partly because the net was a foot high at that time. But then in 1901, the company refined the equipment and changed the name to Ping Pong. What's in a name?'

'Good question. Would tennis have become so popular if its name had stayed as Sphairistike?'

'I'm glad *you* pronounced that one, Warren. Names are important. Many dynasties, especially royal families, repeat a name to create a sense of tradition and longevity around it. Henry I's only legitimate son was called William, a name with special significance for Normans. But Prince William drowned, with hundreds of others, when the 'unsinkable' *White Ship* sank on November 25th, 1120. And the two main claimants, Matilda and Stephen, had to forge identities with no help from the names of past monarchs. Matilda, of course, had another key issue to deal with as *she* tried to build support. A later king had a much easier time securing the English throne. Prince Edward took part in the Ninth Crusade in 1272. His father Henry III died on November 16th. Did Edward rush back to England? No, he waited almost two years before he 'popped' back to formally claim his throne. Richard the Lionheart didn't seem too keen on England either. He didn't speak English and once even offered to sell London.'

'That's right, Angelique. He only 'popped' back once to England after his coronation. And his wife, Berengaria, never even visited these shores.'

'And we Dutch have had a few moments too, Warren. The Orange family name inspired the genetic modification of carrots from their more natural purple. But Orange is a town in the South of France, admittedly where the family had held an estate. It would be like the British royal family calling themselves the Delhis or the Philadelphias, not the Windsors. Rulers often behave in strange ways that would result in mere citizens being laughed at. On November 17th, in the year before the start of the Great War, Kaiser Wilhelm intervened in army discipline. By banning any member of the armed forces from dancing the tango. Last tango in Berlin, perhaps. On the same day, in 1970, a German-*sounding* lady became front page news. Actually, not quite the front page. Stephanie Rahn became the *Sun*'s first 'Page Three Girl'. Although the surname she used was Khan. I wonder what type of audience *her* breasts were aimed at.'

'Talking of which, when is the next life modelling session?'

'That's funny, Skye. Maybe a future model *will* be physically naked. Anyway, next week it's Pippa's turn. She's borrowed one of Seth's full-length mirrors, so it should be interesting. A time for reflection, at least.'

'Last time, we were looking for words beginning with the letter O. What are the final four, Warren?'

'They are ofuro, opsimath, optimific and orts:

While steaming alone in the ofuro,
She pondered that using orts,
Was often optimific.
She was an opsimath, but at least she was learning.'

'And your thoughts on what meaning there may be, Warren?'
'Well, Skye. Does this interpretation make any sense to you?

While steaming alone in the Japanese communal bath,
She pondered that using odds and ends,
Often produced the best results.
She was learning late in life, but at least she was learning.'

'I remember being at an onsen in Nagasaki. There's still quite a lot of Dutch influence there, in that part of Kyushu. You get given a small towel, but it's to wear on your head. Apart from that towel, you're naked. I found it quite liberating. And I think I've now got enough confidence back to try it again, should the chance come. Maybe Hatsu and Seth could work together to create a Suffolk-based version.'

'We might *all* end up in hot water. Which I'd prefer to use for cooking orts. You know, using leftovers and cans from the back of the cupboard to create interesting meals. And yes, maybe including celeriac.'

'You carry on, Warren. We'll let you know if we ever tire of your favourite ingredient. What do you think, Angelique?'

'I agree, Skye. I'm not scared to try any of Warren's creations . . . I was hoping that onomatomania would be included. It means a fear of, or alternatively an obsession with, certain words. With good reason, I have never liked the Dutch word for hospital. It's *het zickenhuis* — the sick house. But even though I don't smoke, I love the word for a pipe — *pijp*.'

'Some words are euphonic. That is, pleasing to the ear. Like mohoohoo or effleurage. Talking of which, I remember a sultry night in Kirkwall when—'

'I found a good song about orts. And it's by one of your favourite bands, Skye. A great use of orts is to make soup. And if you consume a big bowl of it, you might feel jussulent. So this song might be another favourite of *The Clangers*. Here's "Venus of the Soup Kitchen" by Prefab Sprout.'

'I once accidentally ended up in a soup kitchen. I had just arrived in Utrecht, from the south. It was raining heavily and I sought shelter under an archway. A converted van, a bit like yours Warren, was serving soup and bread rolls. I was handed a steaming mug and a warm roll. *"Hoeveel kost het?"* I asked — "How much is it?" It was a bit embarrassing to be told it was free, but I got over it. Even though they wouldn't accept a donation. Though they did give me a tip to go and see an English band called The Cropdusters that night. I'd never seen, or even heard of, pyscho-ceilidh hoedown music before. I enjoyed bouncing around at the front that night. And on many other nights with that band over the years . . . To finish In This Fortnight, I'd like to go back to another event from November 25th. The Great Storm of 1703 is renowned in Britain. Wind speeds of over 120mph resulted in a trail of destruction that killed almost 10,000 people. One fifth of the Royal Navy's ships were lost. One admiral, who survived, had his ship blown from Harwich to

Gothenburg. The storm caused over-revving windmills to catch fire. And we know in Suffolk, as well as the Netherlands, how important windmills are in 'low' country. Over 400 windmills were destroyed. Some historians believe that their loss gave impetus to the Industrial Revolution, as new sources of power were developed and refined. Maybe every cloud *does* have a silver lining.'

~

Life Modelling at the Hop Yard #3

'Please set up your easel at one of the marked points around the room.' Pippa pointed to the four compass points.

Angelique chose 'east', followed, in a compass-wise direction by Kenesha, Marina and Hatsu.

'I shall try and do four poses, but we'll see.' Pippa glanced, with almost a grimace, at the draped mirror she was standing next to. 'I can only cope with fragments of my image. I've been told I'm beautiful, but I see myself differently.'

'But you're a model,' Kenesha said. 'And I'm not surprised. What do you think, Hatsu?'

'I like to look at Pippa. But not just because, to me, she's beautiful.' Hatsu looked down at her feet and shuffled.

Marina rescued her by pointing at the mirror and calling out, from her 'west' position, to Pippa. 'So what's with the mirror?'

'I'm going to try and look at myself in it. Face my fear of fearing my face.'

'Ah, *frente a frente* — face to face. With both of them being yours?'

'That's right, Marina. But for my first pose, I'm going to keep the mirror covered. With George's lovely Edinburgh scarf.' Pippa knelt down, with her fingertips just touching the top of her knees. She gazed at the map and created a journey from some of the names: Charlotte Square, George Street, Heriot Row, India Street. That last name brought her back to the moment. 'I'll start with this pose.'

'So let's see how this works out.' Pippa stood in front of the mirror. She flicked her hair in such a way that it covered her eyes. Then she revealed, to the artists, the exposed mirror. But before the quartet could set themselves, she turned away. With her head in her hands, she began to sob.

A few moments later, a hand on her right shoulder made her jump, but then smile. 'Thank you, Hatsu. I thought I could do this.'

'Let's have a drink and a snack first. Take a break. You're so brave just to try.'

'Hatsu's right,' Angelique said. 'We all have our own hopes and fears. This feels like a good space to explore them.'

'*Todo el mundo* — everybody needs their own way of dealing with things.'

'So what do you want to do?' Kenesha asked.

Pippa clapped her hands and, with a smile, directed the artists to move their easels next to each other. 'I'm going to give it another go. What's the worst that could happen?' She then moved the mirror, from its central position, to the side of the room. And, after blowing air slowly through her lips, Pippa took up a sideways pose which allowed her to see part of her face. 'Mirror, mirror on the wall, I think I'll give you face time after all.'

Chapter 16

'Hi, I'm Skye Hunter and welcome to *Chatter Broth*. It's November 27th and today's guest is George P Salt. I heard, from Angelique, that your Edinburgh scarf came in useful at the last Life Modelling session.'

'Yes, that piece of printed fabric seems to have a life of its own. Though I've got it back, for now.'

'How are your plans shaping up?'

'They're going well. Warren and I have sorted out all the food side. And I'll be re-opening as GPS Maps in January, when I get back.'

'Where are you off to, George?'

'Rapa Nui, also known as Easter Island. Hatsu and I have been talking about how going there, was the spark for her arriving here. And I've found a link to the island too. A link that I want to explore and see where it goes. And maybe I'll take an instant camera with me. Seeing how seventy years tomorrow, was the first day that Polaroid cameras went on sale. You certainly come up with some interesting historical research. Though nothing to do with Portsmouth, this time, Warren.'

'Thanks, George. So what else has caught your interest In This Fortnight?'

'I know about your fascination with the Great Exhibition. On November 30th, 1936, the Crystal Palace was destroyed by fire. I don't understand how a metal and glass building could catch fire.'

'Nor do I. At least some of it remains. The Coalbrookdale Gates, built as the original entrance in 1851, still separate Kensington Gardens from Hyde Park. And Prince Albert was the president of the Society for Improving the Conditions of the Labouring Classes. I know that's a bit of a mouthful, but the Society's architect designed and constructed a model dwelling. Model, in the sense that it was a template for the future. Prince Albert's Model Cottage, as it was known, had some innovative features. Like damp-resistant hollow bricks and a covered communal staircase. Each flat had its own rubbish chute, a heated airing cupboard, and even an inside toilet. It was seen as too radical by some. Working people having decent housing? Scandalous! So it was constructed next to, not in, Hyde Park. Afterwards, in 1852, it was moved to Kennington. Where it became a museum. The building's still there, though it's now the HQ for a charity promoting the importance of urban trees. And the legacy of the Great Exhibition of the Works of Industry of All Nations continues. Prince Albert used some of the profits to buy 87 acres of land in South Kensington. And to establish centres of culture and education. Institutions that developed to become world famous establishments. Such as the Victoria and Albert Museum, the Natural History Museum, the Science Museum, Imperial College and the Royal Albert Hall. The list goes on . . . I wonder what might have happened if Prince Albert had survived as long as Victoria. His early death from typhoid robbed Britain of one of its greatest ever innovators. The Royal Commission for the Exhibition still exists though, and distributes part of its continuing surplus. Some of which is used to fund one hundred Winston Churchill travelling scholarships every year.'

'That sounds interesting. Maybe Colin and I should apply ourselves. And all because millions of people spent a penny.'

'People *did* pay to use the public toilets, Skye. But good profits were also made from the sale of buns, soft drinks and souvenirs.'

'Moving on, I've got three linked events. Back in 1869, on December 10th, Wyoming gave women the vote. Then, in 1890, the US Congress was negotiating Wyoming's bid to become the 44th state of the Union. One condition was that women should lose their right to vote. Wyoming's response? "We will remain out of the Union one hundred years rather than come in without the women." Congress blinked first. Then, in 1966, the Mini skirt was banned from the Houses of Parliament. Why are so many men so scared of women expressing themselves? Although it's not *just* men. There was an interesting decision made by Knutsford councillors four years ago. On December 4th, they voted to allow the widening of the town's pavements. A certain Lady Jane Stanley, in 1794, had financed the construction of deliberately narrow pavements. So that couples could not walk arm in arm.'

'That sounds harsh, George. Maybe she was a Miss Havisham-type figure, with a twisted heart following romantic rejection.'

'So you did manage to sneak a Portsmouth reference in, by using a Charles Dickens character. Good work, Warren. There are many ways to voice and stage protests. Maybe with individuals, like Rosa Louise Macauley Parks in 1955. It was the first day of December, when she refused to give up her seat. But I'm going to finish with an event from 1781. Listeners might have heard of a British ship called the *Zong*. Sixty of the 440 Africans on board had already died when the captain, for insurance purposes, ordered that 133 slaves should be thrown overboard. At a subsequent court case, Lord Mansfield made the landmark comment that humans were *not* just another form of cargo. Public opinion was, slowly, turning against the legal trade in human beings. Six years later, the Society for the Abolition of the Slave Trade was founded.'

'You're right, George. Protest movements take time and sustained effort I wonder how long it will be before young people achieve success in their environmental protests. You know, with their school strike action.'

'Hopefully sooner rather than later, Skye. But for now, I want to reflect more on the impact of trading in humans. I'm building a deeper understanding of my African heritage. And at the moment, it starts with a Spanish brigantine called the *Trouvadore*. My ancestors, on my mother's side, were taken from Africa in 1841. But the Cuba-bound ship, with its Spanish crew, was wrecked en route. At a place just off the coast of Turks and Caicos called, ironically, Breezy Point. The islands were a British colony, and slavery had become illegal less than a decade earlier. So the 192 Africans who survived the crossing *never* became slaves. They were taken, but never sold. Shackled by the Spanish, then unchained by the British. Were my ancestors ever actually slaves? It's a fine distinction, and one that I'm still trying to get my head round. Whatever they were, my ancestors were not free. Most were forcibly apprenticed to work in the salt ponds for a year. Living in small whitewashed huts with basic facilities. Though they were relatively lucky. Freed Africans in the Bahamas often had to serve *fourteen* years of apprenticeship.'

'I thought that freed slaves were sent to Freetown in Sierra Leone.'

'You're correct, Skye. But only if they were rescued near the coast of Africa. The Royal Navy's anti-slavery patrols captured hundreds of slave ships in the 19th century. And over 150,000 Africans were freed. But if they were freed in the Caribbean, they were sent to Trinidad. Or the Bahamas.'

'But your ancestors were rescued from a wreck. Then set to work making salt. Oh, is that where you got your surname from?'

'Actually no, Warren. My father's mother just happened to marry a Welshman called Mervyn P Salt. In addition to their free labour, the new arrivals had to become Christians and learn English. At the end of the year, most went to live elsewhere on the islands. Many to a place on Middle Caicos called Bambarra.'

'Hence the Bambarra Rum bottles over at M3?'

'That's right, Skye. The 15-year-old is named for the *Trouvadore*, but I prefer the 8-year-old Reserve. Best sipped while listening to some music. Perhaps not "Saltwater" by Julian Lennon. Maybe some Ripsaw, the national music of the Turks and Caicos. I've seen people using a screwdriver to play the handsaw that the musical style is based around.'

'The Carpenters?'

'That's funny, Warren. No, the main man is called Lovey Forbes. I like the music, especially when it's mixed in with some Soca and Reggae. What the locals call 'Combina' music. New traditions are another legacy of the slave trade. Most of the Africans stolen from Africa were young and fit. However, it was usually older people, the elders, who knew all the traditions and rites. And they, the elders, stayed in Africa. And with them, most of their deep knowledge. So the new arrivals had to adapt, as they continue to do so. It's understandable, but many of us take salt for granted these days. Celtic tribes used to pour seawater onto charcoal to produce salt crystals. And in the days before refrigeration and canning, it was crucial. Huge quantities were needed. Two pounds were needed to salt just one pound of fresh cod. And salt was almost the only source of profits on the islands. And you should never put all your salt in one sack.'

'How was the salt produced, George?'

'With difficulty, Skye, but there were some natural advantages. At Salt Cay, most of the land was flooded by the sea twice daily. A combination of stone dams, sluice gates and windmills were used to control water flow. The whole process took about three months, with water being moved between ponds to concentrate the saline content. When it had thickened into a salty slush, it was moved into the drying pans. This is where the product went from being semi-liquid to a crystal form. And, in the early days, the salt crystals were scooped up using conch shells. Oh, I'd love someone to walk in now with a platter of deep-fried conch fritters. When done well, with a lime zest mayo, they're mouth-wateringly tremendous. Maybe I'll write a cookbook, to celebrate Warren taking over the food side of things here at the Hop Yard. *A Pinch of Salt*, perhaps . . . You can still see much of the salt industry infrastructure on Grand Turk, including the tiny whitewashed huts. The raking of the salt did cause confusion back in London, though. The colony's badge used to have two piles of salt on it. These were misidentified by a Whitehall official, who added a door to one of them.'

'A door? And I'd love to help you with the cookbook?'

'Yes, Warren. And thank you for your offer. We'll speak more about it later. The official in London thought the salt was snow, and that the piles were igloos. A Caribbean island group in the Arctic? That's too funny. Unlike the working conditions. Mary Prince was a slave on three of the islands for ten years. This was in the seventy-year period, up to 1834, that slaves were used in the Turks and Caicos. It's lucky my ancestors weren't captured in *that* period. Following Mary's arrival from Bermuda, where she had been born a slave, she was sold for one hundred pounds. The next morning, at 4am, she was set to work in the salt ponds until dusk. When dusk fell, there was further work, such as bagging and loading bushels of salt. I've been to the islands a few times, and sunglasses are essential. Salt, like snow, has a very high albedo effect. That is, the amount of light reflected off a surface. So the salt rakers also developed many eye problems. But Mary didn't give up. On Sunday afternoons, she collected soft reeds to place on the bare wooden bed boards, to provide some comfort from salt boils. She wrote, "*people in England, I am sure, have never found out what is carried on there. Cruel, horrible place!*" And she campaigned for a ban on the sale of slaves in the colonies.'

'How did she manage to get a book published?'

'She was clever, Warren. Her fifth owner, yes her fifth, took her from Antigua to England. He described her as his servant, but she knew that slavery was illegal in Great Britain. So she literally walked away, to freedom. And recounted her story to one Thomas Pringle. He edited out some of the more horrific episodes of her life, before having the book published in 1831. This was as part of the soon-to-be-successful Abolitionist campaign. Strangely, or perhaps not, the word slave was rarely used. Especially in the early years of salt production. One reason was that the first salt rakers were often agricultural workers, kidnapped from Ireland. Another reason was that those salt rakers were indentured for 99 years, not for life. If someone reached a century, and had been taken before the age of one, they could be freed. How generous.'

'Last time, we were looking for words beginning with the letter P. Over to you for the final four, Warren.'

'Thanks, Skye. They are pargeting — I can guess why *that* word was chosen — paternoster, phrontistery and popple:

An ancient building with pargeting.
Or a towering paternoster.
Both had doubled as a phrontistery,
To reduce the popple in her mind.'

'And your thoughts on what meaning there may be, Warren?'
'Well, Skye, does this interpretation make any sense to you?

An ancient building with ornamental plasterwork.
Or a doorless, continuous lift in a tower block.
Both had doubled as a place for thinking,
To cool her boiling mind.

The Hop Yard is a place for thinking, and action as well. As for popple, I've chosen "Hot 'N Cold" by Basement Jaxx. It's about things building up, until they reach boiling point.'

'My suggestion was pandiculation, stretching and yawning. No, don't you two start pandiculating. You're the hosts. I even had a song lined up. "Mid Day Crisis" by Carter USM. Though I don't wake up with a smile on my face, I do like to hop straight out of bed in the morning'

'Good work, George. I'll add it to the Four Play list.'

'Thanks, Warren. This place, the Hop Yard, really is a good place for thinking . . . Maybe I'll go to New York on the way back from Easter Island.'

'Why's that?'

'It links to the *Trouvadore*. Even though it might have been called the *Troubadour*. Which is ironic, as troubadours sang about gallantry and chivalry. The complete opposite of what was happening on *that* ship. The New York connection comes from the aftermath of the shipwreck. A letter from a resident of Grand Turk, sent in 1878, decades later, refers to "*Two African idols, of wood with glass eyes, found on board the last Spanish slaver, wrecked in the year 1841, at Breezy Point on the Caicos Islands*". But the wooden figures weren't from Africa. They were from Easter Island. So how did they end up in the Caribbean? I'm intrigued, and want to know more. Maybe partly because it will allow me to think about my Afro-Caribbean heritage, but at one step removed. The figures are now in New York's Natural History Museum. Though that seems a strange place for ceremonial art.'

'That's a fascinating mystery, George. I used to go with Abigail, India's mother, to the British Museum. The Easter Island moai there was something we were always drawn to. Even though she was convinced it was in the wrong place.'

'That's a good point, Skye. Where is the best place to display artefacts? It's interesting that museums and governments are discussing this complex and emotive issue more. London's moai is called Ho'a Hakananai'a. It's unusual in that it's carved from basalt. Most moai were carved from tuff, which despite its name, is much easier to carve.'

'Talking of intricate design, it must be about fifteen years since Marina stayed at the Ancient House. Surrounded by all that pargeting. It still amuses me that Colin has a surname linked so closely to a Landmark Trust property. And there are a few of them linked to your name, Warren.'

'Such as the Old Windmill at Wagstaffe Worthy?'

'One for the future, maybe. No, Skye, I'm thinking of a trio of Bedfordshire properties. Two of which, on the Old Warden estate there, were built on top of warrens.'

'I haven't been back to Stoker's Cottage, my first 'Landmark'. But I cycle to Wicken Fen three or four times a year.'

'I remember the day you arrived here on your touring bike. You looked a little lost, but at least you had a map. You and Marina have both enjoyed staying in rescued buildings. Landmark Trust ones, and here at the Hop Yard. Zoe was only three, when Marina arrived in Great Britain. Which reminds me of a trip I made in the same year, but to a different place. Colin and I were up in Sheffield to see some snooker at The Crucible. Cue for a song, Warren?'

'Hey, I'm the punslinger round here. You'll put me out of a job, Skye. Which I could chalk down to experience, I suppose. What's the link?'

'Oh, yes. Somehow, but it was after a session at the Fat Cat, we ended up at the University's Arts Tower. Which had a paternoster. I remember that there were lots of rules. Such as a maximum of two people per car and no luggage. Also, a warning that although doing a loop was not dangerous, it was definitely not recommended. And it was so strange, a lift with no doors that you had to hop in and out of. While waiting, I thought I saw Jarvis Cocker glide up, but maybe I was mistaken.'

Chapter 17

'Hi, I'm Skye Hunter and welcome to *Chatter Broth*. It's December 11th and today's guest is Hatsu Akahoshi. Welcome back.'

'Thank you, Skye. And hello, Warren Wagstaffe. People have started to buy into the idea of paying to donate books. And the beds are all sold out for the rest of the month. I've loved talking with George about Easter Island. I hope he finds some of what he's looking for there. It's a special place.'

'And it was a stepping stone to you being here. What has caught your attention from Warren's research?'

'We're in a studio, and there are two interesting events linked to the development of radio. In 1896, on December 12th, Guglielmo Marconi performed the first public demonstration of radio, in London. Then five years later, to the day, he managed the first ever transatlantic radio transmission. From Cornwall to Newfoundland. What an achievement. And there are a couple of events, in this fortnight, linked to a women's prison in London. In mid-December 1913, there were a lot of Suffragettes being held in Holloway Prison. Some of their supporters set off an explosion, at the boundary wall there, using dynamite. A noble cause, but one probably not best served by using a Nobel invention. Then five years later, Countess Markievicz won a Dublin seat for Sinn Fein. She became the first woman elected to the British parliament, though she couldn't take up her seat.

As she was in . . . Holloway Prison.'

'Elected members of her party still don't take their seats in London. I wonder under what circumstances, if any, they might.'

'Good thought, Skye. And while you ponder it, here's "Holloway Girl" by Marillion.'

'There's hope in that song. That if you believe, then one day, your prison door *will* be unlocked. It must be very strange being in prison, but hearing the outside world. I visited Alcatraz once. One of the warders said that prisoners could hear music drifting across the water from San Francisco. The main purpose of my visit had been to visit Manzanar, a Second World War camp in California which had housed US-born Japanese internees.'

'Internment is one of the most complex decisions that a government can make. There was a family living in Peasenham at the start of the same war. Because of their German heritage, the father had been sent to the Isle of Man during World War *One*. The Knockaloe camp there, near Peel, was the largest internment camp in the British Empire. Over 20,000 people were held there. The camp even had its own railway line.'

'Did the same thing happen in the Second World War, Skye?'

'Sort of, Hatsu. The family were sent to the Isle of Man. But this time, they were housed in converted boarding houses. The father was separated from the rest of his family, but things were not as strict. Though there was barbed wire, internees often had the chance to earn money on farms and meet up with their families.'

'Have you been there, Skye?'

'Several times, Warren. And I'll be going back when the new internment museum opens. Some of the World War One internees found themselves being guarded by their British-born children. Can you imagine that? So I'll be going back. To see the museum. But also, to ride the heritage lines, eat Davidson's ice cream, and maybe even spot a wild wallaby.'

'A wallaby?'

'Yes, Hatsu. Some escaped from a zoo there and established themselves. You'd like the island as well, Warren. There's a great food and drink festival, and some great locally-sourced food. One of the chefs, in Port Erin, encourages paddleboarders to pick up seaweed for her. Which she then uses in her foraging menu. I think I told you about her before.'

'You did, Skye. And I adapted her idea at the Field Party. Maybe that Manx chef could get some of the TT riders to scoop up wild garlic, as they lean into sharp bends.'

'I think they might have other things on their minds, like avoiding wallabies. Back to you, Hatsu.'

'I'd love to see a wallaby, especially one living up a tree. Though that sounds unlikely. I love trees. Which is why I wrote down quercine, related to oak, on the M3 noticeboard. Was my suggestion successful?'

'Let's find out. Last time, in Lost Four Words, we were looking for words beginning with the letter Q. Which four made it to the front of the queue, Warren?'

'Ha, ha. They are qanat, quahog, quant and quirley:

As a reward for removing the quahog,
With her newly-acquired quant,
From the narrow qanat,
She was offered a quirley.'

'And your thoughts, Warren?'
'Well, Skye, does this make any sense to you?

As a reward for removing the common edible round clam,
With her new pronged bargepole,
From the narrow irrigation tunnel,
She was offered a hand-rolled cigarette.

Which seems quite a strange reward. So no quercine, Hatsu. But I do have a couple of songs for you, and they're both by Rush. First up, in honour of Marconi, I'll play "Spirit of Radio". Then, as a consolation prize for you, "The Trees".'

'Thanks, Warren. Is that song really about trees? I know it describes the oaks and the maples fighting for light. But isn't it really about people? Who, if anyone, wants to live in the shade?'

'What do you think, Skye?'

'Do famous people really want to live in the spotlight *all* the time? So some light, with shade available, sounds ideal.'

'One fact you researched really surprised me.'

'Which one was that, Hatsu?'

'The decision, in 1979, which forced councils to sell their social housing to any willing tenant. A Housing Bill, introduced on December 20th of that year, might have seemed like Christmas come early for many people. But councils were not allowed to use any of the money recouped, for building replacement properties. How crazy is that? Look at the amount of people who are desperate for even basic housing nowadays. Colin and this community do great things on a small scale, but housing should be a government priority.'

'I totally agree. I lived in a council flat in Portsmouth. My mother refused, on principle, to even discuss purchasing our flat. Even when my step-father had access to a decent amount of money. Holloway Prison actually closed in 2016. There's been talk of the huge site being used for affordable housing. Watch this space. But if it was developed, there might be a microbrewery on the site. Perhaps run by the "Holloway Girl". I'm sure her first brew wouldn't be too bitter, but she might name it with a nod to the past. With a tip of the hat to her previous life. Not Jail Ale. That name's already been taken. Maybe something a bit more subtle, like SKP.'

'SKP? Oh, I get it. Back to you, Hatsu.'

'Strange ideas, like the idea that everyone *has* to own their own home, become almost accepted. And decisions can have unforeseen consequences. But I'm going to finish with three events from December 24th. The first two happened, on the same day in 1914, during World War One. A war in which Japan was allied with Britain, not Germany. Now, many people know about the Christmas Eve truce, when many British Army and German troops laid down their weapons. And exchanged gifts and songs. It must have been difficult to go back to firing at each other a few days later. But it might have been made easier if they had heard about another event. At the same time they were creating a strange version of peace between the trenches, a German plane was flying across the English Channel. When it was over Dover, a single bomb was dropped. No-one was killed, but it must have been shocking. Especially for John Banks. He had been up a tree in the garden of a rectory there. The blast blew him from the tree. Luckily, he wasn't seriously injured. The bomb marked the site of the first ever aerial attack on the British mainland. Strangely, in 1965, Christmas Eve was also the date of one of the largest ever meteorites to land in Britain. It weighed almost fifty kilos. That's almost heavier than I am. The people of Barwell must have thought that Santa's sleigh had crashed.'

'I could play that song about a certain reindeer, but I think I'll return instead to No Man's Land on the Western Front. Here's "All Together Now" by The Farm.'

~

Rapa Nui / Easter Island, 2018

George looked down, once again, at the vast expanse of ocean. Santiago, nestled in the shadow of the Andes, seemed more than just miles away. For the past four hours he had seen nothing down there, except water. No landforms, no ships. 'How did the Polynesians navigate?'

'They preferred to use the stars, but they had daytime techniques as well.'

'Sorry, I was thinking out loud. I'm George.'

'My name is Patricia. I'm a teacher from Copiapo, a mining town in the Atacama desert. But my grand-mother is Rapa Nuian. She married an Irish surveyor from County Clare, though he was born in Java. And they met in Costa Rica. What about you?'

'That's what I'm trying to find out. Though there is a link to Easter Island. Sorry, Rapa Nui.'

'Don't worry, the Easter Island name is also important, as it marks the first contact with Europeans. The Spanish name for the island is Isla de Pascua. Which is a little strange, as *La Pascua* is not specific to Easter. For instance, *Felices Pascuas* means Merry Christmas.'

'And festive greetings to you too, Patricia. I'm interested in maps and charts. So can you tell me more about navigation?'

'The skills were based on being able to see beyond the horizon. Not literally, but by using clues. Such as the direction flown by birds at dusk. Or the type of vegetation floating on the ocean's surface. Cloud formations could indicate the presence of yet unseen islands. Rapa Nui was first settled perhaps 1500 years ago. Before New Zealand, but after Hawaii. The *ahu moai* phase began about a thousand years ago.'

'That's interesting. The carved moai figures on their *ahu*, the ceremonial platforms, are rightly renowned. But I'm more interested in the wooden moai — the *kavakava* figures. A pair was found on a shipwreck in the Caribbean. A shipwreck which my ancestors survived.'

'The *Trouvadore?*'

'Yes. I'm shocked to hear someone else mention it.'

'I've heard about that ship at the Anthropological Museum on the island. They've got some wonderful artefacts there, including various wooden figures. Not just the type you're interested in, with their elongated features and visible ribcages — *kavakava* means ribs. But also, the curvier *moai tangata*. The word *tangata* means masculine, but female and animal forms were also produced. You should visit the museum, but not tomorrow, as it's closed on Mondays.'

'I've heard the word *tangata* before, in relation to the birdman cult.'

'Yes, that was known as *tangata manu*, the *manu* part referring, slightly confusingly, to the bird. The cult, based at Orongo ceremonial village, was seen as a replacement for the colossal task of constructing huge stone moai. But the moai in the British Museum, taken from Orongo, has birdman carvings on the back. That's why Ho'a Hakananai'a is so important.'

'Should it be returned?'

'I don't know whether it should be. Though I think, in the next few decades, it will be. Much of our culture, including the stone-carved petroglyphs and cave paintings, is vulnerable. And funding is always too little. Even so, some tourists complain about the $80 National Park access fee. One tourist said that for that amount they could visit all the US National Parks for a year.'

'I think the fee is fair, perhaps even too low.'

'That's good, George. Tourism is very important to the island. For employment, but also to provide funds for research and conservation. There is still so much to be discovered.'

'Like what, Patricia?'

'Jacob Roggeveen, on Easter Sunday, 1722, was the first known European to visit Rapa Nui. Clan warfare had already increased by then, but most of the moai were still standing on their *ahu*. By the time of Captain Cook's arrival, in 1774, most had been toppled. And they were all down by the 1860s. But maybe not all due to human intervention. The great tsunami of 1960 caused massive damage. Perhaps previous events, such as earthquakes, caused some of the topplings.'

'I have a friend called Hatsu. She comes from the Japanese city where the crane company that organised the initial restoration is based. Some of her family were involved, and she has visited. We've talked about the island a lot. It seems to have some sort of magnetic pull.'

'Maybe it does. Perhaps even literally. So back to the moai. They have eye cavities. Only moai placed on their *ahu* had these sockets. So they must have been carved at the sites. And eyes are very powerful, so would have been a massively symbolic final touch. The first eye fragments, made from coral and red scoria, were found in 1978. So as you can see, more research is needed.'

'Including on how the moai were moved? Some of them weigh over 50 tons.'

'Yes, and not all the theories involve trees. Captain Cook wrote . . . Let me just find the quote in my notebook. Yes, here it is. He wrote that he and his crew, "*could hardly conceive how these islanders, wholly unacquainted with any mechanical power, could raise such stupendous figures*". My favourite theory, proposed by a Czech engineer called Pavel Pavel, was based on *walking* the moai. By tilting them from side to side. An idea that fits in with some oral traditions. There are still hundreds of moai, mainly unfinished, at the main Rano Raraku quarry. But there are almost one hundred that were abandoned, en route to their *ahu*. Perhaps they tipped over and couldn't be raised again.'

'So the trees weren't all cut down for use as rollers?'

'Maybe some were. Captain Cook also wrote about not finding a single tree on the island. Indeed, he was distinctly under-impressed with the supply side of things. He wrote, "*No nation need contend for the honour of the discovery of this island, as there can be few places which afford less convenience for shipping than it does . . . Nature has been exceedingly sparing of her favours to this spot*". Captain Cook couldn't even get the islanders to agree on the proper name for the island. Three suggestions offered were Tamareki, Teapy and Whyhu. Though he wrote that the local sweet potatoes were the best he'd ever tasted. And he learned that the word moai meant burying, or sleeping, place.'

'The *Trouvadore* was wrecked in 1841. So contact was increasing.'

'That's correct, George. There was another explorer, thirty years after that, but still relevant I think. He wrote under the pseudonym of Pierre Loti. The island certainly had an impact on him. I have some notes about him too . . . He wrote, "*there exists in the midst of the great ocean, in a region where nobody goes, a mysterious and isolated island* ". But what might interest you is that each islander he met offered him a "*shapeless idol* ". So there was trade, or barter, in the wooden moai. Maybe that's how your figures ended up in the Caribbean. Having passed through many hands.'

'Trade and exchange has always been a driver of the world economy. Not all contact was aggressive.'

'No, though on Rapa Nui it became increasingly destructive. During the 1800s, islanders had been forcibly removed in small numbers. But in 1862, Peruvian slave traders took one and a half thousand people away. That is, almost half of the islanders. Many of them were forced to work mining guano, aka bird excrement. A very strange, but lucrative, kind of white gold. And the Rapa Nuians were struck down by many diseases. A year later, only a dozen managed to return. But they carried smallpox with them.'

'My ancestors were also forced to work for a year, but producing salt. Another strange kind of white gold.'

'Salt and bird droppings. What kind of world do we live in? Back to the mining, and it was not only lives that were lost. So was a key part of the ceremonial culture. Those who knew how to translate the *rongo-rongo* scripts had all died. That two-part word means to recite or chant out. Historians are still not sure whether it was even a day-to-day language. And, unlike the Rosetta Stone, it still hasn't been deciphered. If only Ada Lovelace or Alan Turing had been let loose on it.'

'Which makes the moai in *Night at the Museum* rather poignant. The only thing he said to the Ben Stiller character was "Dum dum".'

'Ah, film culture. One of the best dive sites here is in Hanga Roa Bay. The subterranean moai there is actually a replica from a Kevin Costner film.'

'Let me guess. *Dances with Moai? Ahu of Dreams?*'

'No, just *Rapa Nui*. Don't tell anyone, George, but I'm quite fond of the film. You should see it if you get the chance. And I recommend you go to a show while you're here. My favourite dance group is called Haha Varua. Some people say they're not traditional enough. But I love their moves and energy. And what is *traditional* anyway? Cultures have to adapt, or they become dusty.'

'I couldn't agree more.'

'Oh, and you'll love the food at the show they put on, too. After a taster of ceviche, washed down with a pisco sour, you get a feast. The main ingredients are baked *Umu Pae*-style, in a covered pit. But don't eat too much. You might get asked up on the stage by some of the dancers.'

'That's unlikely, but everything else sounds good. Do they also serve beers, Patricia? A good friend of mine runs a micropub, and I said I'd do some research for her.'

'That's very generous of you, George. I'm not sure if you can get it at the dance show, but Cervecería Mahina brew a couple of beers. My favourite is their Porter, but you might prefer the Pale Ale. Why not try them both? For research, obviously. Maybe we could— ooh, there it is. Can I lean over you, so that I can see it better?'

George carefully positioned his body, to let Patricia get closer to the window. 'That looks like a volcanic crater.'

'Yes, that's Rano Kau, which is next to Orongo. And there's Mataveri Airport, with Hanga Roa just behind it. I hope you enjoy the island and find what you're looking for.'

'It's been lovely spending time with you. I know we've just met, but would you mind holding my hand as we come into land. I get a bit nervous.'

'No problem. Just don't squeeze too hard if things get a bit bumpy.'

Chapter 18

George had found it difficult to sleep. However, in compensation, he had also managed to fit in some rather interesting dreams. Most of them set in a flamingo-heavy desert oasis in Chile. A woman there had been staring at a lump of copper in the road. Like the copper, she was mainly bluey-green. Unlike the copper, she had purple eye shadow and breasts made from pimento-stuffed olives. But then a car from the Paris-Dakar Rally, with an icebox on its roof, had flown past — surely that wasn't right? — and he had woken up with a start.

After a cold shower, he walked from his hotel down towards the coast. A sign with the word *Tahai* on it was just visible in the post-dawn light. And then in the distance, he saw them. A group and an individual. And as he walked nearer, the individual became more distinct. Like most moai, it faced inwards. And this one wore a red hat. And had eyes. Which could not see the approaching cruise ship passing—

'It's just a drive-by, so to speak. A lot of the ships don't actually put passengers ashore here.'

George glanced sideways, and saw the voice's owner. She was smiling, although most of her face was lost in a mass of curls. 'It's my first time on the island. In fact, I only arrived yesterday. But it sounds as if you're more of an expert.'

'I wouldn't say that. Experts first need to understand the big picture. And this island is so full of mysteries. Take the *pukao* —

the red hats. They're made of red scoria and come from the Puna Pau quarry. And were probably quite easy to roll. But how were they carved so accurately? And are they really hats, or actually symbolic top-knots?'

'Mysteries take time to unravel. There's a place near where I live in Suffolk. The owner used to stare at the mounds on her estate—'

'Are you talking about Sutton Hoo and the discovery of a funeral ship?'

'I am. Have you been?'

'Many years ago, with a friend of the family called Colin. So which part of Suffolk are you from?'

George smiled. Here he was, on a remote island in the Pacific, and his map-loving mind was focused on East Anglia. 'It's a place inland from Southwold and RSPB Minsmere. Just off the A1120, heading for Stowmarket.'

'I know that area. Sort of. I have connections in a village between Swefling and Laxfield. Have you heard of Peasenham?'

George snorted, and then quickly rejected the idea that the nearest moai had just glanced quizzically at him. 'I live and work there, at a place called the Hop Yard. My name's George P Salt. And you are?'

'My name's India. India Farr.'

~

George pulled open the door of M3. Ah, that welcoming creak . . . He heard Angelique and Warren talking to Marina at the bar. A few other people were settled around the wood-burning stove.

'Great to see you,' Angelique said, as she wrapped her arms around him.

'And there's a place with your name on it, for lunch

tomorrow,' Warren added.

Despite the cold, George was touched by the warmth of his welcome. It was like coming home. Maybe this place *was* home. 'India's in the Pacific.'

No one in M3 responded to George's statement.

'India,' George repeated, 'is on an island in the Pacific Ocean.'

'And you're supposed to be a Geographer,' Marina said. She nodded towards the world map on the ceiling, while topping up a golden pint of Oakham's Citra IPA.

George smiled and adjusted his black leather baseball cap. 'You're right Marina. I'm talking about India Farr, Zoe's mother. I met her last week. She is, or at least recently was, on Easter Island. In the Pacific.'

'*Asombrosa,*' Marina said. 'That's amazing. Colin drove Zoe to the hospital early this morning. There's a chance the transplant team might have found a suitable kidney for her. Though she's only the reserve.'

'What do you mean?'

'Zoe's the backup. She's there in case the donated kidney isn't a good match for the primary recipient. Can we speak about this later?'

'Of course, Marina. Oh, and Merry Christmas for tomorrow.'

'And *Felices Pascuas* to you as well, George.'

Marina watched as George walked across the yard to his shop, and smiled as he paused to check out the H Van's latest menu. She put her elbows on the bar and rested her chin on her knuckles. Then noticed that she had put on odd socks underneath her wellies. Marina felt sick, excited and empty. She looked up at the map again and placed India. In the Pacific, yes, but surely needed back in Europe? What could she—

'It's great to have George back,' Warren said. 'Hatsu will be so excited. They'll have so much to talk about.'

'And how about George and India,' Angelique said. 'I'd love to hear how they met.'

The door creaked open again, and a well-wrapped figure entered M3.

'I think we should let India know what's happening,' Marina said. 'You know, with her daughter.'

As she finished her sentence, she became aware of the identity of the new arrival.

'It was nineteen years ago tonight that I became pregnant with Zoe.'

~

'Hi, I'm Skye Hunter and welcome to *Chatter Broth*. It's December 25th and today's guest is George P Salt. The last twenty-four hours have certainly been interesting. Have you had a chance to unpack?'

'Not yet, Skye. I'm still finding my bearings.'

'How was your trip?'

'It was good, Warren. I felt a strong affinity to Easter Island, and not just because of the wooden moai. There's a strange atmosphere there, of loss and of hope. Of finding a new way forward, while still learning from past events and newly discovered artefacts. And then there was India. I'd heard about her, but she'd always been in the background. Like an undercurrent, or a ripple. So to spend time with her, on the island and in the States, was—'

'You met her in the USA, as well?'

'That's right, Warren. I stayed with her for a few days in Beacon last week, while she finished sorting out her latest project. It was handy for New York, even though I didn't get to see the *kavakava* figures. Another time, perhaps. I thought she'd flown back to Easter Island, but obviously she didn't.'

'I'd never met her until last night. We didn't talk much, as I wanted to spend time with Zoe. As it turned out, the primary recipient *was* a good match for the donor's kidney. So Zoe stayed on the substitute's bench, if you like. She had some counselling, but she's still quite upset. Though she said she was looking forward to Christmas lunch.'

'By the way, how many place settings will there be, Warren?'

'Let's see. There's the three of us. Plus Angelique, Seth, Kenesha and Hatsu. Then Zoe. That's eight. Not forgetting India, Pippa and Richard. That could be interesting. And Colin, of course. Plus a couple of spare places for *other* unexpected guests. And don't worry. Celeriac doesn't appear in every course. Just three of the four.'

'That was "Uninvited Guest" by Marillion. When a stranger comes riding into town, things change. And often in unexpected ways. Although such people can *sometimes* bring a positive spark to the party.'

'Now, now, Warren. Play fair. We all arrived in Peasenham unannounced. I was evacuated and George cycled in on that August day. You turned up with a rucksack and a shy smile. And look at us now. Shall we move on?'

'You're right, Skye. What have you got for us In This Fortnight, George?'

'I've chosen nine events, so I'm sure we'll hear at least one rumbling stomach by the end. In 1675, three days after Christmas, the British parliament voted to close every coffee shop. MPs saw them as hotbeds of gossip. And in 1887, on December 30th, another group tried to limit gatherings. This time it was women trying to ban the Sunday opening of pubs. So a petition, with over a million signatures, was delivered to Queen Victoria. Then on New Year's Eve, but back in 1795, the window tax came into effect. You can still see thousands of bricked-up windows in every county.'

'I wonder what they, the MPs, would have made of *Chatter Broth*.'

'Oh, I'm sure podcasts would also have been treated with suspicion, Skye. Had the broadcasting technology existed at that time. Moving on, the first all-iron bridge in the world, at Ironbridge, was opened to traffic on January 1st, 1781. What an event that must have been. Though the River Severn coracle men, who had operated a ferry service, were probably not so impressed. And the structure was forged at Coalbrookdale, where the gates were made for the—'

'Great Exhibition! I'd love to visit that area and explore the industrial heritage.'

'It's a wonderful place, Warren. I went with Colin, back in the 1970s. Just before the Landmark Trust opened a property there, overlooking the bridge. I'll look into availability for early next year. There's a double room, and Colin and I could share the twin. We'd been thinking what we could buy you as a present.'

'That would be wonderful. Thank you so much.'

'And if you go, Skye, I'll give you a bottle of beer from Burton. The Bass Brewery there registered the first British trade mark, a Pale Ale label, which included its iconic red triangle, on New Year's Day, 1876. And January 2nd was an interesting day. Louis Daguerre, in 1839, took the first photo of the moon. The light side of it. Then there were two arrests, fifty years apart. In 1932, Mahatma Gandhi was arrested for "*good and sufficient reasons*". Then, fifty years later, Erica Roe ran topless during a rugby match at Twickenham.'

'I remember that, George. The policeman's helmet came in quite handy. I wonder how people move on from events like that.'

'It's a different scenario, Skye. But Kim Wilde is now well

known as a gardener. I think she must get a lot of satisfaction from having dug out a new career. I don't know. It's just a feeling, Skye.'

'You're right, George. We often have an idea about someone. Yet they've moved on. And we haven't . . . What was your next event?'

'Let me take you back to 1066. The year had started well for Harold Godwin. The Anglo-Saxon council, the Witan, had chosen him to be the new king. His coronation, on January 6th, was stitched into the Bayeux Tapestry. As was his death on Senlac Hill, later that year. Although it was probably Harald *Hardrada*, defeated by Harold at Stamford Bridge, who was killed by an arrow to his eye. However it happened, Harold's death was violent. Only his widow, Edith Swan-Neck, was able to identify his dismembered body. By recognising certain marks, known only to her. Only two other English kings, both called Richard, have died on the battlefield. The Lionheart at Chalus, and Richard III at Bosworth Field.'

'I need to check the roast vegetables. I can't imagine what it would really be like to have to fight in a battle. But many people have written and sung about it. So here's "Brothers in Arms" by Dire Straits.'

'You're back just in time, Warren. Last time, we were looking for words beginning with the letter R. So what are the final four?'

'Thanks, Skye. They are ramfeezled, rongo-rongo, rotometer and rupestrian:

Rupestrian research took her to new heights.
Despite using a rotometer,
The hike to the crater left her unexpectedly ramfeezled.
And mist still covered the rongo-rongo.'

'And your thoughts on what meaning there may be, Warren?'
'Well, Skye, does this interpretation make any sense to you?

Rock art research took her upwards.
Despite using a wheeled map-measurer,
The volcanic hike left her surprisingly exhausted.
And mist still covered the undeciphered Rapa Nuian script.'

'Sounds like something that India might have written. On Easter Island. I was talking to her about stone-carved petroglyphs last week. And she borrowed my rotometer up at Orongo, near a volcanic crater. Which was revealed when the mist cleared.'

'Is he right, Skye? Did India write that poem? Or even *all* of the poems?'

'I couldn't possibly comment, Warren. Did you have a favourite word, George?'

'I would have selected rotometer. But also rogitate, to ask repeatedly. Have you got a song for either of those, Warren?'

'I think "Crack the Shutters" by Snow Patrol would be appropriate. Though the rotometer is replaced by fingers, mapping the heights and depths of a lover's body.'

'That reminds me of—'

'The song's about to start, Skye.'

'Pause it please, Warren. I'm thinking about a scene from *The History Boys*, not *my* history. The boys had been reading up on the Western Front. Dakin, played in the film version by Dominic Cooper, is talking to Scripps. About the rebuffed advance on his girlfriend's body. Who had allowed him to go over the top, but had halted his advance. Before he reached her "No Man's Land". Very amusing. I loved the theatre version, too. As you were, Warren.'

'I'll play the Snow Patrol song, followed by "Just Who Is the Five O'clock Hero" by The Jam. In which Paul Weller sings about a worker who's ramfeezled. And that double Four Play, will give me time to check on my avocado and celeriac mix.'

'For the starter?'

'No, George. It's the base for the ice cream that I'm serving with the plum pudding.'

Chapter 19

Life Modelling at the Hop Yard #4

India gave a nod to Warren, indicating that she was happy with the arrangements.

'Is it correct, Ms Farr, that you don't want the curtains drawn?'

'Indeed it is, and thank you Warren. But please call me India. The natural light is perfect for today's Life Model class.'

'Well, if you're sure, Ms Fa— India, and we are due for a cloudburst...'

'If people wanted to peer through the windows, I don't think rain would stop them.'

'I suppose not. Do you need anything else?'

'That's a good question. Thanks again for preparing that festive feast. It held things together, on what could have been a tricky day. And those celeriac soufflés were amazing. I know you're a bit wary of me, and I understand that. But I know that you've really helped Zoe as well.'

'I'm just getting my head round things. I don't really understand why you're here, but Zoe doesn't seem to mind. It was interesting seeing how she looked at you and Richard during the meal.'

'It's only the second time we've met. And the first time was mainly spent watching each other ping table tennis balls at each other. As for Richard, Zoe hadn't seen much of him in her life, and had never seen us together. I was impressed with Pippa.'

'So was I. She helped me finish off dishes, remove dirty plates and quenelle the ice cream. All without any fuss. Which reminds me, I need to get back to the H Van. George is helping me for one last time today, before I fully take over the food side of things.'

India watched him go, a young man finding his way in life. He was someone who cared deeply for Zoe and the community he lived in. India didn't really dwell on the past. For her, guilt was just another word in the dictionary. Nevertheless, India felt a slight rumbling in her stomach. And she didn't think it was just food-related. She was tempted to leave, to just bunker down in Marylebone. It wasn't only about Zoe. There were so many relationships at the Hop Yard that needed to be nurtured. But something had shifted, something that needed to be dealt with. Here in Peasenham, not remotely at Pershore Place Mews.

A sharp patter of raindrops brought India back to the present. The stage was set, yet India felt nervous about how the artists might respond. But she often felt nervous, whether before a long journey, during a three-point turn, or in a room full of people she knew. India peered across the yard and noticed people sheltering under the H Van's awning.

'Right,' Hatsu said, 'apart from Angelique, I think we're all here. She's just finishing up in the studio. I'll give her a wave . . . Excellent, she's pointing to the hall and nodding. OK, let's make a run for it. Bye, George.'

'Hey, India,' Angelique said. 'It's just the five of us today. Skye is planning her podcast, and you can probably imagine why Zoe decided to duck out. And not just because it was her mother's turn to be the life model. Oh, and we got you a ginger tea, to warm you up before you disrobe.'

'Actually, Angelique, I knew about Zoe and so I've decided to shake things up a bit,' India said. 'As you are all quite wet already, *you* might as well strip off. I'll remain clothed, in my dungarees and flip-flops. You, the artists, can draw in the nude.'

'Ooh, I like that idea,' Pippa said. 'Is that why there are partitions on the stage? To conceal our nudity? Rather cheeky, but marvellous. Come on girls, choose your spaces.'

Kenesha, with a shake of her head, jogged up to the stage and elegantly jumped into the middle space. The others used the side steps.

When India looked around, she could see the artists, starting with Pippa on the left, nearest to the north-facing window. She then turned towards the rain-splashed window.

Pippa Luscombe put down her white handbag, then undid her thin leather belt. This released her shiny short-sleeved olive blouse. She then took off her lemon-yellow dress and folded it on the back of the chair. After taking off her unreasonably priced — but reasonably practical — heels, she unrolled her sheer hold-up stockings and pulled her chestnut hair back over her shoulders.

Angelique Vonk took off all but one of her silver rings. Then pulled her black jumper dress off, in one deceptively simple movement. It was tricky to see them on her dress, but she managed to remove a few long hairs from the shoulders and back of it. She then kicked off her clogs before removing her black knickers.

Kenesha Baxter unclipped the pedometer from her running shorts and loosened the Velcro on her trainers. She then carefully placed her pop socks, undies and white sports bra on top of her neatly folded vest.

Hatsu Akahoshi hung up her grey woollen mid-length coat on a peg. She took off her two-tone court shoes, unzipped her miniskirt and then pulled her leggings down. After removing her *katsura* — her wig — she pulled her grey polo neck up over her almost hairless head. She then unlaced her silk camisole and used her thumbs to ease off her French knickers. Then she replaced her wig.

In the final partition, Marina Rueda firmly massaged her shoulders. Then pulled off her wellies and thick socks, and wriggled out of her boiler suit. She then undid the four hooks on the back of her turquoise bra and popped the non-matching briefs into one of its cups.

'I think we'll leave it there.' The hour had flown, though not as a crow flies. More like the freestyle loops and spins of a swallow. A restless swallow that had become detached from its kind. India had found it interesting posing. With her back to the artists. Not seeing their nudity, but perhaps not revealing much of herself either. It would be interesting to see what they had produced. Detail and strong strokes, hopefully. But maybe the results would be a little bit sketchy.

After the artists had dressed, Hatsu asked Pippa to help straighten her wig.

Moving into position behind Hatsu's chair, Pippa snagged her leg on an exposed nail. 'Oh botherboots, I've got a ladder in my stocking.'

'That's not a ladder,' whispered Hatsu. 'That's a stairway to heaven.'

'Hatsu, I think you might have a crush on me. But not as big as the crush I have on Richard. And he needs me, now, more than ever.' *Though it's a pity that you and I didn't meet up a few years ago.*

~

'Hi, I'm Skye Hunter and welcome to *Chatter Broth*. It's January 8th, so Happy New Year to everyone. Today's guest is Colin Pargeter. I must say those purple trousers suit you.'

'I should hope so, Skylark, especially as you gave them to me early. In time for my 85th birthday tomorrow. And as we're talking of presents, I've booked a couple of Landmarks.'

'Two, Colin?'

'That's right. I booked the Ironbridge one for Warren and us, as you suggested. For four nights at the end of the month. Then I noticed there was some late availability for the Martello Tower, just over near Aldeburgh. So I grabbed that one as well. For this weekend. Thought it would be a good place to take India and Zoe. You know, let the coastal breezes do their thing. And Marina's always wanted to stay there. You're allowed two guests as well. To visit, but not to stay. P'raps you might want to visit with Angelique, Warren?'

'That sounds great, Colin. Two Landmarks in a month will really get the year started. Then I can focus on Veg Out, though that's just a working title.'

'Knowing you, it won't involve lying on a chaise longue.'

'Just the opposite, Skye. I've made a list of local people who might enjoy me cooking them a meal. Especially people who don't get out much. Like young carers or people with mobility issues. I can use the surplus fresh produce that we get in, and then take it out.'

'Good chap. I remember you talking about those homes that Prince Albert helped to promote. Maybe you could call it Warren Wagstaffe's Model Mobile Meals.'

'Thanks, Colin. I want to serve good, honest food. But your suggested name? That's a bit of a mouthful. Ho, ho. For now, let's move on with Lost Four Words. Skye?'

'Last time, we were looking for words beginning with the letter S.'

'That's right. The final four are scaffy, schwoomph, scollop and scopa:

In the breeze, it didn't take her much effort
To schwoomph,
But the scaffy,
Used a just-found scollop,
To moor the scopa deck.'

'And your thoughts, Warren?'
'Well, Skye, does this make sense to you?

In the breeze, it didn't take her much effort
To flick her hair over one eye,
But the street-sweeper,
Used a just-found thatching peg,
To stop the Italian playing cards from blowing away.

I wonder if Lady Godiva did a schwoomph, when she rode through the streets of Coventry.'

'At first, I thought the scaffy was using a scallop — not a scollop — as a makeshift paperweight. What about you, Colin?'

'Me too, Skye. My suggestions were selion, a ridge between two furrows. And sukey, a kettle. Shall I get a brew on?'

'The usual for me. What about you Warren?'

'Oh, a white miso soup, please.'

'Sukey sounds quite soothing. Selion makes me think of the fields around here. And of other things too. I remember one lazy afternoon in Riga. It wasn't just the Art Nouveau district that I was exploring. There was also a rather delicious—'

'Time for some more Four Play, I think. First up, it's "Body Talks" by The Struts, featuring Kesha. The woman in the song certainly knows how to schwoomph.'

'And that second song was "Dignity" by Deacon Blue. A song about a scaffy with a secret. A secret that floated his boat. Or at least the dinghy he dreamt of. They're a band I'd love to see live. They played at the Portsmouth Guildhall last year, but I found out too late. I'm sure they'll play there again though. I heard it was a rousing night. For now, what have you got for us In This Fortnight, Colin?'

'I'll start with my birthday, Warren. Now, Jean Blanchard was a clever chap. He invented the parachute. Which was quite useful as, in 1793, he completed the first hot-air balloon flight in the USA. Another pioneer was my hero, Ernest Shackleton. On the same day, in 1909, he decided to turn back just 11 miles short of the South Pole. Maybe Captain Scott should have done the same thing. When *he* reached there, three years later, he wrote, "*Great God, this is an awful place*". Maybe he'd have thought differently if Amundsen hadn't got there first. And talking of ice, it was in this fortnight, in 1814, that the last Frost Fair was held on the River Thames. What a sight that would have been. Much more spectacular than John Hetherington's top hat. Though that caused quite a stir in 1797. He wore the first one and was fined £50 for causing a disturbance. Back to my birthday, and in New York there was excitement on the streets in 1902. Too much, possibly, as flirting in public was banned. How did the cops enforce that law? And six years later, smoking in public was banned there, but just for women. Why not for everyone? I'm on a roll now, but don't worry, just a couple more things.'

'You carry on, Colin. We're impressed with your energy and passion. Not bad for one of the *older* surviving evacuees.'

'Thanks, young vackee! It was four years ago that some

interesting memory loss research came out. Now, we went through a lot with Abigail. 'Specially as she developed memory loss when she was only in her twenties. So this team of scientists announced that the brains of older people only *appear* to slow down. That their brains become full.'

'So they have to dump more recent memories?'

'That's right, Warren. It seems that our brains are like hard drives. Only we can't defragment them, like we can a computer's hard drive. When our brains are full, we can only delete memories, and more recent memories are the easiest to access for deletion. The lead doctor, Michael Ramscar, said, "the brains of older people do not get weak. On the contrary, they simply know more". Now, I've had more than a few warning signs. Like triple-checking that I've locked a door. Or putting towels in the dishwasher. So I await new research and treatments with interest.'

'At least you haven't been putting plates in the washing machine, Colin. Memory loss isn't something that's going to go away. Some of my customers come and ask for the same thing they had yesterday. And the day before that. That's one of the reasons I'm going out from the Hop Yard.'

'You should talk to India. A lot of her clients were people with Alzheimer's, or their relatives had it.'

'Maybe, Skye. I feel a bit awkward with her. I'll see what Zoe says when I meet up with her later. She's out on a walk with Kenesha at the moment. Nothing too strenuous, but it's good for both of them. They've become quite close, and they're both trying to sort out their future lives.'

'As much as anyone can, Warren.'

Chapter 20

Marina's entry in The Martello Tower Logbook, 2019

Over a hundred Martello towers were built during the Napoleonic invasion threat in the early 1800s. This one, 'CC', was at the northern end of the defensive line. Though a fort, the presence of oak and teak in the interior gives more of a naval feeling. The spirit is of a ship, tethered to the coast. A very different 'ship' to a house called Naulakha, in Vermont.

Much of the surrounding coast has been eroded away. The tower is the only structure, in the former village of Slaughden, which has survived the North Sea's gales and high tides. All the other houses have been taken by *las olas* — the waves. But it was built to last. The structure, using over a million bricks, was designed so that cannonballs would bounce off the walls. And, like any major infrastructural scheme, there were complaints about the cost. Especially after the invasion threat had passed.

William Cobbett wrote, '*Here has been the squandering! Here has been the pauper-making!*' However, the tower still had a military role to play. It was used as a semaphore (signalling) post in World War One. Semaphore comes from the Greek words for sign and light. And that sense is retained in the Spanish word for traffic lights — *los semáforos*.

During World War Two, the tower was fitted with anti-aircraft guns. Some Aldeburgh locals claim that shots were fired in anger, well over a century after construction. But the inter-war years sound the most interesting. Another Aldeburgh local liked to scare off lovers, searching for '*sensual space*', with his penny whistle. Then a family bought it from the MoD to use as a monumental beach hut. A later owner, Miss Debenham, had a penthouse added on the roof. I would have liked to have attended one of her cocktail parties. Martello mojitos, perhaps.

And this moated tower is rather odd. It has a drawbridge, but half the moat is missing. So access from the sea side is less restricted. While reading Pat Barker's *Regeneration* — a key scene from it is set here — in the sitting room, I heard a noise at the window (I had decided not to close the wooden shutters). Like moths drawn to light, a family (armed with small stones) was peering up at me. They gestured to the other side of the tower, and I met them at the drawbridge gate. They wanted to pop in for a quick look. Here's a rough outline of what followed:

Jeremy: 'Hello there. What a great place. And you're so lucky to have such a calm, sunny day in January. I'm Jeremy. We'd love to see the view from the top. Me, Tessa and the kids.'

Tessa: 'Just for a few minutes. We'll be gone before you know it. Although if we could have our picnic up there, that would be tremendous.'

Jeremy: 'Could you hurry up and unlock the gate?'

Me (Marina): 'I have a key. But this is a holiday rental, not a museum.'

Tessa: 'That's even better. You're bound to have some ice.'

Me: 'We're only allowed two guests, and there are six of you.'

Tessa: 'That would ruin the picnic. But we could come up in pairs, I suppose.'

Me: 'We already have a guest, and are expecting another.'

Jeremy: 'What a load of piffling tripe. You could fit fifty people in there. So selfish.'

Me: 'Our second guest has arrived.'

Angelique: 'Hello, Marina. What a place. Warren dropped me off in Aldeburgh. I've brought some extra goodies, including pistachio macaroons.'

Tessa: 'I hope you really have been invited, as there's a very mean guest list in operation.'

Elder Daughter: 'Can we go now? We can have our picnic at Dunwich. There are other places I could see an Antony Gormley sculpture.'

Angelique: 'Oh, I would have loved to have seen that, too. But it was only here for a year.'

And the oddness continues inside. Most Martello towers have a central brick column to support the roof. But this one has a curved ceiling. Tales from the logbook tell of epic battles against drips during rainy weather. Clay pots, pans, and even a wellington boot were used as makeshift water collectors. It's dry now, with a log-burning stove making the space rather cosy.

But the curve of the roof creates an unusual acoustic effect. For these, like some others (for example, at St Paul's or in Bologna), are whispering walls. A conversation from one side of the room can be heard on the other side. But *not* by a person standing in the middle. So be careful when you speak. You never know *what* might be overheard.

Marina Rueda, Peasenham, Suffolk

~

'Hi, I'm Skye Hunter and welcome to *Chatter Broth*. It's January 22nd and today's guest is Marina Rueda. What's hopping at M3?'

'Hola, Skye. And thanks for driving us to Aldeburgh, Warren. I hope you enjoy your first *stay* in a Landmark Trust property next week. We don't have any hoppy beers at the moment. Though I'd love to taste some SKP. It took me a while to work that one out. The pun almost escaped me, but then I read the letters out loud . . . Which leads me to a late-January day in 1935. The first ever can of beer was sold on that day in Richmond, Virginia. For decades, bottles were still seen as a superior product, but things are changing. Most of our take-out beers are now canned, rather than bottled. Richmond is an interesting city, with some great museums. One of my favourite museum exhibits is a 3-D installation of a sailing ship and what look like wicker baskets of salt. I'll have to talk to George about that. Maybe there's something for him there. I was also taken by a painting of a woman carrying a basket of tropical fruit. Mmm, ripe mangoes. And there's some great street art. On my first visit, I was looking for a bar made from a fire truck. I didn't find it, that time, but I did come across a magnificent flying woman. She was fragmented, but sort of together too. And longer than the GRTC bus I was riding on. Nearby is the NPS's Civil War National Battlefield at Petersburg. Many people associate the start of trench warfare with World War One. But take a look at some of those photos from 1864, a full half century earlier, and you get a different picture. I'm rattling on. Can you take over,

Skye?'

'That's a core part of *Chatter* Broth. Taking thoughts in different directions. But let's pause In This Fortnight and start Lost Four Words. Last time, we were looking for words beginning with the letter T. Ooh, that makes me feel thirsty. What are the final four, Warren?'

'Thanks, Skye. I'll put a brew. Tea before the T's, so to speak. The final four are tacouba, taradiddle, tiffle and tosher:

Tiffling was losing its appeal,
When a passing tosher,
Directed her to the nearest tacouba.
Complete taradiddle?'

'And your thoughts, Warren?'
'Well, Skye, does this make any sense to you?

Pottering about aimlessly was losing its appeal,
When a passing treasure hunter
— of the kind most often found searching in sewers —
Directed her to the nearest bridge
— in fact, a tree that had fallen across the river.
Complete nonsense?'

'Maybe it is, Warren. While we think about that, I think a spot of Four Play, linked to tiffling, is required. Can you play "Driftwood" by Travis, please?'

'I remember a green Austin Sprite I used to have. Austin had lost the right to use the word 'Healey'. It was a lovely car, but very light. I had to put a couple of paving stones in the boot. That normally did the trick. However, back in January 1973, my luck ran out. When I hit some ice on a bend near Blythburgh, I was spinning for a long, long time. If you catch my drift? Oh, did you suggest a word, Marina?'

'I did. And just the opposite of tiffling. Mine was tummler, a person who causes things to happen. Though, perhaps, not deliberately. People can impact on the lives of others without really realising they are doing it.'

'I'd like to finish with an event from 1896. Walter Arnold became the first British motorist to be fined for breaking the speed limit. And he didn't just *nudge* over the limit. He smashed it. His 8mph might seem reasonable now, but it was four times the limit for town driving. What caught my attention was his arrest. The local bobby, giving chase on a bicycle, caught him after five miles. That's over half an hour of pedalling. I'm surprised Mr Arnold received only a shilling fine. Perhaps if he'd been wearing a top hat, or flirting in public, he'd have been dealt with more severely.'

Chapter 21

'Good afternoon. My name's India Farr. I'm here to meet Harrison Ward, my living donor co-ordinator.'

'Hello India, could you confirm your date of birth and the first line of your address plus your postcode.'

India gave the details, but hesitated after the address part.

'Oh, I see that's in London.'

'Yes, but I also have a base near here, in Peasenham.'

'That's good. My notes show that you've already met Harrison. So if you just wait over there, I'll let you know when he's ready.'

'I gave birth to her, but I'm not really her mother.'

'Well, biologically, you are. But living donors don't need to be related. They just need to be aware of the risks. Just as we need to be aware of their motivation and psychological situation. Also, the testing programme can throw up some surprises. For example, a previously unknown medical condition.'

'I'm as ready, as I can be, for that sort of thing.'

'Why is it only now that you have put yourself forward? What has changed?'

'Zoe has had a few setbacks recently. Two possible avenues were closed. Her being only the reserve on Christmas Eve, following on from Warren having only one kidney.'

'I can't comment on medical issues relating to another

patient, India.'

'I understand that. And now there have been some discussions about Colin, Zoe's guardian, getting involved. Though healthy, he's in his mid-eighties. Also, I've started to get to know my daughter in the last three months. So I've had a change of heart, so to speak. Zoe's not particularly happy with my decision, but she hasn't rejected it. And she understands the likely matching advantages of my being her blood relation. If it came to it, I'd also consider becoming involved in a paired or three-way pooled donation.'

'You have been doing your homework.'

'I have, Harrison. The literature is very good, and Warren has shared his knowledge and experiences of the process with me. So what's next?'

'There have been no medical issues with your initial set of blood tests. So we can begin the next phase. There will be a lot of tests. We need to make sure that your general health is good and that both your kidneys are functioning well. Apart from the medical tests, you will have a series of interviews with a counsellor, Jerry Dangerfield. As it happens, there's just been a cancellation. So you could actually have your first meeting with her a fortnight Thursday.'

'That would be good. Thank you, Harrison.'

'Just double-check at the reception when you leave. Also, towards the end of the process there will be an interview with an independent assessor from the Human Tissue Authority. At our first meeting, we spoke about the risks such as death, organ damage and infections. As well as complications which might impact on your finances or emotional well-being. The assessor will need to be sure that you have considered all the possibilities.'

'It hasn't been an easy decision.'

'And one that's different for every donor, India. But remember, it's your choice and you can change your mind at any time. The team here, including the surgical team, would only proceed if they were confident that both you *and* Zoe were healthy enough. And surgeons have a natural reluctance to remove a healthy organ. Even, if by doing so, they have the chance to save a life.'

'Could you give me an overview of how a kidney transplant works for the donor?'

'Typically, the donor would be under general anaesthetic during the keyhole surgery. Unless open surgery becomes necessary, the donor would be left with a relatively small scar. So perhaps three hours in theatre. Followed by three days in hospital. Then maybe three months to make a full recovery. However, there are no guarantees. It depends on how they react. For example, to the painkillers and antibiotics. In contrast, Zoe will need a range of medications for the rest of her life.'

~

Skye's entry in the Iron Bridge House Logbook, 2019 with additional comments by Colin & Warren

It has been over forty years since this property, then known as 34 High Street, was opened as a Landmark Trust (LT) holiday rental. We took a rather indirect route to get here from Suffolk. Colin and I had never visited Portsmouth, and Warren had never seen the *SS Great Britain* in Bristol (he loved it: Brunel would be a top contender, if Warren produced a shortlist of 'Greatest Portmouthians').

There are some interesting LT links as well. My friend Hatsu gave me a 1977 edition of the LT Handbook last week. It has fascinating snippets* about the properties, but also about the charity. Much of its funding came from the founder, Sir John Smith, via his Manifold Trust. And the old handbook shows financial distributions to 'structures' such as *HMS Belfast, SS Great Britain* and, of course, The Iron Bridge. Other beneficiaries of industrial preservation grants have included a tidal mill (in Woodbridge, just south of where I now live), a pottery and some blowing engines. Whatever *they* are.

Perhaps the answer is in the library. A key person who helped to revive British canals was Sonia Rolt. She also played a key role in forming the libraries and selecting the artwork of each LT property. There are many links in life, and so many of them have understated quality.

* *Some Logbook Snippets*

'I'm afraid our beagle ate several pieces of the jigsaw.'

'A seal swam by me at Thorpeness.
I thought it was an old man.'

'For botanists, there is a very good bog at Tregaron.'

'A troupe of players appeared out of the mists and offered entertainment in return for fare. They played their piece ... which was applauded vigorously (to keep warm).'

And my favourite, written in a logbook at The Pineapple: 'Farewell, old fruit.'

There are also entries for properties, which are now ex-Landmarks, including Edale Mill, the Master's House at the Gladstone Pottery Museum, and the Wellbrook Beetling Mill in Northern Ireland. Apparently, beetling is that part of the linen-making process where the cloth is hammered to produce the sheen.

Reading more of the 1977 Handbook, I was impressed by Sir John's philosophy. He was not interested in depriving people of ordinary 'housing stock'. Sir John focused on buildings that had lost their original function. And which were at risk from neglect, vandalism and the weather. Buildings that could then be enjoyed by thousands of people, rather than become just another under-used weekend cottage.

I love the idea of not doing too much to an old building. Mending and repairing it, if possible, rather than just replacing things. Giving new life to an old building. A building to be used, not just admired. Ah, I see Warren waving at me from the bridge. A signal for me to put a brew on, using the delightful Old Chelsea china tea set.

The History Album states that this area was once the '*most extraordinary district in the world* '. And it was a truly revolutionary place, with a unique bridge. Local coal deposits, transported by barges, fuelled industries such as potteries, tile works and, of course, the iron industry. I can imagine the scene on New Year's Day, 1771, when the bridge was officially opened.

Though not everyone was happy. For example, the local coracle makers lost most of their ferrying income. At least they were given exemption, unlike the Royal Family, from paying the new tolls. Pedestrians had to pay a halfpenny. Even in death you couldn't really escape, as hearses were charged eightpence.

The land on which Iron Bridge House stands was sold, in 1835, to a grocer for £1,400. Grocers were traders who bought in bulk and then made their profit by selling their goods in smaller quantities. Another phrase for bulk buying was by the gross, hence grocer. I didn't know that before today. The bridge and the opening of the Severn Valley Railway (1862) boosted both trade and tourism. Visitors were able to hire canoes, but coracles would have been much safer. The most famous coracle makers were the Rogers family. One of them, Tommy, also supplemented his income with poaching and casual labouring. He helped to build the new Ironbridge police cells. Only to become, ironically, one of the first people to be held in one.

In 1916, Iron Bridge House only fetched £550, perhaps because of the war. And in 1926 there was even a proposal to demolish the bridge. It had survived floods, but had always had problems with ground movements. A limit of two hundred people on the bridge, still enforced, was introduced. Then, in 1946, there were plans to build a replacement bridge next to it. But the bridge survived, and within forty years, gained international protection when the Ironbridge Gorge was given UNESCO World Heritage status.

We love our Ironbridge Passports. They cost 80p in the 1970s, but are still good value at £26.50 (or just £20 for seniors like me). All the sites are fascinating. But I was surprised at just how much I enjoyed the Jackfield Tile Museum. For instance, seeing the tiled book section-markers that were designed for WH Smith. Can you imagine a bookshop today being divided up into areas such as *Sea Tales*, *Engineering Books* and *Ladies' Papers*? The recreation of part of Covent Garden Underground station gave me a slight chill. When the sound of an air raid siren went off, I didn't linger.

However, I did linger next to a glazed multi-tiled depiction of *A Midsummer Night's Dream*. Even though Titania was a little under-dressed . . . There really is something for everyone, now, in Jackfield. I say 'now', because of a quote at the museum's entrance. The quote comes from a speech given in 1870 by a certain Henry Dunhill. As well as owning the tileworks, he was the chairman of the local Reading Room & Workmen's Club.

Dunhill strongly encouraged the members to read widely as, *'it will enlarge your ideas, and help you to understand that Jackfield is not all the world, but a very poor bit of the fag end of it* '. His description continued with examples including rubbish heaps, dilapidated houses and miry roads. But that even though Jackfield was a '*neglected, forlorn, and desolate place*', it was also possible to '*understand and follow the great movements of the world, and to share in the thoughts and emotions of the great leaders of human thought*'.

It has been a tad indulgent, what with us having a library here, but we have visited a few bookshops this week. My favourite was the one just off the stableyard at Attingham Park. I was delighted to pick up a copy of *Iron Bridge to Crystal Palace* by Asa Briggs. Warren enjoyed the copy here, so he now has his very own copy to take home. Colin found a lovely Folio Society edition of *Touching The Void* in Much Wenlock. I understand there might be a stage version later in the year. I hope they don't include the word 'cliff-hanger' in their publicity material.

There's also a weekly Food Bank nearby in Much Wenlock. Warren helped out for an hour, and we donated some soup and teabags. I think more could be done to ensure that people don't go hungry. Jonathan Coe, in *Middle England*, wrote a poignant scene on the subject. One of his characters is embarrassed to open their kitchen cupboard. Because it contained 'economy' packets and tins, and from so many *different* supermarkets.

A teacher friend of ours, Kenesha, said that she used to make extra sandwiches. And gave them, discreetly, to members of her tutor group. She told us there was one girl who came in to be fed, and then would often skip the rest of the school day. Shouldn't money and investment be directed to improve the life chances of people like that girl?

Skye Hunter, The Hop Yard, Suffolk
What a delightful stay in a homely and fragrant gem. If venturing out, get a poke of chips and enjoy them at the Coracle Micropub.

If venturing further, you might well enjoy a glass of Tall, Dark & Damson (Joules Brewery) at The Shakespeare in Bridgnorth.

Thanks to the Housekeeper and the Landmark Trust,
Colin Pargeter, Peasenham, Suffolk

This property has eight windows, plus one above the communal staircase, and you can see the Iron Bridge from all of them:

Window One   The innovative bridge cost almost double its £3,000 estimate. A sum that included fifteen quid for celebratory beers. And at night, the bridge is illuminated by subtle red lighting. The planned green lights had to be changed when it was discovered they bamboozled bats.

Window Two   The War Memorial: '*In grateful and undying memory of the valiant men of Ironbridge who laid down their lives in the Great War 1914 to 1918.*' Fifty-three names are listed. From Adams, Armstrong and Aston. To Watson, Welch and Wilkes. There are also ten men listed from the Second World War. Despite the massive increase in bombing in that later conflict, did World War One change Britain more?

Window Three   Eley's (justly) Famous Pork Pie Shop.

Window Four   The Severn. No coracles* today, but there is an ice cream van parked, just out of reach of the fast-flowing river. A river in which cross-Channel swimmer Captain Webb once saved his younger brother from drowning.

Window Five   The Iron Bridge's Toll House. A foot crossing cost a halfpenny, but a season ticket was available for a guinea (worth 21 shillings or 240 old pennies). I wonder how many were sold. Pedestrians were still being charged within living memory.

*Window Six*** The Cooling Towers. They're scheduled to be demolished this year (a source of sadness for many locals, as it's a "We're almost home" landmark. However, the redeveloped site might include a new railway station).

Window Seven Ironbridge has a lot of interesting shops, including Darlington's. Back in 1982, the brakes on a lorry failed near there. The driver swerved to avoid a group of school children. But smashed into several buildings. The accident resulted in the deaths of six people.

Window Eight The lanes and alleyways and dead-ends of Ironbridge. Rising and radiating, higgledy-piggledy, from the planned order of The Square.

Warren Wagstaffe, Pompey & Suffolk

PS This is the first time I've stayed in a LT property and the first time I've slept in a double bed. A double first, in more ways than one. It was a bit odd though, all that space, but I might be tempted to try it again.

* The logbooks are great sources of information e.g. a gallon of petrol cost 74p in 1976. That's much less than you'd pay for just a litre in 2019. And apart from info, there's some really good art. Coracle makers lived nearby until quite recently. There's an impressive sketch of one of them, Eustace (aka Eusty) Rogers, in the second logbook. P'raps (as Colin would say), he made the coracle used by Shrewsbury Town FC to retrieve lost balls at their old ground (upstream from here).

** The bathroom has some very odd prints of caged birds. Did breeders really feed Cayenne pepper to canaries to give them a cinnamon tint?

~

'Hi, I'm Skye Hunter and welcome to *Chatter Broth*. It's February 5th and today's guest is Angelique Vonk. It's thirty-one years since the first Red Nose Day for Comic Relief. So let's start with In This Fortnight.'

'Hello Skye. It's terrific to be here again. Where's Warren?'

'Oh, he's just helping Hatsu over at Book Bathing. He'll be here soon.'

'I'll start with an event from thirty years ago in Ipswich. That's Ipswich, Australia. Not Ipswich, Suffolk. A storm there produced large quantities of rain, naturally. But also sardines. Can you imagine that?'

'Sounds fishy to me. I think I'd have preferred flapjacks from the sky.'

'That's a sweet idea.'

'It is, Angelique. At least it wasn't hard, knobbly celeriac—'

'Did someone mention my favourite vegetable?'

'Hello, Warren. Angelique and I were just talking about strange storms. Did you get everything done?'

'Just about. A mystery donor left a full collection of Annie Proulx books. Including *The Shipping News*, *Close Range* and *Barkskins*. And they're all signed first editions. There's even a copy of her wonderful book *Cider*. They'll be auctioned in four days' time, and we've just finalised the menu.'

'It's lucky the sardines didn't fall on *Britain* during the mid-to-late 1940s. It might have become smelly, as soap rationing began in 1942. And didn't end for another eight years. Although I'm sure there was an informal market in such goods. Goods and people move across borders, often at night or where things are quiet. And not just here in Suffolk. I was born and brought up near the Dutch-Belgian border. Sort of. There's a book by Nicolas Freeling, *Guns Before Butter*, which captures the atmosphere of that border area very well.'

'What do you mean by sort of?'

'It's like this, Skye. My village of Baarle-Nassau was actually a land island. It was completely surrounded by an area of Belgium called Baarle-Hertog. An area which, itself, was surrounded by the Netherlands.'

'That sounds complicated.'

'It was, Warren. And not just working out the differences between enclaves, exclaves and counter-enclaves. Some houses straddled the border. So the occupants had to decide whether to send mail by PostNL or Bpost. Dutch teenagers, although I had left for Utrecht by then, had to watch 16-year-old Belgians legally drinking beer. There were plenty of other economic opportunities and loopholes. For instance, the Belgians were allowed to sell fireworks throughout the year. But were not allowed to open shops on Sundays, including *adult* stores.'

'Tit-for-tat?'

'I suppose so, Skye. Though the complexity paid a good dividend in 1914. The invading German Army was banned from crossing Dutch borders. So the Belgian 'islands' in the area became a safe sanctuary for refugees. Not so in 1940, unfortunately. During *those* war years another strange flying object was in the wrong place. Not the sardines or flapjacks from earlier, but an aeroplane. Orville Wright had had an argument with the Smithsonian Museum in Washington DC. So in 1928 he sent the original *Wright Flyer* to the Science Museum in London. It wasn't until 1948 that it was returned. Can you imagine that? It would be like us sending Rembrandt's *Night Watch* overseas. Or the Louvre losing *Mona Lisa*. Again. On the same day, February 13th, but in 1987, there was a curious sale in Knightsbridge—'

'Nowhere else in England has more consonants in a row. There are six: G, H, T, S B and R.'

'Thanks, Warren. I admire your thirst for interesting facts. The sale was a broom cupboard, less than twelve by six feet in area, opposite Harrod's. It sold for over £36,000.'

'A *cupboard* in that broom cupboard would probably go for that now.'

'You're right, Skye. I love this country, but I don't understand the obsession with home ownership. And the prices are just astonishing. "*Hoeveel wilt U?!*" — "How much do you want?!" It's a dream that's out of reach for so many people, so why not change the system. Have long-term tenancies at fair prices. It would be a game-changer. I know that you have talked about this before with Warren and Colin. Perhaps there has been a recent shift in public opinion. But I think it might still take decades to get sorted out.'

'I'll play "Our House" by Madness, no pun intended, while we ponder what home means.'

'There's a lot of energy in that song, Warren. Now, Buckingham Palace is an icon. But it's facing some massive repair bills. Why not convert it into flats for public service workers? With maybe some new model apartments in the gardens. That would send out a message, which I'm sure the ghost of Prince Albert would approve of. There's plenty of other royal accommodation: Balmoral Castle, Highgrove, Holyrood Palace, Hillsborough Castle, Sandringham, Windsor Castle . . . '

'That's an interesting idea, Angelique, but it would be very controversial. Maybe something like that could happen in the Netherlands. But here? There'd be more chance of Parliament moving to Coventry. What do you think, Warren?'

'You know my ideas about developing housing partnerships with the National Trust or the MoD. There's that place called Poundbury, which Prince Charles has overseen. It was built on Duchy of Cornwall land, even though it's in Dorset. The Duchy owns land in at least twenty counties. Maybe that's a link that could be developed.'

'Watch this space. Let's finish this part with two marriages, both on February 10th. The first, between Victoria and Albert in 1840, is well known. But there was an even more spectacular marriage ceremony, in New York City, twenty-three years later. Thousands attended the marriage, and even if they couldn't, they were able to pay $75 for a ticket to the reception. Now that's a fair sum of money today, but this was during the US Civil War. And when Mercy Bump married Charles Stratton, it made front-page news.'

'I've never heard of them.'

'Few people have, apart from Warren of course. Charles was born in 1838. He was rented out to a distant relative, for $3 a week, when he was just four. When he was six, he met Queen Victoria. Although she'd been told by Mr Barnum he was eleven and—'

'Oh, it was in that film about PT Barnum, *The Greatest Showman*. So young Charles was General Tom Thumb, and Mercy was Lavinia Warren.'

'That's right, Skye. Lavinia was first named Mercy Bump. Names carry meaning, and mystery.'

'For example, Angelique?'

'Here are a few. Edna Ann was a promising young writer from Norwich. That's Norwich, Connecticut. Not Norwich, Norfolk. She even used the E from Edna in some of her early novels. Like *The Shipping News*.'

'Hey, that's E. Annie Proulx.'

'Top marks, Warren. Then there's Winston Smith in 1984. George Orwell, who had changed his own name from Eric Blair, combined two contrasting names. First, Winston, a name known by almost everyone in the 1940s. Then Smith, a common surname, harking back to a profession that had premises in every

English village. It's where my family name comes from. Vonk means spark. Such as a spark from a blacksmith's anvil. Then there are people with initials, such as JK Rowling, AE Housman and . . . George P Salt. He just smiles whenever I've asked him. Has he ever revealed his middle name to you, Skye?'

'Not that I remember, Angelique. Maybe, back on that hot August day when he first arrived here. Eleven years of mystery, but we'd all be a little bit lost without GPS. I think it's important to have secrets, as long as they don't fester or cause damage. Sometimes telling the *truth* can have unforeseen consequences. Yes, I know some people laughed, but it sort of made sense to me what Donald Rumsfeld said. About there being two kinds of knowns and unknowns. I think there *are* unknown unknowns. Which sometimes reveal themselves. In a great unravel. I know what you're thinking. Skye's had a strange brew. But sometimes my mind just flies, soaring like a carefree skylark. Looping, not loopy.'

'Last time, we were looking for words beginning with the letter U. I wonder what the final four were this week. Over to you, Warren.'

'Thanks, Skye. Our Lost Four Words are ubiquarian, ukemi, umiak and urucu:

She survived the jump into the umiak,
With her urucu intact.
Though not an ubiquarian,
She had learnt ukemi.'

'And your *u*-sual thoughts, Warren?'
'Well, Skye, can you make any sense of this?

She survived the jump into the female-crewed Arctic canoe,
With her body paint intact.
Though not a person who wished to travel everywhere,
She had learnt the Japanese art of falling safely.'

'I suggested umbratile, life in the shade. I've always found it strange that the English have two words for objects that protect a person from the sun. Umbrella *and* parasol. But then use their umbrellas when it's raining, not when shade is needed. I also like the word ukemi. It sounds like a very useful skill. It makes me wonder if Jean Blanchard visited Japan before he invented the parachute.'

'I don't know, but I bet the Beach Boys did. Visit Japan, that is. So linked to ubiquarian, here's some more Four Play.'

'That was "I Get Around". I wonder if one of the band had been a baker. One of the lines refers to really good bread.'

'Oh, Warren. I think that bread was dough, as in dollars.'

'My mistake, Skye. How shall we move on?'

'Every three months or so we have a bit of Slow Dating. And we're just coming up to Valentine's Day'

'Phew, we're back on track. That's right, Skye. So who's next, after Haberdasher and Digs Disco?

'It's Quill Sister:

Paperback writer with coastal views — from a well-feathered, but frequently sand-blasted, nest — seeks dissimilar, I think. Or maybe not. Who knows? Fancy a tingle on the shingle? Or burning the candle in Walberswick? Or even showing your attitude at Latitude?'

'She sounds a bit confused and confusing. What do you think, Angelique?'

'Is she looking to meet a hardback writer, Warren? What

views do coastal people have? Is her home cosy or draughty? So yes. It's confusing. But, definitely original.'

'There you go, listeners. If you fancy being sand-blasted in a novel way, why not reply. Please include 'Quill Sister' on your envelope and send it to the getting less unusual address, i.e. *Chatter Broth* c/o M3 aka Marina's Moreish Micropub, The Hop Yard, Peasenham, Suffolk.'

'Oh, I almost forgot. How was Ironbridge, Warren?'

'It was amazing, Angelique. I loved the Martello Tower, but Iron Bridge House was even better. I could live in Ironbridge. And maybe start another community there, one day. Though with all the manufacturing heritage, we'd have to call it something like the Tile Yard or the Iron Works. It would need to be built on stilts though, as the River Severn is a powerful force of nature.'

'Colin and I were delighted to spend time with you there.'

'It was a lovely present, Skye. I've been looking in the LT Handbook. And they have more buildings with an industrial past. George has told me how much he enjoyed the simplicity of Stoker's Cottage. So I'm going to save up, so that I can host you at another one in the future. Yes, me, Warren Wagstaffe. It's been quite a journey. I quite like the look of Richard Arkwright's North Street in Cromford. It's the site of the first planned industrial housing in the world. The Landmark Trust let out all but one of their properties there to local people. That's a great idea. They do the same thing in Ironbridge. One of the two flats is let to a local. Housing difficulties *can* be sorted out. With a bit of imagination, and some focused investment.'

Chapter 22

'Hi, I'm Skye Hunter and welcome to *Chatter Broth*. It's February 19th and today's guest is George P Salt. His shop, GPS Maps, is now fully up and running. But maybe there's still a part for the *spherical* side of Globe+Artichoke.'

'There is, Skye. Seth has sourced some wonderful reclaimed wood. We hope to finish our first globe by the end of August, in time for the Field Party. That's a key part of the calendar for me. Time ebbs and flows on a slightly different frequency around here . . . I enjoyed listening to your last podcast, and being reminded of my visit to Stoker's Cottage. But was it really a dozen years ago? I've spent more than a third of my life here. By the way, I've heard some great feedback about Veg Out, Warren.'

'It's going well, though not quite as I expected. People *do* like the food. But for some of them, what they really like is getting out of their homes. To be in another space, physically and mentally. Pippa has lent me her Mazda Bongo until Easter. I use it as an informal taxi, now that Colin has sorted out the insurance issues. I'm also planning on doing a big meal here every Monday. Though I haven't worked out a way yet to transport people who have mobility issues.'

'I'm sure you'll find a way, Warren. Shall we continue with Lost Four Words? Last time, we were looking for words beginning with the letter V. What are the final four, Warren?'

'Thanks, Skye. They are vasquine, vergaloo, vogie and volupty:

Although food could make her vogie,
Eating a ripe vergaloo,
And watching the juice drip on her vasquine,
Was closer to volupty.'

'And your thoughts, Warren?'
'Well, Skye, does this make any sense to you?

Although food could make her cheerful,
Eating a ripe white pear,
And watching the juice drip on her petticoat,
Was closer to sensual pleasure.

Food certainly makes me feel cheerful. Especially when I've cooked a meal for other people.'

'That poem paints a picture for me. I remember being told once that the best way to eat a mango was naked. In the rain or under a shower. Now, I remember a steamy night in Pondicherry. A friend of mine had just sourced a full box of juice-rich Alphonso mangoes. So we decided to—'

'George, did you suggest a word?'

'I did. It was vitilitigate, to argue noisily. Though I like the sound of vergaloo. I think it would go well with pecans. Maybe India would have a different suggestion.'

'Or perhaps the lady from "Greensleeves". With her silk petticoat of slender white. I won't play that though. Instead, as part of Four Play, I've chosen a cheerful song. Well, it's *kind* of vogie. It's about two people who would be better off *out* of their relationship. But in a "no hard feelings" kind of way. Here's

"Very Happy Now" by the Grand Slambovians.'

'George, what have you gleaned from In This Fortnight?'

'I think I'll start with some events linked to romance and marriage, Skye. In 1472, on February 20th, Norway was having difficulty raising funds for the dowry of Princess Margaret. So Christian I, King of Norway and Denmark, came up with an interesting idea. In lieu of a payment, he loaned Orkney and Shetland to Scotland. And the loan has never been repaid.'

'I've never been to Shetland, but I love Orkney. There's definitely a different feel to those islands. I wonder if the Norwegians want their islands back.'

'I'm sure they do, Skye. And if Scotland becomes independent, then the Northern islanders might themselves start casting their eyes over the water. And while we're on the subject of Scandinavia, let's go back to 1712. The Swedes needed to adjust their Julian calendar. So they added two leap days to the end of February. Yes, two. So for that year only, there was a February 30th. Anyone born on that day would never have another birthday. To finish this theme, let's go back even further. To the spring of 1693. *The Ladies' Mercury*, on February 27th of that year, became the first magazine targeted at women. Perhaps it was inspired by Henry Robinson's marriage bureau. Who knows? The word magazine comes from the Arabic word for a storehouse — *makazin*. In this case, a paper room of ideas and opinions. A slim room, in that it consisted of just one double-sided sheet. A key feature was its Q&A column. The editor promised to respond to "*all the most nice and curious questions concerning love, marriage, behaviour, dress and humour of the female sex, whether virgins, wives, or widows*". Very inclusive.'

'It sounds like it was written by men.'

'It does, Skye. Especially as replies were to be answered with "*the Zeal and Softness becoming to the Sex*". And that questions should be derived from female observations relating to puzzling male behaviour. There were other guidelines too. A letter explained that its female readers need not bother with the "*examination of learning, nature, arts, sciences and indeed the whole world* "—'

'That doesn't leave a lot, George.'

'Indeed not, Skye. But it seems women were not ready to follow all the advice. In the second issue they were reminded that the magazine only dealt with "*questions of love, marriage and domestic concerns*". Not with "*questions relating to learning or religion*". If the editor had listened and responded to his target audience, the weekly paper might have become established. As it was, it folded on March 17th. Have women always accepted the restrictions placed on them? No. So I'm going to jump forwards in time. Twenty-nine Suffragettes were arrested on February 24th, 1909, for trying to break into the Houses of Parliament. Yet just eleven years later, to the day, Lady Astor became the first woman to speak in Parliament. Almost a century earlier, in 1812, Lord Byron made his first speech in the House of Lords. On February 27th, he spoke on behalf of workers who were suffering from increased mechanisation and rising food prices. And who were banned from forming trade unions. Under the banner of General Ludd, their protests included the smashing of machines. The government's reaction was to bring in legislation that made the destruction of machines a hanging offence. Lord Byron argued their actions were caused by, "Nothing but absolute want".'

'The term "Luddite" is now almost a term of abuse.'

'It is, Skye. But how far can you blame people who feel disempowered by the pace and nature of change? And change can be dramatic. On the same date, but in 1933, the Reichstag — Germany's parliament — in Berlin burned down. A Dutch Communist, Marinus van der Lubbe, was arrested. He had in his possession just a box of matches. Whether or not he was guilty, the Nazi Party used the fire as an excuse to arrest thousands of Communists. The next day, President Hindenburg's Emergency Decree allowed the police to arrest and hold suspects without trial. But that fire was the spark that quickly led to dictatorship. One outcome was the Second World War. Another era that has a long tail, so to speak. For example, I was surprised by an event from 1953. The British government offered amnesties to deserters from that conflict. Over 3,000 missing servicemen applied. That's an incredible number of people, some of whom had been hiding their true identities for over ten years.'

'Lots of people slipped through the cracks at that time. I've never really come to terms with what happened to my parents. I've nowhere to visit to remind me of them. Not even a grave. Though I love the idea of that Japanese phone box . . . I don't even know if my mother survived the war. Without Colin, and our Hop Yard community, I'm not sure how I'd have survived.'

'You're a key part of this place. Ably assisted by our very own Warren Wagstaffe, of course. *Chatter Broth* is so much more than a podcast. It's a space for us to stretch and reflect. Where we can discuss issues and develop plans. So it's appropriate that I'm going to finish with two events linked to broadcasting. Firstly, the microphone was invented by Emile Berliner in 1887. How would we sound without it? Secondly, the microphone was used to great effect on March 4th, 1933. Franklin Delano Roosevelt was another politician who used radio to get his message across. During his first inauguration speech, he spoke about the great task of getting unemployed people back to work. And quickly. My favourite line from his speech was one I think we can all learn from. The line is, "So let me assert my firm belief that the only thing we have to fear is fear itself". Powerful words, which he backed up with decisive action.'

'I half-remember listening to FDR's speeches when I was a child. Colin was fascinated by him. We once visited Great

Malvern, just so that Colin could stand outside a house that the young Roosevelt had lived in. That 1933 speech took place just twelve years after Roosevelt contracted polio. A disease that meant he had to spend most of his waking hours in a wheelchair. So he probably appreciated the opportunities that radio broadcasting gave him. For instance, his confidence-boosting fireside chats. I dress up for our show, but our listeners don't know that. At least, they didn't until now. But it's sound that matters. Even with television, people who aren't deaf get more than seventy per cent of their information through their ears. So I think it will be a long time before people stop saying, "We heard it on the radio".'

~

'Hello. My name's Dr Dangerfield, but please call me Jerry. Is it all right if I call you India?'

'No problem, Jerry.'

'I'm going to start with some scripted questions, and then we'll talk about some issues in more depth. We'll start with a health literacy test. Are you ready?'

'Yes, Jerry. Go for it.'

'I'm going to show you eighteen cards with three words on them. First, I'd like you to read out the top word. Next, I'll read the two words underneath and I'd like you to tell me which of the two words is more similar to, or has a closer match with, the top word. If you don't know, don't guess. Just say, "I don't know".'

'Let's get on with it then.'

Jerry wasn't quite sure whether India was showing nerves or being pushy, but she let it pass. 'Here is the first card. Please, read the top word out loud.'

'Kidney.'

'Which of the two words, urine or fever, is most similar to the top word? If you don't know the answer, please say, "I don't know".'

'Urine.'

'And the next one?'

'Occupation.'

'Work or education?'

'Work.' India couldn't work out why the test was needed. Until she came to the word pregnancy: "birth or childhood?" and later, abnormal: "different or similar?" Maybe Jerry was interested in her reaction to certain words, rather than just her understanding of them.

'And just this last one.'

'Syphilis.'

'Contraception or Condom?'

'It could be either. Knowing someone had syphilis should act as a deterrent. A sheath might prevent syphilis being transmitted.'

'Which one, India?'

'I'll go for condom. I wish I'd known more about them when I was a teenager. Especially, that condoms don't come with a guarantee. How could I have been so stupid? At least, that's what I've thought for most of my adult life. Now? I'm not so sure.'

India read through all the questions on the next part of the test, before marking her answers. She strongly agreed or strongly disagreed with all six statements. India thought that she *did* bounce back quickly and *didn't* have a hard time getting through stressful events. Her self-scoring indicated that she had high resilience. She handed the sheet back to Dr Dangerfield, but couldn't read the expression on the psychologist's face.

'I've now got two questions about your recent mood. Each

with four options. Not at all, several days, more than half the days or nearly every day. Please choose the option that matches, or is closest to, how you feel. Here goes. Over the last two weeks, how often have you been bothered by having little pleasure in doing things, India?'

'Never. That is, not at all. Even though I'm not involved in my usual work at the moment.'

'Secondly, how often have you been bothered by feeling down, depressed or hopeless?'

'In the last few weeks, not at all. My early twenties weren't so good, but I worked my way through.'

'I've now got a series of "yes" or "no" questions. If you're not sure, think about what your answer would be most of the time. Here's the first one. In general, do you have difficulty making and keeping friends?'

'Making them, yes. Keeping them, no.'

'Would you normally describe yourself as a loner?'

'No, though other people might view me as one.'

'In general, do you trust other people?'

'It's not something I've really considered, Jerry. Pass.'

'Could you try and give an answer.'

'For that one, no. Not an honest one, anyway.'

'Let's move on then. Do you normally lose your temper easily?'

'No. I've never lost my temper.'

'Really?'

'I've had disagreements, but I've never lashed out verbally or physically. Maybe I'm *too* calm at times.'

'Are you normally an impulsive sort of person?'

'No, not now. Just the opposite, really. Maybe it's because I don't rush my work.'

'That's interesting, and it links to the last question.'

'What do you mean, Jerry?'

'We'll come on to that later. Are you normally a worrier?'

'No. You make decisions in life and get on with them. Mistakes get made, inevitably. But I go with, "What's the worst that could happen?" Most of the time.'

Jerry was intrigued by India's answers. The phrase "cold fish" came to mind, but then again, smoked salmon was one of her favourite starters. 'In general, do you depend on others a lot?'

'No. Although I've had indirect financial support. I did a lot of temporary jobs in the early years of this millennium. Roasting coffee beans, selling Really Useful Boxes, picking raspberries . . . Before I started my career in decluttering. Other people's lives, that is.'

'That's interesting. It links to the last question, India. In general, are you a perfectionist?'

'No.'

'Even though you suggested you like to take time doing things.'

'I like to do things well, but life is imperfect. I try and do a good job, but I'm not going to lose sleep over any mistakes or omissions. These tests are interesting, but they feel a bit like some of those scenes from *Blade Runner.*'

'I disagree, but you're not the first person to say something like that.'

'I'd now like to talk with you more about your relationship with your mother. And how that might have impacted on your relationship with Zoe. To start, what did you call your mother?'

'Abigail.'

'Not Mum or Mother?'

'No, always Abigail. She never hugged me or told me she loved me, when I went to visit her.'

'Visit?'

'I wasn't allowed to live with her when I was a child. She

blamed me for the death of my twin brother. Though our relationship did improve a bit when she began to forget who I was. Perhaps there *are* some benefits to memory loss.'

'And her symptoms became more obvious soon after your birth?'

'According to Colin, yes. He thinks that the shock of those events in Bologna might have made her illness worse. She had already been diagnosed with some of the signs of early-onset Alzheimer's in her 20s. Not memory loss, at first. The build-up of plaques between her nerve cells, and tangles in her brain cells, was *first* diagnosed when she had problems with her vision. Fortunately, Colin was able to provide a home for her in Marylebone. He had inherited a large property there, with a mews cottage attached to the rear. Though Colin decided to sell the main house, when Abigail's care needs became more complex and expensive.'

'Why do you think he did that?'

'I don't know. But Colin has always helped waifs and strays. Including myself. But he doesn't boss anyone about. He makes suggestions, not orders. Like suggesting that Zoe went and lived with him in Suffolk, after I decided not to complete my university course. Luckily, Marina arrived in Suffolk in 2003. She quickly took Zoe under her wing. I don't think that living with a remote mother would have been a good environment for a young child.'

'Are you still talking about Zoe?'

'Yes, not *my* upbringing.'

'So what was Colin's reaction to your pregnancy?'

'His main concern was for the health of me and my baby. Richard had agreed to take full responsibility for Zoe, but then he went off to Australia just before the birth. He wasn't badly injured in a youth hostel fire there, but he did have some sort of mental breakdown. Colin then agreed a new plan with the

Duffys in Marylebone. He arranged for Zoe to stay with them, with a live-in nanny. I stayed three doors down with a friend called Natalie. Abigail moved into Number 17, with a live-in nurse.'

'So you had contact with Zoe?'

'Not really, though I arranged for my breast milk to be delivered.'

'That's interesting, India. Why did you do that, and for how long?'

'It was twice a day for about eighteen months. Richard's former nanny helped for the first few weeks. I found it really difficult, at first, to express it by myself. There's so much conflicting advice out there. I didn't know then about the differences between morning and evening milk. That was just luck. Or maybe instinct.'

'But why express, India, when you could have breastfed your daughter?'

India shuffled in her seat and looked out over the courtyard garden. 'I make good decisions and bad decisions. I don't always understand why I am making them. Was even giving Zoe my breast milk a good decision?'

'It was a personal one. And an emotional one. A bond with your baby, even though you were one step removed. Living on a street which had three generations of the same family, but all living in different homes. You felt unloved by your mother, abandoned even. And then you followed a similar path with Zoe . . . There are a lot of women who struggle to conceive. Who dream of having a baby. They might find it hard to accept your decision.'

'I've been on the receiving end of that. But I can understand their disbelief and anger. Even now, I don't really understand the reasons behind my decision. But, at least I'm here now.'

'Did Abigail ever reveal the identity of *your* father?'

'No. Just that he was an American. Can an adult be an orphan? That's certainly how I've felt.'

'So why *have* you come back now?'

'For years, I believed in remote control. Well not control, but influence. I encouraged clients I respected to visit Suffolk. To act as extra-curricular tutors and guides. Starting with Marina, who became very close to Zoe.'

'*In loco parentis?*'

'Sort of, Jerry. Not in the place of a parent, but as an alternative. I was able to deal with managing estates, but not my own child. Also, it's now been over three years since Abigail died. I think I've come more to terms with *her* remoteness now. That is, her rejection of me. And realised that I can avoid some of the mistakes that my mother made. Then, last year, Marina engineered a meeting between Zoe and me in Vermont. A few months later, by chance, I met George from the Hop Yard. On Easter Island. I decided to come back, even before Zoe's second chance of getting a kidney didn't work out. So here I am.'

'There are no typical cases in organ donation, but yours is quite unusual. However, I will be recommending to the multi-disciplinary team that you are indeed a suitable candidate. You'll have to face lots more tests, and they might determine that you are not a suitable donor. But, as things stand, you can make your next appointment with Harrison. Oh, before you go. Have you ever been back to Bologna?'

'No, it's not near the top of any of my lists. Why do you ask?'

'It might be interesting. For you, and for Zoe, to see where you were born. Going back, to work out how you might both better move forward.'

'I can understand why you might think that. But even if I came round to the idea, I seriously doubt that Zoe would.'

Chapter 23

'Hi, I'm Skye Hunter and welcome to *Chatter Broth*. It's March 5th and today's guest is Richard Duffy. Now, this is his first time on the show. So can you tell us a little about yourself?'

'Me? In short, I'm a recovering coward . . . I've had a few difficulties in life, but there's really no excuse for some of the decisions I've made. But recently, mainly with the support of Pippa, I've started to find my feet again.'

'Do you mean Pippa Luscombe?'

'I do, Warren. I'm grateful, and a little surprised, that you and Skye agreed to me being your guest. And what you've both done for Zoe is remarkable. Warren, you were even prepared to donate a kidney to my daughter.'

'It's not something I've really talked about, Richard.'

'I understand that, but you still did it. And then found out that you only had one kidney. Sorry, Zoe told me. And she also told me that you persuaded her to go with India to Bologna. Colin will have his hands full on that trip.'

'You've been spending a lot more time with Zoe.'

'I have, Skye. And I was glad to help Hatsu with the auction at Book Bathing. I'm a dealer, though more *Lovejoy* than *Antiques Roadshow*.'

'Whatever your style, you raised over £6,000 for us.'

'And you're very stylish, Richard. I don't know anyone else who could carry off a beard like yours. Which reminds me of one of our Lost Four Words. Last time, we were looking for words beginning with the letter W.'

Thanks, Skye. This time they are waveson, whiskerando, withitness and woofits:

She smiled at the whiskerando,
Admiring his withitness,
As rather than getting the woofits,
He calmly saved the ship by turning cargo into waveson.'

'And your thoughts, Warren?'
'Well, Skye, what do you think of this?

She smiled at the man with abundant facial hair,
Admiring his aura of teacherly confidence,
As rather than choosing moodiness,
He calmly saved the ship by throwing cargo overboard.'

'Ah, I'm a whiskerando. I'll certainly give that word a whirl, or a twirl. Skye, you have withitness. You are the undisputed captain of this sound studio. Our admiral of the airwaves. The woofits? Yeah, I've been there. But waveson, what's that all about, Warren?'

'It's another word for jetsam. That is, goods thrown off a ship, usually as a desperate last measure. Goods, which maybe, will float on waves. As opposed to flotsam, which is floating wreckage. George has spoken in the past about how humans have been treated as cargo. And millions of people are still suffering today. People dreaming of a new life and taking incredible risks to move across borders. Often in sealed shipping containers, holding on to an empty promise of personal and economic freedom. There might even be people being held against their will within a *mile* of us. We shouldn't be complacent. So here's Toots & the Maytals with "Never Get Weary Yet". It's a song about someone who is captured. And thrown overboard. Then, having escaped from a whale, is put in prison. But, despite everything, does not give up.'

'I can relate to that song, but mainly through the notes. Music reaches me, most of the time. I don't really get into words so much. They can be a bit noisy. But Pippa chose widdershins, going in the opposite direction. I don't think that one will catch on. But who knows? I've been looking through the notes Warren made up for me. Alexander Graham Bell patented the telephone in 1876. But didn't seem all that convinced by it, as he refused to have a phone installed in his study. And his wife was deaf, so maybe the phone didn't get answered much in that household.'

'What else piqued your interest In This Fortnight, Richard?'

'Plenty, Skye. But I'm not really convinced by all of them. How do we know that Cai Lun invented paper on March 11th, 105 AD?'

'Maybe he wrote the date. On the first piece of paper.'

'Fair play, Warren. Maybe he did. Marching on, here are a couple of military events. It took until March 13th, 1927, for the lance to be de-listed as an official weapon. That's almost ten years since the machine guns of the Western Front put an end to cavalry charges.'

'There's that scene in *War Horse*. Conflict can be terrible and terrifying.'

'It can, Skye. But also random. The Second World War didn't start very quickly for Britain. Thousands of evacuees drifted back as the so-called Phoney War stretched on. Colin has told me it was a very confusing time. For the authorities, and for families. But relative peace was about to be shattered. On March 16th, 1940, James Isbister became the first person in that war to be killed in a German bombing raid on Great Britain. But where did he live? Dover? London? Portsmouth? No, he was killed at Scapa Flow in the Orkney Islands.'

'A favourite place of mine. But nowhere on these islands was safe. Although if you had to choose a place, then the Isle of Man would have been a good bet. So many Germans were interned or imprisoned there, that German bomber crews almost always gave the island a wide berth. I was too young to remember the bombing raid which killed my father.'

'I'll move on, Skye.'

'You don't have to. Like Colin, I've been thinking about the war quite a lot recently. I cling to the hope that, even if my mother was killed, she didn't suffer. Though maybe she survived, and created a new life for herself. Like those army deserters hiding for years, which George was talking about last time. And people emerging from the jungle, sometimes decades after a conflict had ended. I'll probably never know about my mother. I don't often dwell on the past. But I suppose it always dwells on me. I've never been able to form a long-term romantic relationship. I've had more than a few short-term ones. Don't worry, Warren. I'm not about to regale you with a story about a chance encounter on the castle walls in Harlech. Although, thinking about it—'

'Anything else, Richard?'

'I've struggled with relationships too. In fact, Pippa's my first. You know, the first person I've spent more than one night with. Anyone who knows me was surprised when we had our one-month anniversary. And when we got to a year, people were gobsmacked. Pippa's brought me back nearer to a place I want to be. I still get the woofits, but that's the limit of it. It never got as bad as my next date, but I was down in the depths for years. Skye, you mentioned Comic Relief on the show last month. Their Red Nose Day, in 2001, holds a sad distinction. That was the *only* day between 1993 and 2002 when nobody in the UK killed themselves. I find that uplifting, but also incredibly sad. So many lives. To finish, I've chosen two dates from mid-March. Mahatma Gandhi was jailed in 1922 for promoting public disorder. Eight years later he began his 300-mile march to the sea, so that he and his followers could make tax-free salt. Images from that time, showing Indians being repeatedly beaten by the British, shocked people from all sides of the independence debate. People were also shocked when six agricultural workers were sentenced, in 1834, to be transported for seven years to Australia. Not for forming a form of Trade Union, a Friendly Society, but for making an illegal oath. Public outrage and demonstrations led to full pardons within two years. But it takes a long time to return from Australia . . . '

~

Bologna, 2019

Colin led the way out of Bologna's Centrale station. He stopped underneath the clock, which still read 10.25. 'I was on my way back from Yugoslavia in 1980. President Tito had recently died and there was a strange atmosphere in the Balkans. A sense of a cork being pulled from a bottle, a cloop, but a hesitation to taste the contents. As it happens, I was looking for interesting wines to import and Dalmatia looked a good bet—'

'Dalmatian wines. Wouldn't they be a bit spotty?' Zoe asked.

'Very good, Zoe. Some were, but at least I didn't try 101 of them. Some definitely had a 'Split' personality. Which was interesting, as I was staying in the coastal city of that name. The Roman palace complex was the place for tastings and listening to the *klapa* — a capella — groups. One of the singers, Roko, was my contact at *Dalmacijavino* — Dalmatian Wines. He was a character. It turned out he couldn't sell me any wine, but he did love to eat. He took me to Galija, a new pizzeria. Mine came with olives, pink onions, and carrots. The night got stranger and I ended up missing the ferry. So Roko drove me up the coast to Zadar. That was a drive and a half. Alfred Hitchcock was awestruck by the sunset he saw at Zadar, but all I saw were the lights around the port. I took the ferry across the Adriatic, and got the train here from Ancona.'

India looked over at Colin. 'Ancona. That's where the train caught up in the blast set out from.'

'That's right, India. I arrived here on August 1st, the day before the bombing. The Ancona train was heading for Switzerland. I don't know if the suitcase bomb was deliberately timed to go off while that train was in the station.'

'Where was the bomb placed?' Zoe asked.

'It was in a 2nd class waiting room. It was packed, on that hot August morning, because it had the luxury of air-conditioning. I'd walked into the old city the day before, down Via Galliera, and I was drenched with sweat by the time I found a hotel.'

'And it's quite warm today, even if it is only March,' India said. She had started shuffling her feet and looking at her watch. 'Shall we go to our hotel?'

'Soon. First, I want to see a Number 37 bus go by. It's not on our route, but it's a key part of the history of that traumatic day. The thirty-seven became an emergency vehicle. First, it took some of the two hundred injured to local hospitals. Then sheets were hung from its windows, as it took the dead to the morgue. Eighty-five people died in the explosion. Eighty-five. I heard the sirens from the vegetable market . . . '

~

Bologna, 1980

Abigail struggled to shake off her unwanted guide. She had been caught off-guard by the offer of chilled *acqua*. An offer that had put her in hot water. A drip of sweat travelled from her neck to the small of her back. And a stream of questions and suggestions travelled in strange trajectories through her mind. She was just going to—

'Do you wish to see how and where lepers confessed their sins? We'll go and stand underneath the covered arches behind the Officino Turismo. Between the two palazzos, there is a kind of whispering gallery. I'll go and stand in the opposite corner and we can test it out. No? Another time. Look over there, at those words: *Panis vita. Canabis protectio. Vinum Laetitia.*'

'Bread is life. Cannabis is protection? Wine is . . . ?'

'You've done well. The third part is, wine is joy.'

'I need a map. I'll just go to the tourist office. *Grazie mille* — many thanks, for your kindness to a stranger.'

'First, neither of us are natives of this city. But I've learnt a few things here. So *gratis* — no charge, I'm going to give you a Bolognese word or two. There's *tiro* — the bell you need to ring to gain entry to a communal staircase. Very handy if you've forgotten your key or if you didn't have one in the first place. And there's *socmel* — which you say when something surprises you. It means suck it! But everyone uses it. Are you feeling peckish?'

'No, I just need to get my bearings.' Abigail tried to turn, but her arm was being held.

'There's a lovely market nearby. It sells wonderful arancini. And after, we can get a slice of *anguria* — water melon. I know a lovely quiet route that will get us there.'

~

Bologna, 2019

'Then I headed north. Towards the sound of the sirens. That's where I first saw Abigail.'

'My mother.'

'Yes, and Zoe's granny. She was sitting on the pavement and looking dazed. I helped her up and found a table outside a cafe. The staff were all out in the street. No-one knew what had happened up at the station. There was talk of a gas explosion. It turned out that Abigail had been hurrying away from someone and had tripped on a paving slab.'

'She never told me that,' India said. 'I know she always blamed me for what happened.'

'Why would she blame you?' Zoe asked. 'How could she blame you? What are you talking about?'

India hesitated, then looked at Colin for reassurance. She was relieved when he responded on her behalf.

'Abigail went into labour. Maybe it was the shock of her fall. Or maybe the general air of panic and confusion. Federico, the waiter, found us a taxi and we went to the maternity unit at Maggiore Hospital. The driver, Chiara, didn't charge us. She was heading back to the station to see how she could help. India was born later that evening, after a difficult birth. The staff did everything they could. They saved the lives of Abigail and India. But her twin brother didn't survive.'

'What?'

'Yes, Zoe. My little brother only survived for three minutes. Abigail never forgave me. She loved her son, your uncle. She didn't seem to have enough love to spare for me.'

Zoe stared up at the clock, which still showed the time of the explosion. She then looked back at India, and put her right hand up to her mouth. Then, for the first time in her life, Zoe went to hug her mother.

~

'Ciao! My name is Giuseppina, but please call me Giusy. And yes, it is pronounced like the English word "juicy". Thank you for choosing me as your guide. I often work for this hotel. I actually used to be a chambermaid here during my university vacations. You made a good choice. The *Orologia* — the Clock Hotel, is in a great position. Do your rooms have a view of the Piazza Maggiore?'

'Our suite, actually,' Colin said. 'There was a bit of a mix-up with the booking, my fault entirely. But it was sorted out without fuss. India and Zoe, her daughter, each have a double bed. There's a sofa bed for me.'

'A sweet mix-up. *Meravigliosa* — that is wonderful. I heard from the manager that you, India, were born here in Bologna in 1980 on *Agosto due* — August the 2nd. And that you, Colin Pargeter, came to the rescue of India's mother. And were with her in the delivery room. So if it's not too nosy, why are you here?'

'I'm getting to know my mother,' Zoe said. 'Colin rescued India's mother and he also sort of rescued me. I have a medical issue, and India heard about it. I didn't want her help. She wasn't there for me when I was growing up. So my best friend, Warren, suggested we come here. Back to where everything started. We're starting to understand each other, but it's tricky.'

'*Senz'altro* — Without a doubt.' Giusy gave India a quick glance. But she couldn't read the expression on the mother's face. But her own family situation would be difficult to explain, and she was a professional guide. 'Bologna was founded, as Felsina, by the Etruscans. The Romans came later. You can still see some of their walls and gates. For example, near the station at Porta Galliera. You would have walked past there earlier, on your way to the hotel.'

'Yes,' Colin said. 'After we had paid our respects by the clock.'

'The explosion was at 10.25 in the morning. The station clock was repaired. But it stopped again, sixteen years ago, when I was eight. The city *then* decided to stop it permanently, as a *timely* memorial.'

'We then waited for a Line 37 bus to pass,' Colin said.

'It still exists. It's forty-five years old and has close to 800,000 kms on the clock. *Il trentasette* is still a symbol of Bologna. But I have something else to show you.' Giusy took out a folded A3 print from her hemp bag and placed it on the nearest table. 'This is a copy of a painting by Renato Guttuso. He created it soon after the bombing. Guttuso copied the title from Francisco Goya's *The Sleep of Reason Produces Monsters*. It's a warning that monsters, murderous monsters, will emerge when people aren't focused on what really matters. The bombing was a tragic reminder to stay focused. Politicians can sometimes seem detached from reality, but our president rushed to the scene by helicopter. Sandro Pertini spoke briefly to reporters, but he was in tears. Now, look at this painting. What do you see?'

'It's a mad birdman, with a sickly green body,' Zoe said. 'Its bulging eyes are set in a red face. And it's ready to destroy more. But hesitating, perhaps because of the big white hand behind it.'

'It has a short sword in one hand,' Colin added. 'And . . . '

'It's a portable bomb, a hand grenade,' Giusy said.

'Yes, and a hand grenade in the other. The monster is stalking the land, with its clawed feet, looking for trouble. Like a deranged jester.'

'It's standing on bodies,' India said. 'Walking all over them, with no respect or mercy. It's like a nightmare. One of the bodies is a baby . . . '

Giusy picked up the print and hesitated. She felt strangely responsible for this multi-generational trio of visitors, but was not quite sure how she could assist. Maybe by giving them space and creating a new narrative. As Umberto Eco once wrote, she thought, *"To survive, we must tell stories"*. Or she could assist them by carefully responding to their comments and body language. And definitely by helping them smell, taste and sip the flavours of the city. 'I think it's time to move away from 1980. This city has layers of history, but let's start exploring by heading out into 2019.'

Giusy led them out of the hotel to the Piazza Nettuno and its namesake fountain. 'The local phrase *"Ci vediamo al Nettuno"* — "See you at the Neptune", tells you a lot about Bologna. This popular meeting point has, since 1566, had a complicated history. The fountain was commissioned when the city was part of the Papal States. But it shows a pagan figure. A confident and powerful Neptune. Below him, on all four sides, are cherubs, shields, sea nymphs and dolphins. Two of the inscriptions are *populi commodo* and *aere publico*. Meaning for public use and made with public money. So it was not surprising that the locals used this regular water supply. Mainly for rinsing their vegetables and washing their clothes. For almost forty years they ignored attempts to stop them using the fountain they had paid for. *Al zigant* — the giant, was theirs. So the authorities fenced it off, for almost three centuries. Before I took my final exams, I followed tradition by walking twice anti-clockwise around the fountain. And many people look closely at Neptune, but some don't make the car connection with his trident. Maserati copied it for their symbol in the 1920s. Ducati are from here as well. Driving one of their powerful motorbikes, especially when wearing La Perla lingerie, is a thrill.'

'What do the figures represent?' Zoe asked.

'You see those four little angels — the *putti*. They represent major rivers in the four continents known to the western world at that time: The Danube, Nile, Ganges and Amazon. The four continents are represented by the nereids, or sea nymphs. They are *prosperosa* — buxom. See the water spraying from their breasts. Though, really it should be milk.'

The quartet then walked across the square towards the Palazzo del Podestà. Colin sensed that India had been upset by the sea nymphs on the fountain, but said nothing. He just squeezed her slightly tighter, as they walked arm-in-arm. Zoe followed, just behind, and focused on the geometric patterns laid into the floor of the square.

Giusy held things together. 'Here is an interesting place. Where the walls can whisper. Sound travels between opposite corners. Which was a useful, and safe, way for lepers to confess their sins. Choose a corner and face the wall. Get as close as you can. So you can feel the heat from your breath, reflecting back at you.' Giusy had expected the two women to try the experiment, so was surprised when Zoe gently pushed Colin forward.

'Can you hear me, Colin?'

'Just about, Zoe. Abigail told me about this place. She was near here just before your mother was born.'

'As the *lines* are open, listen to this. I overheard you and Marina talking in Aldeburgh. At the tower.'

'I thought you might have. Not then, but in the days after.'

'You should have told me.'

'P'raps.'

'So why didn't you?'

'We didn't want to worry you. The plans for a new railway station at Peasenham haven't been approved yet.'

'Do you know the Winchester Book, which was completed in 1086?'

'Are you talking about the Domesday Book?' Zoe asked.

'*Giusto così* — that is right. It was originally stored in Winchester, which was then the capital. Domesday was the nickname given to it by the English. 1086 seems a long time ago. But, just two years later, Bologna's university opened. It is the oldest in Europe. Many years older than Oxford University. And there are over 150,000 students here today. And you see that covered walkway? There are more than 25 miles of such porticoes in this city. When constructed, they were the longest arcades in the world. They had to be tall enough for people to use them when on horseback.'

'Or giraffes, looking at the height of them,' Colin said.

'That's funny,' Zoe said, moving slightly closer to him.

'Whatever people encountered in the porticoes,' Giusy said, 'they had to do it slowly. Especially when it was raining. Umberto Eco, who taught here, thought that the network of porticoes provided a good network for the spreading of ideas. And ideas need food. I like to eat in La Scuderia, but it can get a bit lively. So let's go to the Osteria del Sole. It has served wine — my favourite is sparkling Pignoletto — for over five hundred years. And, if you wish, you can take your own food.'

'Last time I was here, I was confused with the different kinds of pasta.'

'There are hundreds, Colin. But perhaps you were thinking about tortellini and tortelloni.'

'Yes, and something to do with them being inspired by a lady's belly button.'

'That's the tradition here, though I'm not into navel-gazing. Tortellini are smaller, but packed with flavour. I prefer them, especially when they are served *in brodo* — in a light broth. Tortelloni are larger, but without meat. Then there is *ragu*. That is the true Bolognese sauce. Though I prefer it with linguine, not spaghetti.'

Giusy paused next to a small window just off the via Piella. 'Bologna has had many names, including *La Dotta*, *La Grassa* and *La Rossa* — The Learned, The Fat and The Red. The last one being from the politics of the area. But we also have millions of terracotta tiles. I've heard people say that sometimes they *dream* in terracotta. But another nickname was *la città delle acque e della seta* — the City of Silk and Water. This street housed some of our silk mills. Other mills were used in the production of hemp. Remember those words we looked up to, before lunch, on the archway — *Canabis Protectio*. But the waterways have been mainly covered over. Though some of the raised pavements around here were canal paths. So look through this *finestrella* at the Reno Canal. To catch a glimpse of our watery past . . . Some of my favourite songs are by REM. One of them is about believing in yourself, that you *can* be your own star. Though I think Michael Stipe was singing about Nevada, not Emilia-Romagna, when he sang "All The Way To Reno".'

'It's not *La Strada per Santiago* — the Road to Santiago, but you might like to walk the full length of Portico di San Luca.'

'Why's that?' India asked.

'It rises almost 4km, to a hilltop basilica. But it's not about the church. Or the view. For that, you could take a bus up most of the way. No, it's about the journey. You'll pass lots of shops at first, but then it becomes quieter after the Meloncello Arch. To the left, are homes hidden behind a wall. To the right, are hundreds of arches. No-one quite agrees on the number of arches you will pass. But that's not the point.'

'We have a friend in England,' Zoe said. 'Hatsu comes from Shikoku, an island famous for its pilgrimage route. There are eighty-eight listed temples. But her favourite is a *bangai*. That is, a temple not on the list. Every *henro* — pilgrim, finds their own path. So let's do it.'

'You young 'uns go ahead,' Colin said. 'I'll go back to the hotel. We can meet up later for dinner. Giusy, I'd like you to join the three of us for dinner tonight. As our guest. Where would you suggest?'

'That's very generous of you. I'll have to think about where, but we can meet up at Enoteca Italiana for a drink, and then decide.'

'Sounds like a plan,' Zoe said. 'We'll certainly work up an appetite on the climb. Shall we see how far we get, mother?'

Chapter 24

Life Modelling at the Hop Yard #5

'I don't want to do it,' Hatsu whispered. 'Not now. Maybe never.'

'That's fine,' Pippa said, swivelling her body on the bookshop's desk.

'I thought I could do it. You were all so brave. I *can* take it off. Just not for too long.' Hatsu removed her *katsura* and smiled up at her friend from her chair.

Pippa reached down to cover Hatsu's hands with hers.

It was only a soft squeeze, but for Hatsu it triggered a wonderful feeling of care and belonging. And a teardrop, too.

Pippa brushed Hatsu's tear away. 'I'll close the shop and you can snuggle down in your bed of books. Or I could ask Warren to rustle up some of his udon noodles.'

'What about the session?'

'I'll take the others out for a walk, maybe up to Sibton or Peasenhall. We might find an old barn, some exposed flints or a solitary tree to sketch.'

'I *will* close the shop, but I would very much like to be with you all. I don't need to explain to them.'

'What's to explain? Come on, Hatsu. Grab a hat and your jacket and we'll get a wiggle on.'

~

'Hi, I'm Skye Hunter and welcome to *Chatter Broth*. It's March 19th and today's guest is Marina Rueda.'

'Thanks for inviting me again. I really enjoyed the walk last week. It was very liberating. There was a moment with Warren and Zoe that was touching. When they were sat on that old Smyth's seed drill, wearing that big rug Richard bought from Campaign in Peasenhall.'

'And I said to Zoe, "Between us, at least we have *one* healthy kidney".'

'That's right, Warren. It shouldn't have been funny, but it was. You should have been there, Skye.'

'I love Campaign. It's definitely my kind of shop. You never know what you're going to find. That's where India got her green coat, with the leather trimming. I had to stay behind. There were some things I had to discuss with Colin. But thanks, Warren, for bringing me back some black treacle ham from Emmett's.'

'You're lucky it made it. It was much larger when I bought it for you. I'll mention no names. But if I had to—'

'I've talked about innovations in the pub trade before. Not surprising, given that I run a micropub. Here's another one. The corkscrew was patented by a New York inventor in 1860. Two years after the combined pencil and rubber was patented in Philadelphia. Both are useful things to have in places such as a pub, but perhaps less so than they were. The way things are valued fluctuates. Take Alaska.'

'Alaska?'

'Yes, Skye. It was bought by the USA for just over seven million dollars on March 30th, 1867. The Russians thought, at around two cents an acre, that they were getting a good deal. Many Americans were dubious. One of them said that the deal seemed to be, "an awful lot of ice for an awful lot of dollars". Reputations change as well. Sir Walter Raleigh was a favourite of the first Queen Elizabeth. But fell out of favour with James the

First of England. Raleigh was freed in 1616, after more than twelve years in the Tower of London. Freed, to go on a fool's gold mission to Venezuela.'

'Maybe he *should* have visited North America. And stayed.'

'Hindsight is a wonderful thing, Warren. Though there's evidence that James didn't want him to return. And he was executed soon after he did. Raleigh brought some dignity to the bloody occasion. After checking the executioner's axe was well maintained, he found time for some gallows humour. By saying, that it was, "a sharp remedy, but a sure one for all ills". And another axe fell in 1963. When the Beeching Report was published on March 27th. It argued that half of all Britain's railway routes were unprofitable.'

'And why shouldn't they be? Was every mile of tarmac profitable? Or every hospital bed? Now, new stations are being built or re-opened. There might even be one here in the next few years. Right here, at the Hop Yard . . . Hopefully there'll be one back in Ironbridge soon. There's even recently been a new railway line built in the Scottish Borders.'

'You can't be Housing *and* Transport Minister.'

'Probably not, Skye. Though it's an interesting thought.'

'Last time, we were looking for words beginning with the letter X. What are the final four, Warren?'

'Thanks, Skye. They are xanthous, xenodochium, xerostomia and xylorimba:

Though not faithful,
She entered the xenodochium.
Xerostomia made her listen even more.
And as she did, a xanthous player's xylorimba
Almost took her back to Africa.'

'And your thoughts please, Warren? I'm very confused.'
'I'm not surprised. It's not my favourite word-starting letter:

Though not of faith,
She entered the religious hostel for strangers.
An uncomfortable dryness of the mouth, encouraged listening.
And as she did,
A yellow-haired musician's large xylophone-marimba
Almost transported her mentally back to Africa.'

'I was hoping that xenophilia might make the shortlist.'
'What's that when it's at home, Marina?'
'More away, than home, Warren. It's a love of foreign things. And not just things like tea or the Falkirk Wheel, if you're visiting Britain. Unlimited refills of coffee or watching the sunset at Bryce Canyon, in the States. Bagpipes and grilled sardines, in Galicia. All good things, for me, but there's more to it. Not just *things*, but attitudes too. Being more open, even if you're nervous about stepping out. Loving your home, yes. But not being afraid of spreading your wings.'

'Sometimes it's better to listen than to talk. It certainly has been for this mush, who used to feel like an incomplete misfit. And talking of listening, here's some more Four Play. There are different reasons why people can't speak, not just because they have a dry mouth. Also, I'm thinking about Marina encouraging us to spread our wings. So hopefully without getting tongue-tied and my words all twisted, here's Pink Floyd. With "Learning To Fly".'

Chapter 25

'Hello, India. This is the first of three interviews. I'll conduct the second one with Zoe later this week. Then we'll confirm a time for your joint interview.'

'That's how I anticipated the process would proceed, Dr Jordan.'

'Good. It's important you know that I, like all HTA independent assessors, am not a kidney specialist. Also, although I'm based here at the hospital, I'm completely independent from your transplant team. So how aware are you of the nature, and risks, of the medical procedures involved in removing your kidney?'

'I have read numerous documents and case studies. And spoken to a range of medical professionals. I'm aware that the most likely technique, including keyhole incisions, would be laparoscopic nephrectomy. That's a name that doesn't roll easily off the tongue. I also understand that should the operation not go as planned, more invasive surgery would be used. In either case, there's the risk of complications, including to nearby organs, and from bleeding and infections. The worst-case scenario, death, occurs about once a year in the UK. But that 1-in-3000 chance is the same as having your appendix removed.'

'Can you tell me about your motivation and reasons for donating, and how you reached your decision?'

'My daughter is at great risk of needing to go on dialysis.

Perhaps for the rest of her life. Donating one of my kidneys gives her a better chance of having a healthy and fulfilling life. I've have been aware of the difficulties she has experienced in finding a suitable donor. Only about one in a hundred people who die have an organ suitable for donation. So I decided to volunteer. Also, I am already a registered donor. I know that the law changed earlier this year and that adults will have to opt-out after March 2020. I think it's known as Max and Keira's Law.'

'That's correct. Its formal name is the Organ Donation Deemed Consent Bill. So how do you feel about donating your organ?'

'A little nervous, but I suppose that's understandable.'

'How aware are you that you can change your mind, at any point?'

'That option has been made very clear to me, many times.'

'If you did change your mind, would you feel able to do so?'

'I don't see any reason why not. I've made some difficult decisions in my life.'

'Has anyone put any pressure on you to donate? This includes the recipient or any other person.'

'Just the opposite, really. My daughter was initially very reluctant for me to get involved.'

'We can explore that more in the joint interview. Do you feel that you are under any obligation to proceed?'

'No, it's something I want to do.'

'Has anyone threatened you, verbally or physically?'

'Again, no. Why would they?'

'That's one aspect of the process that this interview is designed to explore. I have to be confident that you're here voluntarily. With no pressure being applied or rewards being offered. Do you understand that it's illegal to offer or receive payment, or any other reward, in exchange for an organ?'

'I do. That was a key part of the legislation underpinning the

Human Tissue Act.'

'Has anyone promised you an offer of a reward, either monetary or a gift, if you donate?'

'No, and I'm financially independent.'

'What about any non-monetary offers, such as a holiday.'

'Nothing like that. Zoe's guardian, Colin, has made arrangements to pay my basic expenses while I recuperate. That's alright, isn't it?'

'Yes, reasonable expenses are allowed. Sometimes they are covered by the NHS.'

'I wasn't entirely sure. That's why I waited to sign my donor declaration form. I'll do that now.'

~

'Hi, I'm Warren Wagstaffe and welcome to *Chatter Broth*. It's April 2nd and today's guest is India Farr. This is her first time on the show. I'm sure we'll be hearing about her decluttering business and her plans for the future.'

'Hello, Warren. Where's Skye?'

'She's been delayed, but phoned in to say she'd make it back, for at least *some* of the show.'

'Maybe she wanted us to spend some time with each other. Seeing as we've both had experience of the donation process.'

'A process which is currently the subject of much research. And changes too. In the States, there has been a huge rise in kidneys sourced from people who had overdosed on opiates. In Iran, it's legal to sell a kidney. Though there are very strict guidelines in place.'

'There are so many ethical issues, Warren. Especially as living donors have become more common.'

'You're right. Kidneys offered, both by altruistic and known donors, *are* becoming much more common. Some researchers believe that such donations will rise, within fifteen years, to levels that would cover almost every patient on dialysis. And it would need fewer than one in a thousand adults to achieve that. But it can be awkward. There are many reasons why people don't donate. And those that do, quickly become aware of some quite unexpectedly negative reactions or comments.'

'I've had that too, Warren. Including from you.'

'I think I was over-protective of Zoe. And I didn't know you. But I'm glad that you're doing well in the process.'

'Why did *you* volunteer?'

'It felt like the right thing to do, India. I certainly didn't do it for the increased life expectancy.'

'What do you mean?'

'It's a bit odd. Kidney donors, on average, live longer than non-donors do. Not because they donate, but because of all the health checks involved.'

'So why you?'

'Oh, yes. I'd read about a lad from Yorkshire who donated a kidney when he was just twenty. Sam, his name was. That was a factor. And I saw a piece on a website about an author who refused offers of a kidney from people he knew well. He only relented after an argument with his daughter, who told him how selfish he was. Zoe and I didn't argue, but it did put a strain on our friendship. Especially when we were talking it over with Marina and Colin.'

'There is a lot of pressure, in the process, not to proceed. The NHS wants your kidney, but not as much as it needs to limit risk to the health and mental state of the donor.'

'I found that too, India. Obviously, I had to drop out. But there were still lots of warnings.'

'They'll continue right up to the operation. So how do you feel now?'

'I'm fine about having just one kidney. It's the transplant being delayed, and the impact that's had on Zoe, that's been more difficult to deal with. So overall, it's good that you're here.'

'That's not the warmest welcome I've ever had, but I value your honesty. Even if the operation is totally successful, I'm not sure how my relationship with Zoe will develop.'

'So first you have to persuade someone that you're the right person to be let loose, alone, in their property.'

'I don't persuade them, Warren. Just the opposite, really. It's a bit like the donor process. They've got to convince me that they want me to proceed. A lot of emotions can get stirred up. For example, the property might have been inherited. Or a surviving parent might have needed to move out for medical reasons. Many families are geographically distant, or just can't spare the time.'

'But, a stranger?'

'Maybe it's easier, for me and for my clients. Not that it isn't emotional. I've sometimes gone through a room, struggling to find anything worth recycling. Let alone selling. And then you find something. Maybe a medal, a photograph, or a certificate. Something that means something. That's such a good feeling. You need moments like those, as it can be an overwhelming experience. Even for a stranger. Sometimes you see homes that have been cleared without any care. Personal items just scattered, maybe getting ruined by the rain. I stayed at Shelwick Court once, with a band. You'd have liked them, Warren, as they all drank tea. While there, I found a quote written by Sir John Smith.'

'The founder of the Landmark Trust?'

'That's right. He wrote something that at first upset me, and then motivated me. I always carry it in my wallet. Sir John wrote about how Shelwick was *before* the Landmark Trust became involved. A farmer had lived there by himself. His home became so dilapidated that he was forced to move into a caravan. Following his death, there were plans to demolish Shelwick. Sir John then wrote, "*When we first saw it, the doors stood open to every passer-by . . . minor possessions, rifled and damp, lay strewn all over the house*". I just hated the thought of that scene, particularly the rifled and damp possessions.'

'I can see how that would be upsetting. What's the best thing you've found?'

'There have been so many, Warren. Though my clients have such varied reactions. Some just wanted the house cleared and any valuables sold. Others could get very emotional about an old toy or a battered suitcase. Sometimes I found things that shed new light on their family history. Perhaps even the existence of previously unknown family members. Those kinds of finds needed to be dealt with sensitively. But the best? I think it was an engagement ring I found in a tin of paperclips. Which were in a box that looked like it hadn't been opened since the German Army invaded Czechoslovakia. How that box got from Bohemia to Flagstaff, I have no idea.'

'It sounds like you really do help strangers.'

'And not people closer to home?'

'It looks a bit like that.'

'But are they strangers? My clients approach me after hearing about me from someone they know. And most of them have spent time here in Suffolk. Experiencing a different way of life and enriching Zoe's.'

'So you just dumped some of the responsibility, of raising your daughter, on them.'

'It's unlikely we'll become best friends, Warren. But I did, and do, care about Zoe. As do you. You helped make our recent trip to Italy possible. It was difficult being in Bologna with Zoe. Though it was necessary for us. And, I think, for Colin too. I've often found it difficult to cope with life. Some of the decisions I made might seem quite stony-hearted. Who knows what is really best for their child? Not me, for starters. Yet, I see the close relationships that Zoe has, and has had. Anchored by Colin, but supported by people who are here because of me. People like Marina and Angelique. Gita and Hatsu. And others who were here before you. Like Ana, Zeb and Kayleigh . . . '

'So it's almost four hundred years since the first banana was sold in Britain.'

'What else caught your eye In This Fortnight, India?'

'I've got three more, Warren. Samuel Johnson's *A Dictionary of the English Language* was first published in 1755. Despite being paid 1,500 guineas, Johnson's dictionary was six years behind schedule. Maybe he just kept finding new words. I'll finish with two events from April 2nd. Horatio Nelson was in action at the Battle of Copenhagen in 1801. Not wishing to cease fighting, he disobeyed an order from Admiral Parker. He put his telescope to his blind eye and said, "I have only one eye. I have a right to be blind sometimes. I really do not see the signal". I sometimes wonder, as Hatsu did, whether Nelson had a death wish. And then there's Lady Zazal. In 1877, she flew through the air in London. A trained acrobat, she became the first human cannonball. How do you train for something like that?'

'Maybe you plan, thoroughly, and then hope. Oh, here's Skye. I'll just move back to my normal place.'

'I got back as soon as I could. There were some legal matters that Colin and I had to sort out.'

'It was strange sitting in your seat. You're just in time for Lost Four Words.'

'Last time, we were looking for words beginning with the letter Y.'

'Why indeed, Skye?'

'What do you mean, Warren?'

'Why, and how, were the final four chosen?'

'I couldn't possibly comment.'

'What do *you* think, India?'

'My suggestion was yegg, an itinerant safe burglar.'

'Hmm . . . The final four are yestreen, yperite, yugen and yukata:

Strolling in her yukata,
Yestreen,
She was struck by the terrible contrast
Between yugen
And the almost hidden terror caused by yperite.'

'And your thoughts, Warren? On the interpretation, that is.'

'I catch your drift, Skye. Does this make more sense?

Strolling in her Japanese cotton dressing gown,
Yesterday evening,
She was struck by the terrible contrast
Between the concept of almost hidden beauty
And the almost hidden terror caused by mustard gas.'

'So the word yperite comes from Ypres, where gas was first used as a weapon.'

'That's right, Skye. If enough of the chlorine gas became liquid in your lungs, you would drown.'

'That's a terrible use of scientific knowledge. And about as far away from yugen's hidden beauty as you could get. What do you think, India?'

'I agree. Yugen is a beautiful word. Fleeting moments, like a pink blossom floating down against a pink sky. Or a snowflake landing on a pond. It's not quite the same, but I'm reminded of a poem called "Love Story" by John Clare. Here is the verse that really appealed to me:

"I do not love thee,
But thy handsome ways,
Bring me in absence,
Almost hopeless days."

That sounds like hidden feelings, confused feelings. I also like yestreen as a word. A word that might sound a bit strange to our ears. But words and phrases often shorten over time. And become established. Like fortnight, shortened from fourteen nights.'

'Yestreen has got a chance, India. While we think about that, here's some linked Four Play. Music can be a powerful force. So here's Indeep with "Last Night a DJ Saved my Life"—'

'That's reminded me of something, Warren. Zoe was born, prematurely, in August 2000. Richard was just back from Australia, well physically at least. Though I think that he's made some really good progress this year. He visited the two of us in the maternity ward, but didn't give either of us a hug. Anyway, he left me his magazines. They weren't really my thing, but I do remember a glossy double-page ad in one of them. It was for Bacardi Breezers. The left-hand page showed a young woman doing the washing up in what looked like a tower block flat. She was holding a phone between her head and shoulder. Her hands had plates in them. On the opposite page, her body was in almost the same position. But the woman had been transported to a DJ booth in a club. She was using headphones, rather than a telephone. And she was holding vinyl records, rather than plates. She still had a miniskirt on. But it was all pink sequins, rather than denim. I think that ad had a lot to do with my later decisions. Not that I saw myself mixing tracks at 3am.

But I did need my life to change, though I had no idea how.

There's a different spirit in everyone.'

~

'Do you think that the donor feels under any pressure?'

'It feels strange calling my mother the donor.'

'The questions are designed to be as neutral as possible, Zoe. But I'll try to use mother rather than donor.'

'Thank you, Dr Jordan. I'm sure that my mother is under no pressure to donate. And it's not a decision she rushed into.'

'Have you placed any pressure on your mother to proceed with this donation?'

'No. I even tried to persuade her not to. At first.'

'How would you feel, Zoe, if your mother changed her mind?'

'Phew, that's a difficult question. I've had a few bumps and disappointments during this process. If my mother changed her mind, she'd only do it for a good reason. I know that a lot of planned donations do *not* go ahead, and not just for medical reasons. So, I don't know how I'd feel, but it's not something that I'd argue with her about.'

'I think it's something you should discuss with her during the joint interview.'

'Why is there a third interview, Dr Jordan?'

'It's a chance to see how a donor and recipient respond. You and your mother, together. Seeing you together, including how you both interact, will inform my final decision.'

'How long will your decision take?'

'I'll present my report to the HTA within two weeks of the final interview. Their decision can take some time.'

Chapter 26

'Hi, I'm Skye Hunter and welcome to *Chatter Broth*. It's April 16th and today's guest is Colin Pargeter. It's an unusual show, as we've come to the end of the season. So In This Fortnight will also include April 30th. And I'm not quite sure how the next season will unfold.'

'The show will go on, Skylark. We might just be on the road, for some of it, finding ourselves on some lost highway.'

'Seth has said George and I can come and live with him and Angelique in Laxfield. So I could continue my Veg Out service.'

'P'raps you won't need to, Warren. I haven't worked through all the options. George has come up with a cracking plan, which might just work. Whatever happens, we'll still all be here for the Field Party. Hatsu is making *hanko* — personal seals — for us. She hopes to have them all finished by then.'

'I hope the 'personal' seals don't munch through Warren's celeriac store . . . Onwards and upwards, Colin. As we have been doing, for a fair few decades now. What have you spotted from Warren's notes?'

'Money facts cropped up quite a bit. On April 18th, 1968, Robert McCullough bought London Bridge for one million pounds. Marina's seen it in its new home in Arizona. He might have liked to have paid with £1000 notes, but the government stopped printing them in 1943. And £1 notes were replaced with coins, in April 1983. The year before, on April 23rd, Key West made a bid for independence. It declared it was seceding from the USA. I wonder if Gita's uncle was involved. Anyhow, the so-called Conch Republic failed in its attempt.'

'Couldn't we try something similar here?'

'That would be a last resort, Warren. A sort of *Passport to Peasenham* kind of thing. But the new railway station has to go somewhere, and it looks like it's going to be here. At the Hop Yard. At least we're not going to be bombed out . . . The first prefab home went on display in London on April 30th, 1944. The government was already planning how to house bombed-out families and de-mobbed members of the forces. Over half a million of those homes were constructed. The motor industry was directed to produce them. Perhaps the engineers were inspired by their boxy shape. As, four years later, to the day, came the launch of the first, distinctly uncurvy, Land Rover.'

'And for the last time we— Sorry, last time, we were looking for words beginning with the letter Z. What are our *final* four?'

'Thanks, Skye. They are zampogna, zingiberacious, zugunruhe and zumbooruk:

The strange sounds of the zampogna
And of the sizzling zingiberacious curry
And of the zumbooruk.
They all triggered zugunruhe in her.'

'And your thoughts, Warren?'
'Well, Skye, this was a really tricky one, but here goes:

The strange sounds of the Italian bagpipe
And of the sizzling ginger-infused curry
And of the camel-mounted gun.
They all triggered migratory restlessness in her.

I've got two linked songs as part of our Four Play. First up Katy Perry's "Last Friday Night". It sounds like she had quite a time of it. What, with her ripped outfit and short-term memory loss. But at least she had the presence of mind to think about getting a ginger ale.'

'And that was Donna Summer with her "Highway Runner". Maybe some people are born restless. Always looking for something new.'

'I wonder how restless I would have been. Had I not been rescued by Colin, that is. It's not that I've been cooped up. Far from it. I've explored a few places and had more than a few adventures. I remember one morning in . . . '

'Go on, Skye.'

'Oh. I thought you were going to interrupt me, Warren.'

'It didn't seem right. Sometimes a mush needs to keep his mouth closed. And listen.'

'I'm not sure I want to continue *that* story, but thank you. Although, there was a rather delightful afternoon in Verona—'

'I was hoping that ziff, a beard, would be chosen. That would be a good word to be restored, for a whiskerando like me. What do you think, Skylark?'

'You'd have to speak to India about that . . . Oops!'

~

'Hello Zoe, it's Harrison Ward.'

'Hi, Harrison. Oh, it's gone 10pm. Is there news?'

'There certainly is. Do you have any medical issues at the moment?'

'No. I had a sniffle last week, but it's cleared up.'

'Good. We'd like you to come to the transplant centre at 5am tomorrow. Remember not to eat or—'

'It's tomorrow? The operation? The joint interview with my mother was only just over a fortnight ago. I thought there would be a longer delay.'

'We were set up for another operation, but there were complications. So we have decided to bring your operation forward, as the surgical team is in place. Oh, and no drinks either. There needs to be a fasting gap, of at least six hours, prior to your operation. Please bring any medicines you're using with you.'

'I've already packed my bag.'

'Well done, Zoe. Remember that you, and your mother, will need another medical assessment. Just to make sure that neither of you have developed any new medical conditions. Then, after a pre-med, you'll be given general anaesthetic before being moved to the operating theatre.'

'Third-time lucky.'

'Hopefully everything will be fine, and you'll be out of hospital within a week.'

'Could it be longer?'

'It could. The team needs to check you are fully mobile, are managing your pain and that you can pee. They also need to confirm that there will be at least one adult with you for the first few days after you leave us.'

'But I'll return as an out-patient?'

'You'll become an expert in the layout of this hospital. There'll be over twenty appointments in the first year, but around half will be in the first month.'

'What if I move?'

'How do you mean?'

'I'm not sure what my plans are. I'm planning to start university in London next year. I still have my deferred place on the archaeology course. And I'm not quite sure what's happening at the Hop Yard.'

'Just keep in touch, Zoe. We can liaise with other hospitals if necessary. For now, gather your things. We'll see you by 5am. Oh, I'm sorry. I forgot to tell you something.'

'Is there a problem, Harrison.'

'Not at all, Zoe. As your mother is the donor, you're not just the primary recipient. You're the *only* recipient. As long as there are no issues, you'll receive her kidney. I know that you had mixed feelings last time, when you weren't needed as a backup. So get some rest and we'll see you in just under seven hours.'

~

'All the tests have gone well, India. For both of you.'

'That's good news, Harrison. I wonder how the process will have developed by the time Zoe needs *another* donated kidney. Hopefully mine will last her for at least twenty years. I've read about research into artificial kidneys and even kidneys from pigs.'

'Yes, porcine xenotransplants are indeed the subject of recent research. But for now, the focus is on matching human kidneys. And there's one more thing, India. You'll be asked, one last time, just before you go into surgery, if you still wish to go ahead.'

'Yes, it's the last part of what has been a very thorough process. I know what my answer will be.'

'Next up, you'll receive your general anaesthetic. Then you'll be taken to an operating theatre. Zoe's already next door, ready to receive her new kidney.'

January 2020

Colin and Zoe walked slowly along Weymouth Mews. And then retraced their steps.

'It's not here', said Colin.

'What's not?'

'The Dover Castle, Zoe.'

'Didn't you know, Colin? It's called the Jackalope now. India brought me here for spicy noodles back in November. And she had a beer, whose name might amuse you, called Skylarking IPA. Shall we go in?'

'Another time, maybe. It'll be gone now, anyway.'

'The beer, Colin?'

'No, Zoe. The photograph. My mother rarely went into pubs, but I know she visited this one. It had a pull for her. I think it might've been where she met my father. There *was* a photo, up on the wall. From that era. P'raps my father was one of the people in it.'

'You never knew him.'

'No, but I think my parents might have kept in touch. I hope so anyway. Let's get back to Number 17. You need to pack for your Landmark Trust stay. I'll pop in here another time. Not to check, but just to say a goodbye. Use it, like that phone box Hatsu was talking about on *Chatter Broth* last year.'

'That sounds like a good plan, Colin.'

'Thanks, Zoe. And what's a bloomin' jackalope anyway?

It looks like a hare that's had antlers stuck on its noddle . . . '

Zoe headed outside into Pershore Place Mews. A few olive leaves, blown from the zinc planter over at Number 22, swirled around her feet. Normally she'd have turned left, and headed south towards Marble Arch tube station. The Duffys had said Richard was doing well. And that he hoped that Zoe would visit him. She also wanted to thank her father for a book he had given her, *Daisy Jones & The Six*. The paperback edition had only just come out, on Colin's birthday. One of the novel's characters, Karen, had become pregnant. But decided *not* to have the baby. Zoe's mother, who had made a *different* decision, had gone on ahead to stock up on a few 'essentials' from Muji. India had said she would meet Zoe under the big clock at Waterloo. Before the two of them got the train down, together, to Devon.

~

Zoe's entry in the Peters Tower Logbook, 2020 with additional comments by India

William Peters had this tower constructed as a memorial to his wife, Mary Jane. It was intended to serve as a refuge for stranded fishermen. It has certainly been a shelter from the storm, for me and my mother. In addition to the tower, he paid for a *'commodious block of twelve cottages, suitable for small families'*. William's father had made a fortune trading with the American colonies. But he set up estates for his three sons (including William's, here in Lympstone) in completely different parts of the country. That seems odd to me.

The clock on this tower would have been useful for the local fishermen. Its bell would have sounded, even if the clock was not visible in foggy conditions. One thing I've learned this week is that a cubic metre of air weighs 1.3 kilograms. So we're all under a lot of pressure. Also, that sound (allowing for temperature and wind variations) travels at 1,110 feet per second. So the 'bongs' of Big Ben take eight seconds to reach Speakers' Corner. But another six seconds to reach the western end of Hyde Park. My mother seemed particularly interested in that fact.

We have explored the coast and the Exe Estuary. It's so handy having a railway station nearby. The views from the Avocet Line up to Topsham* and Exeter** are lovely. But they're even better when you head down to Dawlish Warren, and look back towards Lympstone. I certainly think so. Others, in the past, have not been so sure about the view. A travel writer in 1907 wrote, '*There it nestles . . . set down in an opening between two little cliffs of red, red sandstone; but . . . Lympstone is modern . . . and an ornate clock-tower, Jubilee or other, flaunts it insolently.*' Perhaps the writer was suffering a headache after a lively "jam or clotted cream first?" debate.

I'm glad the Landmark Trust put in a spiral staircase during the restoration. It must have been a real struggle on the steep stairs. Even now, it's best not forgetting something. As the bathroom, kitchen, living room and bedroom are all on separate floors. All the polished brass and varnished teak make it feel like a vertical yacht, complete with cosy berths (I chose the top bunk).

The views, depending on the weather, are wide-sweeping. Down on the shore you can see and hear children playing. Instead of wellies, some of them have bin bags tied around their shoes. And, using the binoculars, I've seen Exminster and the hills behind it. Yesterday, I thought I saw a family on one of the slopes playing croquet***. But maybe I imagined it.

We hadn't planned to, but we saw a film in Lympstone today. We'd been loaded down with goodies from Dart's Farm (beautifully designed, and so much more than just a farm shop) and the local RNLI bookstall. A sudden shower sent us scurrying to a doorway, which was opened with a cinematic welcome. What a friendly place. We were even offered tea while we watched *Little Women*.

This is the first time my mother and me have really spent time together. Time alone, that is. It's been interesting staying here, on so many levels. We've become better at sharing things, and not just her spare kidney. We're also sharing a home, temporarily, as I prepare to start my university course.

And who knew that jigsaws could be so fascinating? Not me, for sure. I love the curious whimsy pieces (especially the candlestick) and the fact that some of the so-called edge pieces have no straight edges. That took some working out! There's a leaflet in the box that says you can send in a photo and get your own whimsical jigsaw made.

I thought of getting one made for my guardian, Colin. Of a place we used to all live and work together in, called the Hop Yard. But that might make him sad. I'm sorry, in one way, for rambling on. But places like this are spaces to breathe.
And think. And recover.

Zoe (F-D) Pargeter, Marylebone

* I loved the quay at Topsham. With its Dutch-influenced buildings and interesting shops, not least the two Devon Air Ambulance outlets. And it was lovely to sit in the snug at the Bridge Inn. It still operates using World War One hours, which helps to give it a timeless feel. Although pubs don't have to be old to be a classic.

** There's a new-ish place in Exeter called The Pursuit of

Hoppiness. When we went in there, the locals were having a discussion about the delights, or otherwise, of coriander. Then it was onto whether coconut was an appropriate ingredient to add to beer. Conversations similar, in style and theme, to ones I've heard in M3. A micropub that used to be based in Suffolk, but is now 'resting' before it finds a new home. A home that might be in Bridport. Or Barra. Or even in Boise.

Gandy Street was interesting. It's said to have inspired JK Rowling's Diagon Alley. She was at university here, so who knows? And it's next to a marvellous museum, the RAMM. The exhibits are displayed really well, and I loved peering down onto the wooden model of Exeter.

But my favourite place in the city was the Devon and Exeter Institution. It's a subscription library, but we managed to get a guided tour. It is magnificent. Umberto Eco would have loved it. I think it was him who once said, "I love the smell of book ink in the morning". The Institute sits on the edge of Cathedral Green. I looked for a shop, called Lugets of Exeter, on behalf of Colin who had bought himself some rather exotic trousers from there in the past. But the shop was gone. And so was the Royal Clarence Hotel. It had been a well-loved landmark, but it burned down four years ago. I hope that something beautiful rises from the ashes. The executive chef who had worked there, Michael Caines, has recently opened a place near here called Lympstone Manor. Not bad for someone who rose to the top, despite losing one of his arms. India, my mother, is taking me there for lunch tomorrow.

*** I'm rather fond of regulation hoops, alternative balls and balanced mallets. Yes, like Thursday Next in *The Eyre Affair*, I'm a fan of croquet. I was tempted to play nearby at Budleigh Salterton. But their lawns sound too flat. I prefer a few hills and obstacles.

I, India Farr, am so proud of my daughter. Living her life to the full, despite having to face a daily regime of drugs and dietary restrictions. Performing so well in the petanque competition at the World Transplant Games last August. And Zoe will need another kidney transplant in the future. In fact, probably more than one. So it was good to see that a recent Nobel Prize (surprisingly for Economics, not Medicine) was awarded to a professor, Alvin Roth, whose work focused on matching non-related kidney donors.

I could have spent much more time with my daughter over the years. For instance, at The Library (another Devon LT property). But I chose not to then, remaining HiDdEn in my EnOrMoUs bedroom. So should I have done things differently? That's a question I'm sure most of us ask of ourselves.

India Farr, Marylebone

India closed the logbook, and returned it to its place in the compact library. She watched as Zoe carefully made her way down the stairs. As her daughter picked up their paperbacks, from the inner edge of each step. Peters Tower had been a book sanctuary, harboured safely above the foreshore. And the spiral staircase was a novel library extension, for sure. Could she ever tell her daughter that she *had* taken the full course of morning-after pills? Probably not. She had become pregnant, but then decided to go ahead with her pregnancy anyway.

India thought back to the final scene from *Boyhood*. Set down in Big Bend National Park, as the sun was setting. Where the two new students, Mason and Nicole, were shyly sorting out their feelings for each other. And talking about whether you can seize the moment. Or whether the moment actually seizes you.
India wasn't sure either.

She wasn't quite ready to come down. From the tower, and from her old way of life. But she would. And when she did, she would be ready to start a new chapter in her life. Though there was *still* a lingering unease within her. She had read once that,
'*On this earth, we are nothing but couriers*'. If so, had she delivered? India didn't feel it in her core, but maybe she was guilt-edged.

The End

A Note from the Author

The Hop Yard and Peasenham are imaginary places.
All other places, including the Landmark Trust properties, are real.
However, the logbook entries
(with the exception of the Ironbridge 'snippets',
quoted from the 1977 edition of the LT Handbook)
are the product of the author's imagination.

Different Advanced Reader Copy and Print 'editions'
(introduced, mainly, to iron out errors) can be identified by the first
beer poured in M3. Adnam's Ghost Ship became Titanic's Plum
Porter, then Woodforde's Wherry, and then Adnams (without an
apostrophe) Old Ale. For this edition, brought out to celebrate the
launch of the eBook, Oakham's Citra IPA was the beer of choice.
Cheers! Who knows what will be poured in the film adaptation?

All the words used in 'Lost Four Words' (with one exception)
can be found in at least one of the full-size English dictionaries.

I would like to thank all the people who provided feedback to
earlier versions of this novel. Any errors and omissions are mine.
In relation to factual errors, it's over to Warren Wagstaffe:
'How do you check your facts, Warren?' (from Gita, on page 119)
'I use magazines, books and online resources. I visit libraries and
archives. I even speak to people. I'm sure that mistakes still slip
through, or I'm unaware of new evidence that makes a 'fact' redundant.'

Future ideas for novel titles include:
*Dover Seoul, George P Salt Takes A Dip, Longshore Drift,
Deal Ahoy!, Withitness, Hooks in You* & *On The Other Side Of A Sleep.*

Please send enquiries (including those related to book tours,
festival bookings, interviews & film/radio/TV adaptations to:
figfarmbooks@gmail.com

Re: Cover Design

Paul Tippett aka The Beer Hunter is the creative force behind VitaminP and Danforth & Pape. You might have met him at a Rush convention in Canada, the USA or Europe.

His first cover design for me was for The Extraordinary Word Cup (2014). His design echoed a Brazilian football stadium. Typing the title in a search engine would invariably bring up a "Did you mean WorLd Cup?" message. This may have accidentally contributed to book sales.

While writing Glimpses of India, I mocked up a draft cover. This was later used for the proof copies. The cover photo was one of a series of over three hundred that I took through the 'Water Window' at the National Gallery of Victoria in Melbourne. This was the same window that Keith Haring used to create a giant mural on in 1984.

Once the novel was completed, Paul Tippett was given a brief design brief. He then came up with the current novel cover and the 'figfarm' logo. It was interesting that the novel appeared higher in the rankings as a travel book, rather than as a novel. Title are very important!

My current novel had the working title of 'A Pinch of Salt'. But searches turned up dozens of books, mainly cook books, with the same title. As the novel is set in East Kent, the current working title hovers between 'Raw Deal' and 'Deal Ahoy!'

I look forward to seeing Pauls' cover concept. Maybe over a beer at M3? Other pubs are available . . .

This page was added, with examples of the cover designs, to the eBook edition of this novel in 2022.

To be continued…